An Introduction to Statistics for Canadian Social Scientists

Michael Haan

OXFORD
UNIVERSITY PRESS

OXFORD

UNIVERSITY PRESS

70 Wynford Drive, Don Mills, Ontario M3C 1J9
www.oupcanada.com

Oxford University Press is a department of the University of Oxford.
It furthers the University's objective of excellence in research, scholarship,
and education by publishing worldwide in

Oxford   New York

Auckland   Cape Town   Dar es Salaam   Hong Kong   Karachi
Kuala Lumpur   Madrid   Melbourne   Mexico City   Nairobi
New Delhi   Shanghai   Taipei   Toronto

With offices in

Argentina   Austria   Brazil   Chile   Czech Republic   France   Greece
Guatemala   Hungary   Italy   Japan   Poland   Portugal   Singapore
South Korea   Switzerland   Thailand   Turkey   Ukraine   Vietnam

Oxford is a trade mark of Oxford University Press
in the UK and in certain other countries

Published in Canada
by Oxford University Press

Library and Archives Canada Cataloguing in Publication

Haan, Michael, 1974–
An introduction to statistics for Canadian social scientists / Michael Haan.

Includes bibliographical references and index.
ISBN 978-0-19-542608-3

1. Social sciences--Statistical methods--Textbooks. I. Title.

HA29.H22 2008   300.1'5195   C2008-905042-8

Cover image: Ryan McVay/Getty Images

This book is printed on permanent acid-free paper ∞.

Printed and bound in Canada.

1 2 3 4 — 12 11 10 09

Contents

PART 1: Introduction and Univariate Statistics

PART II: Bivariate Statistics

PART III: Multivariate Techniques

PART IV: Advanced Topics

Preface

Most undergraduate social science students are required to take at least one statistics course as part of their training; usually in their second or third year. Since there is a shortage of high-quality, non-technical Canadian textbooks in this area, professors almost invariably choose an American text for their course. The upside of this is that they have a wide choice of excellent examples from which to choose; the downside is that the substantive content is largely foreign to students—examples and sample datasets are almost always from the US. I believe that this is one of the reasons that students complain about the difficulty and, of greater concern, the irrelevance of statistics for their studies.

Not only do students suffer; using a US text compounds the dismay of professors of subsequent courses about the overall lack of familiarity among students with the basic statistical characteristics of Canadian society. Things like age distributions, city populations, median income, population changes over time, etc., could easily be used to exemplify statistical terms and concepts (like means, medians, variances, normal distributions, etc.), but with current textbook offerings students learn these characteristics about US society. Teaching students with Canadian content promotes greater familiarity with these topics, while at the same time teaching the universal language of statistics.

Since the best way to learn statistics is 'hands-on' (particularly with the recent proliferation of computers in social science departments), a 'knowledge-through-discovery' approach is ideal. Instead of providing the platform for lectures with little or no application, effective pedagogy requires students to apply what they learn in each chapter through practice questions and laboratory exercises (included as accompanying handbooks for SPSS and Stata, two of the most popular statistical software packages).

Finally, I wanted to produce a text that fits the needs and budgets of students more closely. Several statistics textbooks retail for over $200 CDN, an exorbitant amount, made worse when instructors don't even come close to covering all of the topics in a semester. To remedy this, I've written this text so that there is approximately enough material to fill one semester. Consequently, this book is shorter than most, yet there is still plenty of material for a semester- or year-long course.

In summary, with the growing demand for statistical analysis and analysts (both because of the growing availability of data and the massive retirement wave occurring in Federal and Provincial governments) the time is ripe for a Canadian introductory statistics text. That is why Oxford University Press decided to publish the text you are now holding.

When I began writing this text in the fall of 2006, I didn't realize how difficult it would be to fulfill the goals I'd outlined above. I thought that teaching statistics through a textbook would require minimal modification from my in-class lectures of the past few years. Now, nearly two years after beginning, I'm acutely aware of just how different textbook instruction is to lecturing. Perhaps the most notable difference has been that I'm unable to stop at certain points in the lecture to ask students if my explanations are clear. I must assume that the presentation in the pages that follow is clear and organized, and that my audience is following along. Perhaps I should apologize now if I'm mistaken.

This text is broad enough to be used in several social science departments. Although I'm trained as a sociologist, my goal has been to keep examples diverse enough to be of interest to both sociologists and non-sociologists. I hope you'll enjoy (or at least not loathe) what I consider to be one of the most fascinating and useful topics in academia today.

About the Author

Michael Haan is an Assistant Professor of Sociology, and Winspear-Archer Research Fellow, at the University of Alberta. He is also a Faculty Research Fellow at Statistics Canada. Professor Haan has published numerous methodological and substantive articles in the fields of urban sociology, social demography, the sociology of religion, immigration, and homeownership. He teaches social policy, methodology, and statistics courses at the University of Alberta.

Acknowledgements

Many people had a hand in the development of this text. Special thanks go to the Fall 2007 Sociology 210 students at the University of Alberta, who collectively demonstrated a good deal of patience with the irregularities in an earlier version of this text. In addition, Gregory Bowden, Rachel Campbell, Laura Murphy, Shanna Rauckman, and Laura Templeton helped by either proofreading sections of the text or helping with practice questions. Julie Hudson almost single-handedly wrote the accompanying lab manuals, so she deserves full credit for those documents. Thanks to Jennifer Charlton and Lisa Meschino at Oxford for their help and guidance in the early phases, and to Dale Ballucci for her unwavering support throughout the process.

PART ONE

Introduction and Univariate Statistics

CHAPTER 1

Why Should I Want to Learn Statistics?

Learning Objectives

This chapter will help you to understand why you should want to take a statistics course. This is accomplished by:

- giving some of the concerns that might be causing you to not look forward to this course
- putting each of these concerns into context
- discussing the merits of learning to think statistically

Introduction

I bet you're reading this book involuntarily. You've probably enrolled in introductory social statistics in one of the social science departments (history, political science, psychology, sociology, etc.) at your college or university. The course is likely required for your degree or diploma. If you're like most other students, you've dreaded taking statistics for some time now. I'd also bet that you wouldn't take this course if it wasn't required.

You're not alone. I believe that very few people actually *want* to learn statistics. I didn't, and neither did most of my colleagues (some of whom now teach statistics courses). Like you, we were forced by our undergraduate university bureaucracies to enroll in stats. In my case, I'd never met the person, or people, who made this decision for me; they didn't follow my progress through the course, and after I'd finished they didn't ask me if I agreed with their decision to require me to take it.

That was probably a good thing, because I would likely have told them that I dreaded statistics more *after* taking the course than I did before. Sure, I'd learned a few things, but the information was so abstract that it didn't seem relevant to my day-to-day life. Up to that point, I'd survived without knowing what a standard deviation or a z-score was, and I was quite certain that I would have continued to survive without this knowledge. After completing my undergraduate statistics course, I still hated statistics. So did most of the people in my class.

Why Do So Many People Hate Statistics?

Looking back, I think I had at least four reasons for disliking statistics. First, I found it to be little more than useless math and equations, which made the material impenetrable and unintelligible for me. In my mind, the abstract equations discussed in class bore very little relevance to the *practice* of doing statistics. Second, I found the logic, and the assumptions, to be shaky at times. Why, for example, did we often have to assume that variables were normally distributed (we'll discuss what this means later), when this is so rarely true? Third, if statistics are so important and 'objective', why do people often use them to buttress or refute their claims to knowledge? Finally, my professor (who will remain nameless), though a capable statistician, was not very adept at, or perhaps interested in, making assumptions, concepts, and equations palatable to me as a 19-year-old. You may share some, or all, of these reasons for hating statistics.

It is likely, however, that someone in your college or university has decided that that you too should learn statistics at some point in your undergraduate career, making the debate about whether you 'should' learn statistics moot.

Let's see if this is going to be as bad as you fear. You are probably dreading the math and the equations. We'll review the necessary math in chapter 2, but for now you can be assured that to use statistics well you don't need to know a lot of math or to understand equations that you didn't learn in elementary or high school. Similarly, while some of the equations look complex, the principles behind them are generally quite easy to understand. Whenever a new equation is introduced the text will explain, in everyday language, what that equation does. These explanations should be easy to understand because most social statistics concepts are 'results driven'. Once you understand what a certain procedure is designed to do, using it will be easier.

The second reason many people hate statistics is that they don't trust them. Darrell Huff's *How to Lie with Statistics* (1954) is the best-selling statistics book of all time, which suggests that statistical doubters are plentiful. Sure, statistics can mislead, but this can be said about any type of argument. It is your responsibility to assess the validity of any claim, and you can only do that if you understand the tools (be they statistics, rhetoric, logic, etc.) that are being used. Statistics are a tool for constructing a narrative, and one of the goals of a college or university education is to help you use that tool and know if others are using it effectively.

This also applies to the way people use statistics to support their claims to knowledge. For example, say that your friend tells you that he believes all people from Moose Jaw are affluent. Before believing his claim, you might want to analyze it yourself. You might ask:

1. Do you accept the definitions being used? (What exactly is 'Moose Jaw'? How much of the population of Moose Jaw must be considered affluent before Moose Jaw can be called affluent?);
2. Do you agree with the underlying assumptions? (Is 'affluence' a meaningful concept? Can you determine the affluence of one place without comparing it to the affluence of other places?);
3. Do you accept the methods that are being used to arrive at the claim? (e.g., which residents of Moose Jaw answered census questions about their affluence?);
4. Do you believe that the population exists for whom the claim is assumed to be valid (e.g., who lives in Moose Jaw, what are the boundaries on this population, etc.).

You might choose to reject your friend's claim about the affluence of Moose Jaw, because you are unsatisfied with the answers to one or more of those questions. This is the point of using statistics in the social sciences: to provide a framework for assessing claims in a systematic manner. People lie with statistics, but that makes it *more* important for you to understand statistics to identify how the claim was made and decide whether you agree with it. Statistics is just a set of tools and concepts that help you do what you already do countless times every day.

Finally, statistics is just as hard to teach as it is to learn. Students aren't in class because they want to be, and teaching students who would rather be just about anywhere else is difficult. A quick check of www.ratemyprofessor.com shows that statistics professors often receive the harshest criticisms. For this reason, I believe that many professors don't bother trying to make the subject matter more bearable. They don't believe that they can get students to like the class, no matter what they do.

To liven things up, I have used the most interesting and/or relevant examples I could find. Canadian introductory statistics courses are often hurt by the use of US texts, which contain examples that Canadian students can't always relate to. I have tried to rely exclusively on Canadian examples and content, with the hope that you will find the examples relevant.

Each chapter starts with a list of its objectives. Words that you may find unfamiliar will be **highlighted** throughout the text. You can find the definition of each highlighted word in the glossary of statistical terms at the back of the book. You may still find the material to be difficult. If you require further help there are several soothing reads on statistics, including *Statistics without Tears* (Rowntree, 2000) and *Statistics for the Terrified* (Kranzler & Moursund, 1999). As long as you read this text and listen to your professor's lectures, I hope you won't need those resources.

This book adopts a 'knowledge-through-discovery' approach. Instead of abstract lessons on statistics with little or no application, you will apply what you learn in each chapter with laboratory exercises using Canadian data sets (such as the 1881 Census of Canada, the Canadian Community and Health Survey, or one of the General Social Surveys). I hope that they will help you see the links between what you learn in the classroom and what you do in the lab, closing the gap between the theory of statistics and its practice.

Learning to Think Statistically

Using statistics as a toolkit to make claims about the world has only become common practice in the last 200 or so years. In 1975, Ian Hacking, a prominent Canadian philosopher of science (now jointly appointed to the Collège de France and the University of Toronto), published an influential book titled *The Emergence of Probability* (Hacking, 1975). Hacking claims that one of the defining characteristics of the nineteenth century was that people began to see the world less in terms of indeterminism and chance, and more in terms of laws and **probabilities**. One of the consequences of this was what Hacking refers to as the onset of an 'avalanche of printed numbers'. In less than 20 years (from around 1820 to 1840), there was 'an exponential increase in the number of numbers being published' (186). The newfound popularity of numbers caused a shift in the public's view, and understanding, of the world.

Hacking documented the change from not collecting statistics to collecting them, and more importantly a change in the nature of knowledge. He showed that the adoption of statistical methodology changed the dominant way of thinking, learning, and, ultimately, knowing about the world.

Learning statistics is as much about learning a new way of thinking as it is about introducing new subject matter. Consequently, this course will be an introduction to a new way of thinking for many of you.

Understanding the World with Numbers

Since the 'avalanche' began, the topics of statistical inquiry have ranged widely. Numbers and statistics form the basis for many of our understandings: aging, Americanization, apartheid, apple growth patterns, astronomy . . . you name it. Although the focus here is on social statistics, the sheer diversity of topics that statistics are used to study shows that the world can be understood from within the framework of stats.

Consider a recent study of cellular phone usage among teenage girls (Campbell, 2006). Teenagers in North America crave style, friendship, and individuality. Companies that sell cell phones are well aware of this, and present their product to teens as a way to *enhance* individuality, while at the same time promoting conformity to the norms of their peer groups. Most teenage girls can choose whether or not to have a cell phone, and they see their choice as an act of individuality. They and many of their friends have already chosen to have a cell phone (in 2003, roughly half of all teens had a cell phone). Social scientists try to explain this sort of social behaviour. Statistics may or may not help.

If I Don't Plan to Ever Use Statistics in My Career, Should I Still Learn Them?

Of course you should! Within your discipline, there are conversations occurring between several communities. Some of them will assume that you have a certain level of statistical competency. To understand those discussions you need to be at least somewhat statistically savvy.

I also have a philosophical reason for believing that everyone should learn some statistics. Often there are internal divisions within Canadian social science departments—those who don't use statistics in their research do not engage with those who do use statistics (and vice versa). This division hurts both sides. It stymies the intellectual cross-pollination that occurs when different methodological allegiances are combined. To prevent these 'disciplinary silos', and get people with different methodological beliefs to read each other's work, it's important to understand how and what all members of your discipline think. It is equally important, and beneficial, to learn how more theoretically oriented and qualitative researchers think.

Organization of the Book

The next chapter looks at some of the basic mathematical concepts you'll need to learn statistics. Many of these are basic, but you should still take the time to review them. They are the building blocks for the course, and they will help you decode and demystify the subsequent chapters. The topics of chapter 2 (logarithms, exponents, order of operations, fractions, and decimals) are all used quite commonly in statistics, and it is crucial that you become familiar with them.

We'll look at univariate (one variable) statistics in chapter 3, probability in chapter 4, and the Gaussian or normal curve in chapter 5. The methods discussed in chapter 3 (frequencies, percentiles, etc.) are used to give vital information about a particular variable, including the arithmetic average (mean), the median, or the mode. This information can be an end in itself—for example, it is useful to tell people that the median total income of individuals in Canada in 2004 was $24,400 (Statistics Canada, 2006). Once we begin to think in terms of distributions, as we will do in chapters 5 through 7, we begin to think about further analysis of our data.

Assessing variable distribution allows us to determine if we can extend conclusions from a sample to an entire population. Statistics can explain trends in certain populations—such as the population of Red Deer, Nova Scotia, or all of Canada—but because it's almost impossible to talk to everyone in a population, we often only use data on a portion of the population. Sometimes this results in a 'mismatch' between the group being used in analysis (the sample) and the entire population. This is known as sampling error. There will almost always be some sampling error, but there are ways to reduce it. These strategies will form the basis for chapter 8. Chapter 9 will focus on techniques that can help to determine how closely a sample resembles the population it was drawn from. It will also cover the different ways to extract a sample from a population.

Once you understand the distribution of variables, the next logical step is to begin identifying relationships between two variables. This is known as hypothesizing relationships, and in Part Two of this book we'll look at how to cast and test hypotheses with statistics. You probably already hypothesize and test for the existence of relationships all the time, but in chapter 10 we'll begin to look at how to do this a little more systematically.

Chapter 10 also covers methods to test for relationships between two variables (such as gender and income, skin colour and alcohol consumption, rural/urban living and pickup truck ownership). These methods are useful, because they allow you to establish the existence of relationships. They also allow you to quantify the magnitude and direction of those relationships—Canadian men, on average, earn more money than women, but how much more? White people consume more bottles of beer in a year than Asian people, but how many more?

Since we're almost always dealing with samples, we need the skills to determine whether the difference between two groups is statistically significant—that is, does it mean anything? Assessing statistical significance allows you to determine whether the differences you observe in your samples are due to peculiarities in the data (such as sampling error), or if you could expect to find similar differences in the total population. This will be the focus of chapters 10 through 15.

Chapter 16 will cover techniques for moving beyond studying two variables, to focus on multivariate statistics. Multivariate statistics are often superior to bivariate statistics because they allow you to control for the effect of one or more other variables. For example, you could use them to determine if men make a higher average wage than women because of differences in their educations. On average, people with a higher level of education earn more money, so maybe men earn more than women because they go to school longer or get more advanced degrees (they don't). Alternatively, maybe people who live in the country are more likely to own pickup trucks because many of them are farmers. Since pickup trucks are useful on farms, perhaps the rural/urban difference in vehicle choice disappears when we control for the distribution of farmers (it doesn't). Chapter 16 will also look at multivariate techniques for continuous outcomes, allowing us to answer questions like, are gender pay differentials due to an education gap across genders?

Chapter 17 will focus on qualitative outcome variables, like whether a person owns a pickup truck or not. Chapter 18 discusses techniques for diagnosing regression results, which compare many variables at once. Finally, chapter 19 covers techniques for dealing with missing data, which occurs when an individual is unable or unwilling to provide you with some, or all, of the information you request in a survey.

After working through these chapters, the statistics that you know will allow you to perform rudimentary analyses on most data sets and understand much of what is published in the journals of your discipline.

CHAPTER 2

How Much Math Do I Need to Learn Statistics?

Learning Objectives

To learn statistics you will need some background knowledge. Luckily, most of you have already been exposed to the information you need in your earlier training. In this chapter, we'll cover:

- the order of operations
- fractions, decimals, and logarithms
- the four levels of measurement (and their truncations)

BEDMAS and the Order of Operations

Mathematics is the foundation of statistics, and math has its own internal logic that is not always intuitive; why, for example, must you multiply before you add? One of the most basic of all mathematical principles is the **order of operations**. We'll briefly review it here, because it will provide a roadmap for solving problems and equations.

For example, the following equation predicts the average number of hours per month a teenager in Canada spends at the mall:

$$\text{\# of hours at mall} = 0.2 * \text{\# of friends} + (0.01 * \text{disposable income} - \text{age} * 4) - 0.2 * \text{\# security guards at mall} + 2. \qquad (1)$$

At first, this equation seems daunting, but it can be reduced to something much simpler—the slope y-intercept form:

$$Y = ax + b \qquad (2)$$

Hopefully, this equation looks familiar; you probably learned it in high school as an introduction to linear algebra. Both of the equations above describe the characteristics of a trend. In basic statistics, this trend is usually a straight line.

First, let's discuss the second equation, then apply what we learn to the first equation. Typically, a and b are constants that you know the value of. The first constant, b, refers to the value where the trend line (also called the **line of best**

fit or the **ordinary least-squares regression** line) crosses the y-axis when x is set to zero. The other constant, a, is the slope of the line, which means that it describes the rate at which the line goes up or down as the value of x increases. The relationship between equations one and two is straightforward; the last term in both (the number '2' in equation one and the 'b' in equation two) represent the same thing, which is the value of Y (our outcome of interest) when x is set to zero (meaning that a is multiplied by zero). You can see the proof for this if you imagine that in the second equation x is equal to zero. No matter what the value of a is, the product of $a * x$ is zero, therefore Y would equal zero.

Let's apply these principles to equation two. Essentially, the value of b is two (it's the last term in equation one), and in equation two ax corresponds to everything else on the right side of equation one (0.2 * # of friends + [0.01 * disposable income – age * 4] – 0.2 * # security guards at mall); a is replaced by four known values (0.2, 0.01, 4, and 0.2) to collectively become the slope term. '# of friends', 'disposable income', 'age', and '# of security guards at mall' represent x. The big difference between equations one and two is that the slope terms in equation one are expressed by a single term in equation two. Finally, Y in equation two is equal to what you are interested in predicting in equation one: number of hours at the mall.

The goal of both statistics and linear algebra is often just to simplify equations as much as possible in order to derive values of interest—or points on the line for individuals that you want to know something about. In other words, you seek a unique solution for Y (# of hours at mall) and try to use factors that you think will help you do this (# of friends, disposable income, age/4, and # of security guards at mall). These variables are related to one another, which is why you need to be familiar with the order of operations.

To solve the equations you will need to use BEDMAS, an acronym that tells you what order to perform each operation in an equation. BED-MAS stands for Brackets, Exponents, Division, Multiplication, Addition, and Subtraction. For multiplication and division, the order in which you solve the problem doesn't matter. The same applies for addition and subtraction, so BEDMAS could as easily be BEMDAS, BEMDSA, BEDMSA, etc. It is still important to remember that multiplication and division must be done before addition and subtraction. To illustrate, let's solve equation one for a person who has three friends, makes $10,000 per year, is 20-years-old, and is at a mall with 25 security guards.

Following BEDMAS we know that the first part of the equation to solve is the portion in brackets (0.01 * disposable income – age * 4). Within these brackets, there are two multiplication terms (0.01 * disposable income, and age * 4), and a subtraction term (disposable income – age). Using BEDMAS again, we know that the first problem to solve in the brackets is the multiplication. Once you've solved for disposable income and age, you can do the subtraction.

Now that you've solved everything in the brackets, if there was an exponent (the 'E' in BEDMAS), you would need to calculate that. At this point we're going to ignore exponents. Substituting our known values in for the unknowns, the right hand side of the original equation:

0.2 * # of friends + (0.01 * disposable income – 4 * age) – 0.2 * # security guards at mall + 2

Becomes:

0.2 * 3 + (0.01 * 10000 – 20 * 4) – 0.2 * 25 + 2

Then:

$$0.6 + (100 - 80) - 5 + 2$$

And finally:

$$0.6 + 20 - 3 = \textbf{17.6 hours per month}$$

This equation predicts that a person with the observed characteristics (three friends, income of $10,000 per year, age 20, at a mall with 25 security guards) will spend 17.6 hours per month at a mall.

If we believe that our equation does a good job estimating our outcome of interest, we could use it to predict the number of hours for a 45-year-old earning $50,000 at West Edmonton Mall, a 100-year-old person who earns $5,000 per year at Square One, a 5-year-old at Scotia Square Mall . . . just about anyone. We'll learn more about how to do this in later chapters.

Fractions and Decimals

In the example, we had to deal with decimals to find the predicted value. The product of the parts of the equation that involved decimals (the constant for number of friends, and number of security guards) is not usually a round number—that is, it is a non-integer. To deal with non-integers you have to be comfortable with fractions and decimals. You should note that decimals and fractions are just different ways of stating the same thing. For example, the fraction $1/4$ is equal to 0.25. You'll probably prefer to work with decimals.

Exponents

To successfully use statistics you also need to understand exponents. They are typically used to simplify calculations, and take the following form: X^m, where m (the exponent) stands for how many times X is being multiplied by itself. The exponent always appears in the top right-hand corner. The larger character, X, is called the base. Using exponents is also called 'raising to a power', where the exponent is the 'power'. It would not be uncommon to hear X^m referred to as 'X raised to the power of m', or 'X raised to the mth power'. To illustrate, if $m = 3$ then $X * X * X$ would be represented as X^3.

If you're working with two or more exponents with identical bases, and you need to multiply them, you can add the exponents together. Rather than relying extensively on multiplication, it is possible to rely more heavily on addition. For example, $X^a * X^b$ is the same as X^{a+b}. This can only be done when the bases are the same. $X^a * Y^b$ is not the same as XY^{a+b}.

The **inverse function** of an exponent is the root: $2^2 = 4$, then $\sqrt{4} = 2$.

Logarithms

A logarithm is a special form of exponent, where the base is either 10 or 2.718 (the transcendental number). When the base is 10, we're dealing with common logarithms, whereas a base of 2.718 brings us to natural logarithms, which is what we will use in this text. We'll return to these in chapter 17 when we discuss logistic regression.

 BOX 2.1 LOGARITHMS: HISTORY OF A TERM

Scottish Baron John Napier (1550–1617), a prominent politician and Protestant advocate (Hald, 1990), introduced logarithms in 1614. Logarithms were a hugely significant arithmetic advance: they provided the tools for scientific progress in a number of fields. Logarithms make calculations much simpler and faster. Logarithmic identities and derivates allow complex operations to be simplified, and aid in integration and differential calculations. They are also useful for surveying, navigation, astronomy, and anything else requiring complex calculations.

For logarithms to be useful, one needs *logarithmic tables*, huge reference tomes providing the means for logarithmic calculations. Napier and Henry Briggs (1561–1630), a British math professor at Oxford, developed base 10 logarithms. John Napier spent twenty years constructing logarithmic tables, as did Briggs, who eventually published the *Arithmetica Logarithmica* (1624), which includes the 'logarithms of the natural numbers from 1 to 20,000 and from 90,000 to 100,000 to 14 decimal places' (Hald, 1990: 17). Adriaan Vlacq (1600–1667) was a Dutch mathematician who also contributed to these tables, occupying himself with the logarithms for numbers 20,000 to 90,000, completing Briggs' tables.

Consider that Briggs began his *Arithmetica Logarithmica* in 1617, after publishing his first table of logarithms, then he worked out 30,000 cases over the next seven years. That amounts to just over 11 per day, every day, from the time he was 56 to the time he was 63!

Levels of Measurement

When looking at the world statistically, it is useful to think of information as falling into four categories, or **levels of measurement**. These categories are: nominal, ordinal, interval, and ratio. The primary distinction between the levels stems from the relationship that exists between different possible values of the variable. For example, take the numbers on the jerseys of the BC Lions. The Lions have retired the jersey numbers of Jamie Taras (#60) and Jim Young (#30). You can't use the jersey numbers to argue that Taras was twice as good a player as Young. In fact, you can't use the numbers for any purpose other than identification. It is not possible to rank players or judge playing ability by looking at jersey numbers alone. (Although you could assert that players who wear #13 are likely to be less superstitious than average.) Variables with those characteristics are called **nominal**—that is, the numbers are really only names of things. With nominal data, it isn't possible to rank subjects based on value, or to usefully measure the distances between response categories. For statistical purposes nominal variables, such as religion or hair colour, are used to distinguish among respondents.

The next level of measurement is **ordinal:** data that can be organized into an order. A good example of this is the order that students finish in a foot race. By knowing how a person placed, you would be able to assess how well they did relative to other students. What you would *not* be able to assess by looking at the order of finish is the differences in athletic skill. The first-place student could have finished a second ahead of the last-place student, or could have finished a month ahead. With ordinal variables, a ranking is possible, but it is not possible to know the exact distance between values of the variable. Without knowing exactly how long a person took to complete the race, it's not possible to accurately compare the runners' athletic ability.

Another example of ordinal data: When you respond to a telephone survey on the degree to which you agree that *Survivor* is the best television show ever, for example, you might encounter a scale from 1 (strongly disagree) to 5 (strongly agree). This is an ordinal level question (the intermediate scores would represent more moderate levels of agreement or disagreement). We know that there is a difference in the level of agreement between 'strongly agree' and 'strongly disagree', but we cannot accurately measure this distance.

Interval data can be organized into an order and can be added or subtracted but not multiplied or divided. Counts are interval, such as the number of Conservative votes or number of bullets in a corpse. Temperatures in Celsius are also interval, because the zero point is arbitrary. If the temperature is zero degrees it does not make sense to say that there is no temperature. When measuring temperature in Celsius, zero has the same qualitative meaning that one does. Interval levels of measurement are much less common than those at the ratio level.

With **ratio** data it is possible to rank individuals and to accurately measure the distance between them. Most data are ratio. You can add, subtract, multiply, or divide ratio data. In ratio data, zero means that there is none of what you are measuring. Ratio data can be in fractions or decimals—it doesn't have set intervals, like some kinds of interval data. In the racing example, a variable revealing the time it took to complete the race contains this information. With ordinal data, it is not possible to measure how closely the first- and second-place contestants were when they finished. The time of completion, however, allows us to not only identify the first- and second-place finishers, but to determine how big the gap between them was. As with the other levels of measurement, examples of ratio data abound. Age, income, body temperature, airfare ticket prices . . . the list of ratio variables is almost endless.

When Four Levels of Measurement Become Three . . . or Even Two

Many believe that maintaining the four levels of distinction is excessive. Very few people see any purpose in maintaining the distinction between interval and ratio levels, so these variables are often collapsed, leaving nominal, ordinal, and interval/ratio variables.

Others collapse the levels even further, only making the distinction between categorical and continuous variables. Categorical variables include the nominal level of measurement, and continuous variables include interval and ratio levels of measurement. Ordinal variables can either be considered categorical or continuous, depending on the situation (often ordinal variables with two or three levels are considered to be categorical, whereas those with greater than three values are continuous, although this generaliza-tion can be problematic). To help you get a better sense of how this works, consider table 2.1.

The motivation, and justification, for doing this is largely procedural. For most statistical techniques, the type of analysis used depends on the data available. We'll discuss these distinctions more when we get down to doing some analysis.

Table 2.1 Levels of Measurement and Their Classifications

Level of measurement	Can you rank response categories?	Can you measure distances between response categories?	How else might this variable be described?
Nominal	No	No	Categorical
Ordinal	Yes	No	Categorical, Continuous
Interval	Yes	Yes	Continuous, Interval/Ratio
Ratio	Yes	Yes	Continuous, Interval/Ratio

PRACTICE QUESTIONS

Please replace the question marks below with the appropriate answers:

1. $10 + 15 = ?$ 25
2. $10 + 15 - 5 = ?$ 20
3. $10 - (-2) = ?$ 12
4. $(10 + 15) - 5 = ?$ 20
5. $(10 - 15) - 2 = ?$ -17
6. $10 * 15 = ?$ 150
7. $10 * 15 - 5 = ?$
8. $10 * (15 - 5) = ?$
9. $10 * 15 - 15/5 = ?$
10. $10/5 * 15 - 5 = ?$
11. $(X * Y)^a + b = X^? * Y^? + ?$
12. $(X^a)(X^b) = X?$
13. $\sqrt{x} = x^?$
14. if $e = 2.718$, $y = 5$, and $\ln 5 = 1.61$, then $e^{1.61} = ?$

Identify the levels of measurement (nominal, ordinal, interval, or ratio) for the following:

15. Percentage scores on a math exam. R R
16. Letter grades on a math exam. O O
17. Flavours of ice cream. N
18. Fitness training levels on an exercise machine classified as: Easy, Difficult, or Impossible. O
19. Ethnic origins. N
20. Political parties. N –
21. Commuting times to school in kilometres. R
22. Years between important historical events. R I
23. Age (in years). R
24. Amount of money in your savings accounts. R.
25. Temperature on the moon, measured in degrees Celsius. 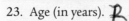 I

Answers to the practice questions for chapter 2 can be found on page 186.

CHAPTER 3

Univariate Statistics

Learning Objectives

In this chapter, we'll look at more ways of studying the characteristics of data by using:

- frequencies
- rates and ratios
- percentages and percentiles

Frequencies

In this course you will learn how to make large, unwieldy sets of numbers more intuitive and comparable. Part of your role as a social statistician is to be a numerical translator. It is your job to turn numbers that only a few people can understand into something that's easy to explain to anyone.

One of the most basic translation tools is the **frequency** table. Typically used for nominal or ordinal data, frequencies tell us the number of times an item, or response category, comes up in a sample. If, for example, we wanted to know how many males and females there are in Canada, a good way to present this information is in the form of a frequency table like table 3.1.

There are five columns of information in the table. The first, labelled 'Sex', is the name of the variable: the sex of the respondent. Since 'Sex' is a nominal variable, the order in which the response categories are presented is arbitrary (the information for males could appear before females, although it is good practice to present your data in alphabetical order). The next column provides the frequencies for each of the categories. Now we know that as of 15 May, 2001 (the census reference date), there were 15,074,757 females and 14,564,275 males living in Canada. As the column 'per cent' tells us, this translates into 50.86 per cent of the Canadian population being female and 49.14 per cent being male. 'Cumulative frequency' is a running total of the frequency of observations

Table 3.1   Number of Males and Females in the Canadian Population, 2001
Census of Canada

Sex	Frequency	%	Cumulative frequency	Cumulative %
Female	15,074,757	50.86	15,074,757	50.86
Male	14,564,275	49.14	29,639,032	100.00

Source: 2001 Census of Canada
Note: Includes all Canadian citizens and landed immigrants who have a usual place of residence in Canada, or who are abroad either on a military base or attached to a diplomatic mission.

in each category (thus the 29,639,032 beside male equals the total number of males *and* females), and 'cumulative per cent' tells us the same about the percentage of observations in each category (since everyone is male or female in the Census, the total beside male is 100 per cent).

There are several alternative ways to present the same data. In figures 3.1 and 3.2, bar charts are used instead of numbers. Many people prefer that format because it provides a visual aid that can be quickly and easily understood. Figure 3.1 shows the number of observations in each category.

Figure 3.2 shows the percentage of observations in each category. As you can see, the horizontal, or *x*-axis, is the same for both graphs (sex of respondent), as are the height of the bars. The only real difference between the two charts is that figure 3.1 has the number of observations in each category as the unit for the vertical or *y*-axis, and figure 3.2 has the per cent of total population as the *y*-axis.

In both of the charts it appears as though females outnumber males because the bar that corresponds with frequency, or percentage, of women is almost three times higher than the bar for males. This is deceiving. To create a more representative chart it would be necessary to begin the *y*-axis at zero, or zero per cent, respectively.

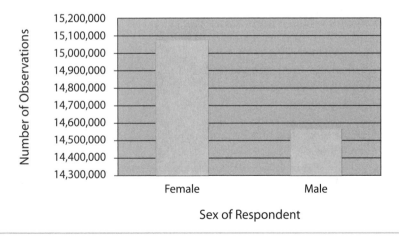

Figure 3.1   Bar Chart of the Number of Males and Females in the Canadian Population, 2001 Census of Canada

Source: 2001 Census of Canada
Note: Includes all Canadian citizens and landed immigrants who have a usual place of residence in Canada, or who are abroad either on a military base or attached to a diplomatic mission.

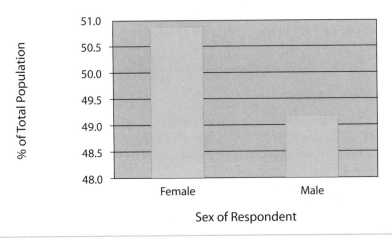

Figure 3.2 Bar Chart of the Percentage of Males and Females in the Canadian Population, 2001 Census of Canada

Source: 2001 Census of Canada
Note: Includes all Canadian citizens and landed immigrants who have a usual place of residence in Canada, or who are abroad either on a military base or attached to a diplomatic mission.

Rules for Creating Bar Charts

You need to know a few things about using bar charts.

First, the response categories should always appear on the *x*-axis, and the frequencies (whether stated as a percentage, or as the number of observations) should always be on the *y*-axis.

Second, the title should only describe the output and the data sets; it should not impose an interpretation of the data. **Axis titles** should be brief and non-repetitive. It would be unnecessary to use 'sex of respondent in the Canadian census' as the *x*-axis for figure 3.2, because that information is in the title of the chart. **Axis scales** should present data as efficiently as possible, without using too many numbers. In figure 3.1, it would be acceptable to remove some of the zeros in the scale, and express the numbers in units of 10,000, 100,000, or even 1,000,000—so the first number would be 14,300, 1,430, or 14.3, respectively. When the numbers on the *y*-axis are smaller they become easier to interpret. However, it will be necessary to do some mental math to interpret the data. Using either the full or the reduced number is acceptable.

Third, the numbers should be listed in equal increments, so that the scale is consistent for each axis. For example, a *y*-axis should never be

0, 2, 4, 20, 100, 10,000. If you see a chart that looks like that, be suspicious! **Legends** often appear alongside bar charts. In figures 3.1 and 3.2 the nominal variable has only two categories, and the data were simple enough that a legend is not necessary. Later examples will use legends to help clarify the data.

Fourth, list the data source, usually in a smaller font, below the chart. The readers will need to know the source of the numbers if they want to replicate the results. If there are notes about your sample, those should also be included. Notice the notes regarding the section of the population included in the sample at the bottom of figures 3.1 and 3.2.

Data can also be presented in a pie chart, as in figure 3.3.

The rules for bar charts apply to pie charts. Legends are helpful, titles should be brief and descriptive, and data sources should be listed beneath the figure.

Translating Frequencies

Frequencies can often be misleading and/or difficult to work with. The numbers are often large and difficult to simplify. Presenting data in percentages, as in figures 3.2 and 3.3, is one method of simplifying frequencies. Percentages

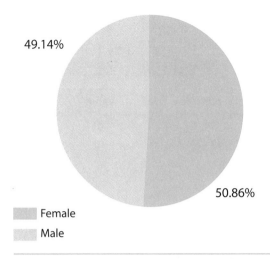

49.14%

50.86%

■ Female
■ Male

Figure 3.3 Pie Chart of the Percentage of Males and Females in the Canadian Population, 2001 Census of Canada

Source: 2001 Census of Canada
Note: Includes all Canadian citizens and landed immigrants who have a usual place of residence in Canada, or who are abroad either on a military base or attached to a diplomatic mission.

are a good way to translate simple statistics because it's easier to remember that 50.9 per cent of all Canadians are female than it is to recall the number 15,074,757.

Two other translation tools are **ratios** and **rates**.

A ratio is the number of observations in one category, compared to the number of observations in another category. For example, we could report the 2001 census data as a ratio and say that there are 15,074,757 women for every 14,564,275 men in Canada. We would probably want to reduce these numbers to make them easier to digest. That can be done by expressing the numbers as fractions and cancelling out common factors in the numerator and denominator. By dividing the number of men and of women by 100,000, 151 women can be substituted for 15,074,757, and 146 men can replace 14,564,275 (15,074,757/100,000 ≈ 151; 14,564,275/100,000 ≈ 146). Thus we would have a ratio of 151:146.

Rates are closely related to ratios, but the denominator is usually a round number (1,000, 100,000, etc.), or an intuitive number (kilometres per hour, heartbeats per minute, GDP per capita, etc.). For example, for the female popula-

tion we could say that there are approximately 509 women for every 1,000 Canadians. Ratios can be used to compare categorical and continuous data, while rates are usually used to present continuous data. Rates are one of the most common methods for presenting univariate data in the social sciences; examples include crime rates, death rates, birth rates, fertility rates, unemployment rates, and inflation rates. To further illustrate rates, look at the Canadian crime rate for the period 1962–2002 as shown in figure 3.4.

In 1962 the crime rate was approximately 2,800 for every 100,000 people. It continued to inch upward until about 1993, when there was a dramatic reversal. As of 2002, the rate was still declining and stood just below 8,000 per 100,000 people, about three times as high as in 1962.

Rates are a more elegant way to present data because they use the same denominator (100,000 in this case). Presenting crime statistics (or birth statistics, death statistics, unemployment statistics, etc.) as a frequency would be cumbersome, because a more detailed explanation would be necessary.

Rates, ratios, and percentages are attractive because they are **standardized.** That is, they use the same unit of measurement, and can be compared across countries, over time, or any other way you choose. When using rates, ensure that

Rate per 100,000 Population

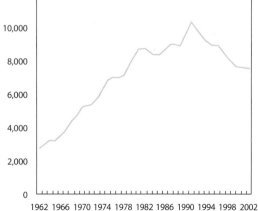

Figure 3.4 Crime Rate, 1962 to 2002

Source: *2002 Juristat* (Canadian Centre for Justice Statistics, 2003)

the denominator is the same across comparison groups (i.e., make sure all ratios that you compare are based on the same 'per X population'). With percentages that are already done for you, the denominator is always 100.

Percentiles

The Canadian Oxford Dictionary defines percentile as 'one of 99 values of a variable dividing a population into 100 equal groups as regards the value of that variable'. You determine the percentiles by slicing your sample into 100 groups, making sure that each group has exactly the same number of people (the best you can, without slicing a person in half). If there were 30,000,000 people in Canada and we were sorting them by age, each group would have 300,000 people. Each of those groups would represent one percentile, and the age values used to delineate the 100 groups would form the cut-points of the percentile.

Returning to the 2001 census, the age value for the first percentile is zero because of all the babies who haven't had a birthday yet. Showing all 100 percentiles in a table makes for a very big, clumsy table, so you usually only show a few of them, as in table 3.2. It is also common to show deciles (10, 20, ...) or quartiles (25, 50, 75, and 100). Table 3.2 shows that age 19 is at the 25th percentile (or first quartile), meaning 25 per cent of the total population is below the age of 19. The 50th percentile (where the Canadian population is evenly divided in half), is at age 37.

The 50th percentile is the median, since half of the population is at or above 37, and half are below. The 75th percentile is those who are at, or over, the age of 52, and the 100th percentile cut-off is age 85. This number is lower than you might

Table 3.2 The Age of the Canadian Population by Percentile Cut-Offs, 2001 Canada

Percentile	Value
1	0
25	19
50	37
75	52
100	85

Source: 2001 Census of Canada

expect because Statistics Canada recodes all values above age 85 to 85, to ensure confidentiality.

Here's an example of percentiles that you are very familiar with: test scores. If you scored 91 per cent on a test, you would know that you were 9 percentage points from 100, and 91 points from zero. This would give you an idea of how you did on the test. Let's suppose lots of people did well on the test, and that 91 per cent was actually the score for the 50th percentile (or the median). You could be proud that you beat half of your classmates, but the other half of them would also have tied or beaten your score. Depending on the measure of central tendency, your 91 per cent might only be average, not the exceptional grade that you thought it was. Percentiles rank you in relation to your peers, not just on a scale of 100 that doesn't relate you to anyone else. They are often used in standardized testing, such as the Scholastic Aptitude Test (SAT), the Law School Admission Test (LSAT), the Graduate Record Examination (GRE), the Medical College Admission Test (MCAT), or the American College Test (ACT).

PRACTICE QUESTIONS

A. Jorge placed 113th out of 1,432 people in a national spelling bee by correctly spelling 37 of the 40 words he was given.

  1. What is the ratio of correct to incorrect responses?
  2. What is his score stated as a percentage?
  3. What is his rank in percentiles?

B. Ethel is conducting a telephone survey to determine the approximate number of people who are interested in lobbying the federal government about recent changes to the Canada Pension Plan. Over the course of a week, she calls 541 people. Of those people, she contacts 432, and identifies 112 individuals who are willing to participate in the lobbying effort.

1. What is her contact rate per 1,000 people?

2. What is her contact/non-contact ratio in lowest terms?

3. What is her lobbying participation rate as a percentage, using only contacted individuals?

C. Charles, a woodchuck with ego problems, thinks that he can chuck more wood than any other woodchuck. But he is insecure and decides that he'll ask 30 of his closest woodchuck friends if they agree. To his chagrin, he only reaches 22 of his friends, and only 5 agree with him. Although he didn't reach 8 of his woodchuck friends, he is certain that they'd agree that he's the best woodchucker out there. To celebrate his accomplishment, he decides to make a poster to hang on the wall of his dwelling, but doesn't know how to calculate any univariate statistics. Help Charles out by calculating the percentage, and the ratio, of woodchucks who think he is the king of all woodchucks.

Answers to the practice questions for chapter 3 can be found on page 186.

Introduction to Probability

Introduction

A standard deck of cards has four suits (spades, hearts, diamonds, and clubs), and 13 cards in each suit (ace through king). Let's assume there are no jokers in the deck. If each card is equally likely to be drawn, is it possible to calculate the likelihood of drawing a particular card?

The answer is yes. Any time you identify how likely an event is to occur, what you're really doing is calculating a probability. A **probability** is a number between zero and one (or zero to 100 per cent, when stated as a percentage), where zero refers to an event that never occurs, and one to an event that definitely occurs. The event can be anything imaginable, from a coin landing heads-up, to a car accident on the way home from work. It doesn't really matter. What does matter is that a calculable chance, or probability, can be attached to the competing outcomes.

This chapter will cover the basic types of probabilities, and identify some of the laws that make probabilities work in statistics.

Some Necessary Terminology

To discuss probabilities, you need to know the vocabulary. These concepts will be used throughout the text, so it is important to understand them.

Sample Space

A **sample** space contains all of the theoretically possible outcomes of an event. Each probability is a fraction of the sample space. The sum of the probabilities of all possible outcomes equals one. The probability of the occurrence of an event is one minus the probability that it won't occur.

If the probability of picking a green apple from a barrel containing 44 green apples and 56 red apples is 44/100, or 11/25, then the probability of *not* picking a green apple is equal to 1 – 11/25, or 14/25. When there are only two possible outcomes (picking a green apple or a red apple), 14/25 is also the probability of picking a red apple. The probability of picking a red apple plus the probability of picking a green apple is 14/25 + 11/25, or 25/25. If you pick an apple, you can be certain that it will either be green or red.

Random Variables

What makes a variable 'random' is that the value is subject to variation from known or unknown sources. The value of a random variable is not predictable, but the probability of certain values can often be calculated. A random variable has a value that is the result of a process or experiment, such as tossing a coin or splitting an atom. Like other types of variables, random variables can take on different values, but the entire sample space is usually already known.

Imagine a coin tossing experiment. Create a variable (let's call it X) for whether the coin will come up heads or tails. Since it was 1) created by a particular process or experiment (tossing a coin), 2) has a known sample space (heads and tails), and 3) it is not possible to predict outcomes perfectly (that is, whether a toss lands heads or tails), we know that we are dealing with a random variable.

Trials and Experiments

Discussions about probability, or statistics, are usually conducted in terms of trials and experiments. A trial is an individual exercise that, when taken alongside other exercises, will collectively form the data for the experiment. A trial is part of an experiment. Suppose you were calculating the probability of randomly selecting a person with a PhD in your student union building. The exercise would form the experiment, and each person selected would count as a trial. If you did this 100 times, the point of the experiment would be to calculate the probability of randomly selecting a person with a PhD, and the results would include the data from the 100 trials.

The Law of Large Numbers

The **law of large numbers** states that if you repeat a random experiment (such as tossing a coin or rolling a die) many, many times, your outcomes will approach a level of 'stability'. Pretend that you have a coin, and that you tossed it in the air 100 times. How many heads would you expect to get? In a 100-toss event, you wouldn't be able to perfectly determine that, but you could make a pretty good 'guess'. Let's say that you predicted the coin would turn up heads half the time.

One hundred is a lot of tosses. The law of large numbers states that you'll probably turn up heads closer to half of the time tossing it 100 times than if you only tossed 10 times. The law also states that if you tossed it 100,000 times, you would get even closer to your predicted ratio. The more times you toss the coin, the closer you'll be to your calculated theoretical probability value of half heads.

Types of Probabilities

There are numerous types of probabilities—so many that there are university courses dedicated just to that subject. We won't cover all of them. Instead we'll focus on some of the more common types.

Empirical versus Theoretical Probabilities

There are two ways to calculate the probability of an event.

First, you can conduct an experiment, and use the results to calculate the probability. If, for example, you wanted to know the probability of drawing a spade from a full deck of well-shuffled cards, you could draw single cards over and over again, and use your results to calculate the probability of drawing a spade. If you conducted 100 draws, and pulled a spade 26 times, you could conclude that the probability is equal to roughly 26/100, or 26 per cent. Since you are using real data, that number is an empirical probability.

Second, you can create a theoretical probability using your powers of deduction. Instead of conducting an experiment, you could determine the total number of spades in a deck (13) relative to the total number of cards (52), yielding the **theoretical probability** of 13/52, or 25 per cent.

You can see that there is a difference in the results for the empirical and theoretical probabilities. This can be due to a random, or non-random, error in the empirical probability. Perhaps the deck wasn't shuffled perfectly, or there weren't enough draws. If there were more trials (draws), the law of large numbers says that the empirical probability will converge with the theoretical probability.

To make things simple for now, let's pretend that we have a sample large enough to make the differences between empirical and theoretical probabilities negligible.

Discrete Probabilities   *outcome has equal probability*

A discrete probability has clearly defined, non-overlapping outcomes. These variables often have an equal probability of occurrence for each value. For example, the roll of a single die has six discrete possible outcomes. We can assign equal probabilities to each outcome. In this case, the probability would be 1/6, the frequency of each outcome over the total possible number of outcomes.

Tossing a coin is another example of a discrete outcome. The coin will either land heads or tails, and if there is no reason to suspect that the coin comes up one way more often than the other, we can assign the probability of 1/2 to each of the outcomes.

In both examples each outcome has an equal probability, but it isn't necessarily so. For example, if there is a 15 per cent chance of rain, we assign a probability of 0.15 to the chance of rain, and a probability of 0.85 to no rain.

Discrete probabilities are easy to work with due to their intuitiveness. If all of the possible outcomes are known, the sum of probabilities will equal one (at least one event in the sample space will occur). For example, the die-tossing scenario has six outcomes, each with a probability of 1/6. If we sum these values, we get 1/6 + 1/6 +1/6 +1/6 +1/6 +1/6, which equals 6/6, or 1.

Even when probabilities are not equal, the sum is usually one. The chance of rain in the earlier example is 0.15 and the chance of no rain is 0.85. The probability of either rain or no rain is 1 (0.15 + 0.85 = 1). State the probability as a percentage and it's 100 per cent.

In reality, the probabilities never quite total one because of the possibility of unforeseen, very unlikely, events: a bird swoops down and catches your coin; the planet explodes before you can determine whether it rained.

Discrete probabilities are also called simple probabilities, because they involve only one set of outcomes. In scenarios where more than one outcome is likely, calculating probabilities is more difficult.

The Probability of Unrelated Events

If one event does not affect the probability of another event, then the events are **independent**. Suppose you're calculating the probabilities of

BOX 4.1 THE STEPS: CALCULATING A DISCRETE THEORETICAL PROBABILITY

1. Identify the experiment of interest (coin tossing, card drawing, etc.), and be sure that the outcomes are mutually exclusive.

2. Determine the sample set, or the total number of possible outcomes. This will be the denominator of your probability calculations.

3. Determine the frequency of occurrence of your outcome of interest (a coin landing on heads, drawing a spade, etc.). This will be the numerator of your calculation.

4. Divide the numerator by the denominator to determine the discrete probability.

two unrelated activities. An example would be rolling two sixes in a row with a six-sided die. The probability of rolling a single six would be equal to 1/6. But what about rolling two sixes in a row?

First, calculate the two discrete probabilities, p(A) and p(B). Then use the multiplication rule of probabilities, which states that observing two independent outcomes in succession is equal to the product of the probability of the two individual outcomes. In our example we have two independent probabilities, p(A) and p(B), with respective probabilities of 1/6 and 1/6. To identify the probability of rolling two successive sixes we multiply these numbers together:

$$p(A \text{ and } B) = p(A) * p(B)$$
$$= 1/6 * 1/6$$
$$= 1/36$$
$$= 0.028$$

The equation yields 0.028, so there's about a 3 per cent chance of rolling two sixes in a row.

The Probability of Related Events

If one event affects the probability of another event, then the events are **dependent**. Solving problems involving related events is more complicated because an intermediate calculation is required. Let's use a bag containing 40 marbles in it to illustrate. Ten of the marbles are green, 10 red, 10 yellow, and 10 blue. Suppose that we wanted to know the probability of pulling out a green marble then pulling out a red marble. How would you figure it out?

Pulling out the red marble is only of interest when the first marble that's pulled out is green. Additionally, the number of marbles changes across experiments, from 20 to 19, thereby altering our probability calculations. Event A is pulling out a green marble first. Since 10 of the 40 marbles are green, p(A) = 10/40 = 1/4. If the first marble is green, what is the probability that the second marble will be red? Of the 39 remaining marbles, 10 are red, so p(B|A), or the probability of B given A, is 10/39. The probability of A then B is therefore equal to:

$$p(A \text{ then } B) = p(A) * p(B|A) \text{ (this is}$$
read as the probability of B given A)
$$= 1/4 \times 10/39$$
$$= 10/156$$
$$= 0.064$$

There's a 6.4 per cent chance of pulling a green and then a red marble in succession.

Mutually Exclusive Probabilities That Are Interchangeable

To determine the probability of either of two mutually exclusive events occurring, it's necessary to add the independent probabilities. If you wanted to know the probability of a die roll yielding *either* a one or a six, you would need to sum the two independent probability calculations:

$$p(\text{one}) = 1/6$$
$$p(\text{six}) = 1/6$$
$$p(\text{one or six}) = 1/6 + 1/6 = 1/3$$

This is the **addition rule of probabilities**.

Non-Mutually Exclusive Probabilities That Are Interchangeable

When two events can occur simultaneously, they are considered non-mutually exclusive, or interchangeable, probabilities. With non-mutually exclusive categories, there is a danger of double-counting. When that occurs it's necessary to subtract values that have been double-counted.

Consider the following scenario: In Dodge City in 1810—a town with a population of 200—there are 40 people who smoke but don't drink and 60 people who drink but don't smoke. As well, 98 people both smoke and drink. What is the probability of randomly picking a smoker p(A), a drinker p(B), a smoker and a drinker p(A and B), or a smoker or drinker p(A or B)?

- For a smoker, it is p(A), which is 138/200 (40 smokers, and 98 smokers and drinkers)
- For a drinker, it is p(B), which is 158/200 (60 drinkers, and 98 smokers and drinkers)
- For a smoker and a drinker, it is p(A and B), which is equal to 98/200
- For a smoker or a drinker it becomes more complicated because of the risk of double-counting. In this case, we'd need to add p(A) to p(B), then subtract the duplicates p(A and B), yielding

$$p(A \text{ or } B) = p(A) + p(B) - p(A \text{ and } B)$$
$$= 138/200 + 158/200 - 98/200$$
$$= (138 + 158 - 98)/200$$
$$= 198/200$$
$$= 0.99$$

BOX 4.2 HOW TO CALCULATE PROBABILITIES FOR NON-MUTUALLY EXCLUSIVE EVENTS

1. Calculate the probability of event A.
2. Calculate the probability of event B.
3. Subtract the number of duplications.

The formula takes the form:

$$p(A \text{ or } B) = p(A) + p(B) - p(A \text{ and } B)$$

These are also called cumulative probabilities, because the outcomes overlap to some extent.

Continuous Probabilities

There is another class of probabilities for variables that don't have exact values, such as time or height. There are no discrete, exact measures of these variables—you can always measure them more precisely. There are an infinite number of possible values. Consequently, the probabilities are also continuous. Although it is possible to calculate continuous probabilities, these are beyond the focus of this text.

Conclusion

To check the plausibility of your calculations, keep in mind that:

1. The probability of an event that cannot occur is zero.
2. The probability of an event that must occur is one.
3. Every probability is a number between zero and one, inclusive. As a percentage, it will range between zero per cent and 100 per cent.
4. The sum of the probabilities of all possible outcomes of an experiment is one.
5. When thinking about probabilities, remember what Aristotle said: 'The probable is what usually happens.'

It is useful to think of statistics as an elaborate way of calculating probabilities.

PRACTICE QUESTIONS

1. Which of the following is the sample space when 2 coins are tossed?

   a. H, T, H, T
   b. H, T
   c. HH, HT, TH, TT
   d. H, H, T, T

2. At the University of Regina, 3 out of 5 students graduate with a Bachelor of Arts degree. The remainder receive a different degree, such as a Bachelor of Science. What is the probability that a randomly chosen graduating student will *not* be getting a Bachelor of Arts degree?

3. A pair of dice is rolled. What is the probability of getting a sum of 2?

4. There are 2 soccer teams in Winnipeg with 30 players in total. One team (Team A) has 16 players and the other (Team B) has 14. Five of these players are left forwards, 3 of whom are on Team A. If a player is chosen at random, what is the probability of choosing someone on Team A, or a left forward?

5. In Canada, roughly 52 per cent of people wear a seat belt while driving. If 2 people are chosen at random, what is the probability that both of them wear a seat belt?

6. Three cards are chosen at random from a deck *without* being replaced. What is the probability of getting a 3, a 9, and a jack, in that order?

7. In poker, one of the better hands is a flush. A flush is 5 cards of the same suit (all hearts, all clubs, etc.). Calculate the likelihood of being dealt a flush (hint: there are 4 suits in total, 13 cards to a suit, and 52 cards in a standard deck). State the likelihood as a decimal, rather than a fraction.

8. Ryan only had time to study 6 of the 8 essay questions that could be on his sociology exam. His professor will be choosing 2 of the 8 questions for the exam. What are the chances that both of the questions that Ryan didn't study will appear on the exam?

Answers to the practice questions for chapter 4 can be found on page 187.

out of 13 pairs.
pull one(1) —>
the next, etc.

1	2	3	4	5.
$\frac{1}{52}$ ×	$\frac{12}{51}$ ×	$\frac{11}{50}$ ×	$\frac{10}{49}$ ×	$\frac{9}{48.}$

multiply top, then bottom, then divide to get answer in decimal

The Normal Curve

Now that you've learned about probabilities and how to describe data, chapter 5 will expand on those topics. You will learn:

- how data are distributed
- principles of the normal distribution
- measures of dispersion
- how probability is related to the normal curve

The History of the Normal (Gaussian) Distribution

Imagine that you're a gambler and want to know how frequently an outcome (such as the number of times a coin will turn up heads in 100 tosses) will occur. A safe guess would be to predict 50 per cent of the time. Usually that's pretty accurate, but gamblers often bet on something *other* than the most obvious outcome. Since coin tossing is a **random process**, the outcome won't always be the most obvious or intuitive one. There could be 53 heads and 47 tails in one set of tosses, 65 heads and 35 tails in another, and 75 heads and 25 tales in yet another. It is theoretically conceivable that

you could get 95 heads and 5 tails in one round of tosses. Anything between zero heads and 100 tails and 100 heads and zero tails is possible.

Imagine that you've been hired to predict the likelihood of an outcome—say 53 heads. Your gambler boss wants to know which outcome you think would be most likely (and therefore which outcome he/she should bet on). Depending on how risk-averse your boss is, you probably wouldn't choose 95 heads and 5 tails, given the over-representation of heads and the low likelihood of that outcome. Instead, you might suggest placing a bet on a more evenly divided outcome because it makes more sense to you, and everyone else, which is also why it wouldn't pay

BOX 5.1 THE NORMAL CURVE: HISTORY OF A TERM

The reason the normal curve is sometimes called the bell curve is because of its bell-like shape. It is often (mistakenly) called the Gaussian curve, to pay tribute to the work of Carl Friedrich Gauss on the distribution of errors in an ordinary least squares regression equation. Gauss argued that the distribution of errors in the equation is random, and that their shape therefore assumes a normal distribution. Since de Moivre used the curve first it should bear his name. The fact that it doesn't follows the law of eponymy, coined by statistician Stephen Stigler, which states that 'no scientific discovery is named after its original discoverer.'

as well as a more extreme bet. By considering these possibilities, you're applying some of the general principles of **probability**, the **central limit theorem**, and the **normal curve**.

This is what Abraham de Moivre, one of the Western world's earliest statisticians, did for a living. He was born in 1667 in Vitry-le-François, France, and moved to London around 1685. There, in addition to being a tutor and mathematician, he served as a gambling consultant at a local coffeehouse. It is likely that de Moivre frequently faced problems like the coin toss example above, because he derived an equation that allowed him to estimate the probability of any of the 100 possible outcomes. He could do that because he noticed that when the number of events (coin flips) increased, the frequency of outcomes approached a smooth and predictable bell-like curve. This observation later became known as the central limit theorem, and the curve he saw is known today as the **Bell**, **Gaussian**, or **normal curve**.

Illustrating the Normal Curve

Although de Moivre's equation is actually calculating probabilities, it's not yet important to understand how probability relates to the normal curve. Instead, let's look at the central limit theorem and determine its relation to the normal curve. A simplified version of the central limit theorem states that if any variable (such as a variable that contains the number of times a coin toss shows heads) has a known range, then it will increasingly approximate the normal curve as the number of samples increases.

To illustrate the normal curve, let's continue using the coin toss example. You would start out with a small exercise, like 100 tosses performed once.[1] Once you've flipped the coin 100 times (yielding 55 heads and 45 tails), you have completed one **experiment**. This probably took some time to do, but it is not even *close* to the number of tosses needed to see the normal curve. In fact, in figure 5.1, the 100 toss experiment was repeated 100 times (that's 10,000 tosses).

This type of graph in figure 5.1 is a histogram. Histograms are often used to assess **distributions**. The x-axis represents the frequency with which heads was observed in each experiment; the values on the y-axis are the proportion of the experiments where each frequency of heads was observed. The y-value of the tallest bar (which is the mode, and has an x-value of 49 heads) is 0.09, meaning that in 100 experiments, 49 heads were observed 9 per cent of the time, or in 9 experiments. On either side of this value are shorter bars with values of 0.07, meaning that 48 and 50 heads were observed in 7 experiments.

The thin, black curvy line in figure 5.1 represents the normal curve. Typically, the normal curve will be bell-shaped, as the black line shows. As de Moivre noted in the central limit theorem, the fewer the number of tosses, the worse the ap-

---

[1]To experiment with coin-tossing, check out UBC economist Ken White's website: http://shazam.econ.ubc.ca/flip.

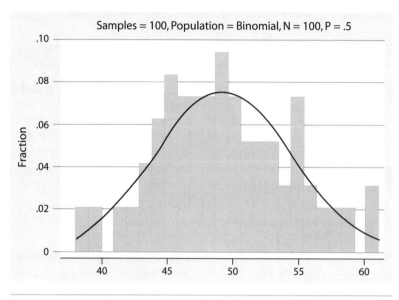

Figure 5.1 Results from 100 Coin Toss Experiments, 100 Tosses
        per Experiment

proximation of the normal curve will be—creating more gaps between the bars of the histogram and the normal curve line. Figure 5.1 represents 100 sets of tosses, each set containing 100 tosses. You can see that the tails are thicker than the normal curve would suggest, and that there are several instances where the bars don't align with the curve. The values of 40 and 59 don't even occur.

In figure 5.2, the number of samples is increased to 1,000 (each experiment still contains 100 tosses). Notice how much closer the distribution of data is the normal curve.

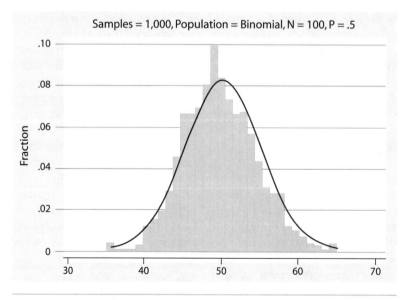

Figure 5.2 Results from 1,000 Coin Toss Experiments, 100 Tosses
        per Experiment

There are far fewer gaps between the normal curve and the data, but the graph still doesn't follow the curve exactly.

When the number of samples is increased to 10,000 (figure 5.3), the fit shows even more improvement. There is very little difference between the results and the overlaid normal curve.

As the exercise demonstrates, the distribution of data, here the proportion of heads in each set of 100 tosses, more closely resembles the normal curve as sample size increases. This is the crux of the central limit theorem, which states that observed data approaches the normal curve as the number of observations increases. Knowing this made it possible for de Moivre to predict how often a set of tosses would return any combination of heads and tails. The curve can also be used to predict other kinds of outcomes. If there are enough trials, it's possible for the distribution *within* a sample to approach normal distribution.

As figure 5.3 suggests, the normal curve can also be used as an **asymptotic** approximation of the distribution of a continuous variable, such as income. There are some necessary qualifiers for income though. Since it has a wider range of values than the coin toss, one large sample can approach the normal curve. Also, unless you are self-employed, it is difficult to earn less

than $0. Finally, a few people in Canada earn a lot more money than could be randomly predicted. These people (such as Kenneth Thomson, Galen Weston, the Irving brothers, Jim Pattison, etc.) are known as **outliers**, because their earnings are sufficiently unique that they will never fall within the parameters of the normal distribution (perhaps this is why they are in the news so often!). Those who earn less than $0 are also outliers.

Some of the difficulties with examining income can be resolved by focusing only on the self-employed (since it is possible to lose money if you're self-employed), and by eliminating the wealthy.

Figure 5.4 is a histogram of income for the approximately 130,000 people who were self-employed in 2001. Once again, the normal curve is overlaid. There are considerable gaps in the plot versus the normal curve. Ideally, the number of observations would be increased to produce a better fit, but that option is not available; everyone who was self-employed in Canada in 2001 is already included.

The example shows that there will almost always be a level of misfit between observed data and the normal curve. However, we often decide that our data is close enough to normal so that

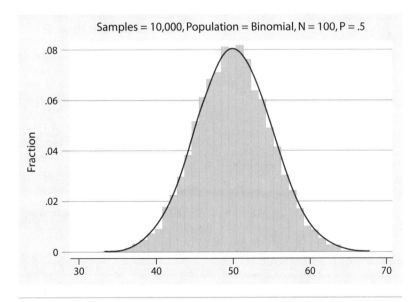

Figure 5.3   Results from 10,000 Coin Toss Experiments, 100 Tosses per Experiment

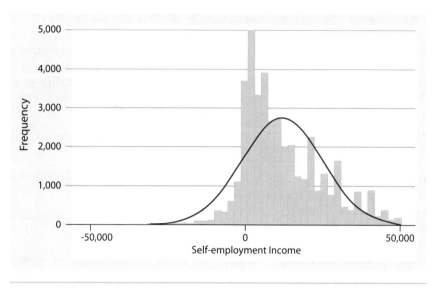

Figure 5.4 Self-employment Income for Those Earning between −$30,000 and $50,000

Source: 2001 Census of Canada

the same statistics that would be used to assess and describe a variable that is normally distributed; such as averages in a coin toss.

Some Useful Terms for Describing Distributions

Below are several useful terms for describing histograms:

a. Symmetrical: Exactly half of the scores fall above the mean, and exactly half of them fall below the mean. Both sides of the mean have the same pattern of distribution.

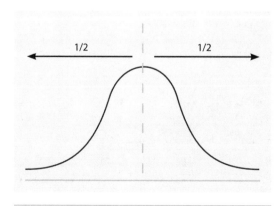

Figure 5.5 Symetrical Curve

b. Skewness: The opposite of symmetrical. Occurs when there are more scores on one side of the mean than on the other, resulting in one of the tails of the histogram being longer than the other. If the right tail is longer than the left (meaning that high values are more spread out than lower values, as in figure 5.4), we say that the histogram is positively skewed, or skewed to the right. Histograms with a longer, lower tail are negatively, or left, skewed.

c. Kurtosis: Refers to how flat or peaked a distribution is. If a distribution is flatter than usual, it has negative kurtosis; if it is more peaked than normal, it has positive kurtosis.

d. Unimodal: A distribution is unimodal when there is only one mode. Histograms of unimodal distributions will have only one major 'hump' in them. The income histogram (figure 5.4) is a good example of this.

e. Bimodal: A distribution with two modes is bimodal, and will have two major 'humps'.

f. Multimodal: Any distribution that has more than two modes.

g. Bell Curve: As shown in figure 5.10, the normal curve is shaped like a bell, so it is often called a bell curve.

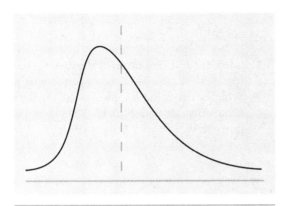

Figure 5.6a   Positively Skewed

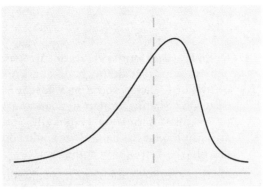

Figure 5.6b   Negatively Skewed

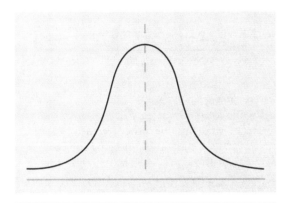

Figure 5.7   Unimodal Distribution

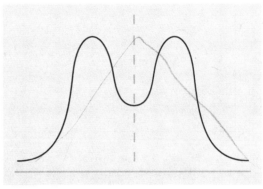

Figure 5.8   Bimodal Distribution

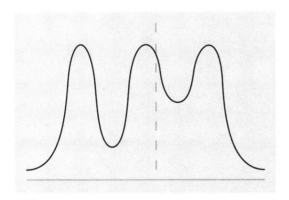

Figure 5.9   Multimodal Distribution

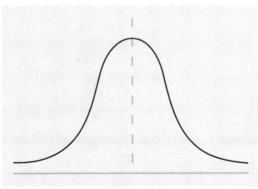

Figure 5.10   The Bell Curve

PRACTICE QUESTIONS

1. Dr Knifewell performs pancreatic surgeries, and has found that although most patients get released quickly, sometimes infections occur, necessitating a longer stay. She wants to see this information graphically, and asks you to plot the data. How would you describe the distribution of the data?

2. Describe the distribution below. Would you say that it is unimodal, bimodal, or multimodal? Is it skewed to the left or the right?

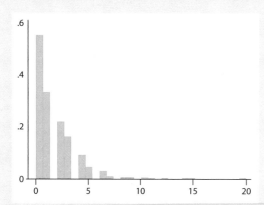

3. Look at the distribution of the variable below, with a super-imposed normal curve. What is the value for the largest outlier? What effect do you think it's having on the kurtosis value of the normal curve?

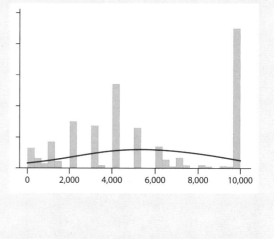

Answers to the practice questions for chapter 5 can be found on page 187.

CHAPTER 6

Measures of Central Tendency and Dispersion

Learning Objectives

This chapter will examine statistical measures used to understand the distribution of any variable. We'll be studying:

- measures of central tendency
- measures of dispersion

Measures of Central Tendency

Depending on the nature of your inquiry, frequencies, percentages, rates, and/or ratios, might not produce the information you want. For example, if you wanted to know how much most Canadians earned in a given year it would be difficult to get that information by using any of the methods that you've already studied in this course. There would be too many categories for you to present in a table.

This is also true for the distribution of variables. To solve the problem you can use the **measures of central tendency** instead of the variables themselves. A common word for a measure of central tendency is an 'average'. It is a 'typical' observation in your data set. Which measure of central tendency you choose to report will depend on the level of measurement and (if your data is continuous) the distribution of your data.

Mode

One measure of central tendency is the **mode**, which is the most frequently occurring value in your data set, on a variable of interest. Suppose we are looking at ethnic origin in the 2001 Canadian census. The mode, or most frequently occurring answer amongst all ethnic-origin categories, would be Canadian (nearly 32 per cent of all respondents checked this box). More census respondents identified as Canadian than any other ethnic origin. Modes are most commonly used for nominal or ordinal data, although they can be used with any level of measurement.

Mean

The most commonly used measure of central tendency is the **mean**.

Suppose that you and nine of your classmates just received the grades from your first Intro Stats exam. The grades were: 25 per cent, 35 per cent, 45 per cent, 47 per cent, 53 per cent, 64 per cent, 67 per cent, 75 per cent, 85 per cent, and 95 per cent (your grade is the 67 per cent). You want to know how you compare to your classmates. One way to do this would be to compare your grade to the arithmetic average, or mean, for the class. To do this, you need to add up all of the individual scores (25 + 35 + 45 + 47 + 53 + 64 + 67 + 75 + 85 + 95 = 591), and divide the sum by 10, the number of observations. This would yield 59.1 per cent (591 ÷ 10 = 59.1 per cent). The difference between your score and the average is 67 per cent – 59.1 per cent. So your score was almost 8 percentage points above the mean.

The mean can be expressed as the sum of all values of a particular variable, where the level of measurement is continuous, divided by the total number of observations used to calculate the sum. As you know from your past exam scores, the mean tells you the value of a 'typical' person.

Let's put that information more formally. The equation for deriving the mean is as follows:

$$\overline{X} = \frac{X_1 + X_2 + X_3 + X_4 + ... + X_N}{N}$$

Or, more simply,

$$\overline{X} = \frac{\sum\limits_{i=1}^{N} X_i}{N}$$

In these equations $\overline{X}$ is equal to the mean of a variable (e.g., age).

$X_1, X_2, X_3,$ etc. are equal to the individual values of X (e.g., person 1 is 20, person 2 is 40, person 3 is 19). X_i indicates the value for individual i (e.g., person 10,763 is 32).

N is equal to the total number of observations (e.g., $N = 10,763$). The second equation merely simplifies the first. Thus $\sum X$ = the sum ($\sum$) of the X values for the sample (replacing the $X_1, X_2, X_3... X_N$, etc.). The denominator does not change.

Here's another example of the mean. Let's suppose that we have five yearly income values: $5,000, $10,000, $15,000, $20,000, and $25,000. The mean is obtained by summing the five values ($5,000 + $10,000 + $15,000 + $20,000 + $25,000 = $75,000), and dividing the sum by five, or the number of observations. This gives us $15,000, which is the income of the average person in the sample.

The average person is an abstraction. There does not need to be someone in your sample with the mean value. A test average could be 59 per cent, even if no one received that score. The average value is still useful because it tells you how you rank compared to the average.

Median

The third measure of central tendency is the **median**. Let's return to the five income values that we used to derive the mean. Sort the incomes by their value, and find the value that falls exactly in the middle; that's the median. In this example we have five observations, so the third individual is the person in the middle, and their income ($15,000) is the median of this sample. If there were an even numbers of observations (say, six instead of five), the calculation would be more complex. We would need to find the middle pair of numbers (the third and fourth observation), and then find the value that's halfway between them, by adding the values together and dividing by two.

In this example the median and the mean are the same. This is often the case when data is normally distributed—something we'll cover in chapter 7. Often there will be extreme values (very high or very low ones), which have a much stronger impact on the mean than the median. The total average income earned by everyone over the age of 14 in the 2001 Canadian census was $27,395.70, but the individual values ranged from negative $50,000 to $200,000.[1] Since there is a substantial number of Canadians earning a large income, the mean will be affected by the extreme values. With variables that have extreme values, like income, the median is the preferred measure of central tendency, because it provides a truer picture of the average person. How typical is a person earning $200,000 or more? The answer is 'not very typical', but these high earners have a huge impact on calculation of the mean (imagine how many people it would

---

[1]Yes, some people in Canada have negative income! Can you think of when this might occur? Hint: in some years, some businesses and investments lose money. Also, Statistics Canada recodes everyone earning more than $200,000 to prevent breaching confidentiality.

Whose idea was it to compute summary statistics, and for what purpose? 'Mean' is a very old term (Walker, 1929), sharing its roots with 'median' from the Latin *mediānus*, for 'middle'. Although the concept of an average is quite common, the use of the mean has a long history. The mean is largely a descriptive and utilitarian measure (Stigler, 1986). In the eighteenth century, astronomers would average measurements, but only a small number and only if they were all taken under similar conditions. These measurements of celestial bodies were taken for the purposes of navigation. Pierre-Simon Laplace (1749–1827) worked on the mean in that context by comparing three observations, and published a paper on the subject in 1776.

Adolphe Quetelet (1796–1874) advanced the work of Laplace. Quetelet was an astronomer, statistician, and sociologist. He was interested in the mean as more than a descriptive measure. 'The stability of statistical aggregates, and hence of mean values, was the foundation of the science of social physics that Quetelet announced in 1831. Its key concept was *l'homme moyen*, the average man (Gigerenzer et al., 1991: 41). Quetelet measured physical characteristics, finding their distribution and mean. From that he equated the normal with 'the good', and deviation with deviance. Quetelet believed that if God produced man in His image, but in an imperfect way, some men came closer to the perfect, or divine, image of man than others.

take to remove the impact of 10 people earning $200,000!). When you have extremely high values, the median will be lower than the mean; when there are extremely low values, the median will exceed the mean. Since we have a cluster of people earning $200,000, the median is significantly lower than the mean, at $20,517.

Measures of Variability

The normal curve doesn't just describe a **distribution**, it refers to assumptions about the data. Those assumptions grant statisticians access to a rich and diverse toolkit for data analysis. But to get to that point one must understand measures of variability.

The Range

The range is the easiest to understand of all of the measures of variance. Range is the lowest value subtracted from the highest value:

$$Range = H - L$$

Where H is the highest value of your variable, and L is the lowest. For the example of the five yearly income values, the range would be $25,000 – $5,000 = $20,000.

Mean Deviation

The range is useful for revealing how 'wide', or spread out, the values are. What it cannot tell you is how far the 'average' person is from the mean value. For example, it is possible that all values but two (one extremely high and one extremely low) are tightly clustered around the mean, but you would not know that by looking at the range.

The simplest method of determining how an observation ranks in the sample is the mean deviation. Defined as the average 'distance' that each variable is from the class mean, the mean deviation is superior to the range because it reveals more than the difference between the highest and lowest scores (i.e., the most extreme values); it shows how far the average is from the mean. This shows how similar the individuals in your sample are, rather than just the highest or lowest-scoring person. The equation for the mean deviation is:

$$MeanDeviation = \frac{\sum |X - \overline{X}|}{N}$$

The mean deviation is the sum of the **absolute values** of the distances from the mean, divided by the total number of observations. Continuing with our income example, we'd subtract the mean

BOX 6.2 THE STEPS: MEAN DEVIATION

The mean deviation for any sample can be easily obtained:

1. Subtract the mean from each value.
2. Sum the absolute values.
3. Divide the sum by the number of observations in your sample. This is the mean deviation.

from every value (5,000 – 15,000 = –10,000; 10,000 – 15,000 = –5,000; 15,000 – 15,000 = 0; 20,000 – 15,000 = 5,000; 25,000 – 15,000 = 10,000), sum the absolute values (10,000 + 5,000 + 5,000 + 10,000 = 30,000), and divide by the total number of observations to get $6,000 ($30,000 / 5 = $6,000)

Although you've probably encountered absolute values already, it's good to be reminded that absolute value refers to the positive score of every value. The absolute values of –1, 2, –5, 11, and –100 would be 1, 2, 5, 11, and 100, respectively.

Variance and the Standard Deviation

The mean deviation is a useful measure of the **dispersion** of values for a variable, but since the absolute value has no straightforward mathematical relationship with the location of reported values, it is not usually used. Luckily, there are more desirable measures.

Two alternatives to the mean deviation are **standard deviation** and **variance**. Both are closely related to the mean deviation, but neither uses absolute values.

The **variance** is the average *squared* distance (as opposed to absolute value) from the mean value. Squaring values eliminates negative values. Each observation contributes to the overall calculation of deviation. The equation is:

$$s^2 = \frac{\sum (X - \overline{X})^2}{N}$$

In the equation, the numerator is also known as the **sum of squares.** It represents the sum of the squared deviations from the mean (note: we will use this frequently in the remainder of the text).

The standard deviation is the square root of the variance. Here's the equation:

$$s = \sqrt{\frac{\sum (X - \overline{X})^2}{N}}$$

Although there are similarities between the standard deviation, the mean deviation, and the variance, researchers most often use the standard deviation for dispersion because it can easily be related to the normal curve.

BOX 6.3 THE STEPS: VARIANCE AND THE STANDARD DEVIATION

The variance for any sample can be easily obtained by:

1. Subtracting the mean from each value.
2. Squaring the differences calculated in step 1. These are the squared deviations.
3. Adding the squared deviations together.
4. Dividing the sum by the number of observations in your sample.
5. To get the sample standard deviation, take the square root of the variance.

BOX 6.4 VARIANCE AND STANDARD DEVIATION: HISTORY OF TWO TERMS

The term 'standard deviation', and the symbol σ (the Greek sigma), were first used by Pearson in 1893 (Walker, 1929; Pearson, 1894). Variance was first employed by R.A. Fisher, in 1918 (Walker, 1929).

Pearson developed standard deviation in the context of evolution, using the error curve, or *normal curve*. When discussing biological matters, there is not uniformity and universality of specimens. To understand and describe genetic and population variations, not only is it important to recognize the measures of central tendency at work, but it's also important to have a formalized manner of discussing the ends of the curve, and the population described by the curve's extremities.

PRACTICE QUESTIONS

1. Last year a small statistical consulting company paid each of its 5 clerks $22,000, 2 statistical analysts earned $50,000 each, and the senior statistician/owner $270,000.

   a. How many employees earn less than the mean salary?
   b. What is the salary range?

2. The following 10 numbers represent the number of times a random sample of celebrities has signed autographs in the past month:

   46 57 68 2 4 14 0 0 2 101

   What is the mean, and mean deviation, for these numbers?

3. A sample of underweight babies was fed a special diet and the following weight gains (in lbs) were observed at the end of 3 months:

   6.7. 2.7 2.5 3.6 3.4 4.1 4.8 5.9 8.3

   What are the mean, standard deviation, and variance of the weight gains?

4. If most of the measurements in a large data set are of approximately the same magnitude, except for a few measurements that are quite a bit larger, how would the mean and median of the data set compare, and what shape would a histogram of the data set be?

5. A sample of 99 distances has a mean of 24 metres and a median of 24.5 metres. Unfortunately, it has just been discovered that an observation erroneously recorded as '30' actually has a value of '35'. If we make this correction to the data, what would happen to the value of the mean? What about the median?

6. Whenever means and medians are compared for income in Canada, the mean is higher. Why do you think this is?

7. Over the past 100 to 200 years, several things have happened to the age distribution of Canadians. First, family sizes have been decreasing, which means that couples are having fewer children. Second, Canadians are living longer. Third, rates of premature death have declined. Thinking about these 3 changes, discuss what you believe has happened to the mean, median, range, and standard deviation across the time period.

Answers to the practice questions for chapter 6 can be found on page 187.

CHAPTER 7

Standard Deviations, Standard Scores, and the Normal Distribution

Introduction

The crime rate in Prince Edward Island is 8,963 per 100,000 persons. That might seem high (or low), but how can you know? How does PEI's crime rate compare to that of other provinces? What about US states? If the rate is high, how high is it relative to other places? If there's a difference between them, is the difference meaningful? What if it's due to chance? These questions lead to the focus of this chapter: how do we compare the values of different groups within a sample?

To answer those questions beyond comparing the means, we'll need to apply and expand on what was covered in the previous chapters. By the end of this chapter, you'll have enough statistical knowledge to place observations on a normal distribution, and to rank values on a common metric using the **standard score** (or **z-score**). Before we examine crime rates, you'll need to know how the mean and standard deviation relate to the normal curve.

How Does the Standard Deviation Relate to the Normal Curve?

First, let's discuss σ, the population standard deviation. Move beyond the detached calculations in the last chapter, and think of the standard deviation as a unit of measurement along an already-known continuum. The continuum is the **normal curve**. The standard deviation and standard score are used to determine the rank of an observation. Understanding these concepts will allow you to discuss your data with other people, even if they don't know the particulars of your study area.

For example, say you sell boats, and need an accountant to increase your business's profitability. She wouldn't need to know the boat business to help you. She knows about money, and money remains the same across all businesses.

The standard deviation is like money: both are units of measurement. Although not as common as money, the standard deviation is used to describe characteristics of the normal distribution. Using the mean and standard deviation, the normal curve provides information about the characteristics of a variable. As in the example, it is not necessary to know anything about a variable or a study to see if its results show important differences between groups.

More on the Normal Distribution

Most observations lie beneath the normal curve, and are subject to the rules of normal distributions. Because of that, there are standardized cut-points (standard deviations) that give a metric for determining the proportion of all observations that lie in six predetermined distances from the mean (which is usually denoted by μ, the Greek letter mu). There are usually three or four of these points above the mean, and three or four below. To further illustrate this, consider figure 7.1.

Figure 7.1 is a plot of the means of 10,000 samples of 200 observations. Or, the average of 200 observations on an interval/ratio variable (number of strikes at a plant, number of children, heart rate, yield per acre, or anything else), repeated 10,000 times. Don't worry about this too much. We'll talk about it more when we get to **sampling distributions**. At this point, think of each mean as an observation.

As we saw in the previous chapter, the mean is useful because we know that 50 per cent of all observations have values that exceed the mean, and 50 per cent have values that do not (assuming a normal distribution). By knowing the mean and the score on a particular variable, we can determine whether a person is in the top or bottom half of the sample. The mean provides a useful 'cut-point' for assessing how an individual ranks. Suppose you wanted to find other cut-points. You would need to use the standard deviation, which you learned about in the last chapter, and the **standard score** (also known as the **z-score** or **normal score**).

The standard deviation allows more cut-points (usually six or eight) where the distribution of observations is known. The standard deviation shows what proportion of the sample, or population, lies on either side of certain key values. These values are given by the standard deviation, and they are denoted with red lines in figure 7.1. The line in the centre of the histogram is μ (mu), the mean, and has a value of zero. The mean value of the raw

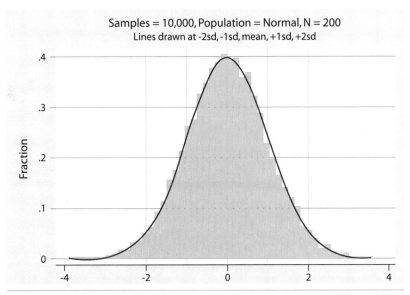

Figure 7.1 The Normal Distribution with Normal Curve and Standard Deviation Lines

scores is not necessarily zero, but when the values of a variable are standardized zero is used for convenience. The red lines that move away from the mean are standard deviation markers. In the case of figure 7.1 they are at ±1σ, ±2σ, and ±3σ (note: ± is shorthand for plus or minus, so ±1σ is 'plus or minus one standard deviation from the mean').

Using the central limit theorem, we know that approximately 68.26 per cent of all observations lie between ±1 standard deviations from the mean, that about 95 per cent of all observations can be found between ±2 standard deviations from the mean (the more accurate figure is 95.44 per cent), and almost all observations (about 99.74 per cent) lie between ±3 standard deviations from the mean. To see exact percentages in your data the sample size would have to be very large—larger than what's usually available. The data would also have to be *very* normally distributed.

Consider this scenario: suppose that you want to know the average number of people kayaking around the Champlain Bridge area of the Ottawa River per day. Since you want a good number of time points, you decide to use an hourly average for each experiment. You stretch your study out over the June–August period, yielding roughly 1,000 data points (you take a few vacation days off). Your sample mean is 32.3, and your standard deviation is 10.2. You could graph these data as a histogram like the one in figure 7.2.

Following convention, the mean for figure 7.2 is given a value of zero. Values higher than the mean are positioned to the right of zero, and negative values are to the left. This is done so that anyone can understand the data without knowing anything about the subject matter. The numbers across the horizontal axis don't refer to the number of kayakers per hour, but instead to the numbers of kayakers expressed in standard deviation units. Since the standard deviation is a commonly used measure, it is possible to use the information from other, unrelated data sets to study kayaking traffic on the Ottawa River. The *y*-axis is the fraction of experiments.

Even with 1,000 observations, the data for the number of kayakers approximates the normal curve fairly well, despite some gaps between the normal curve line and the bars representing the data. If we continued to stand on the Champlain Bridge and observe, the fit would improve. Since we know this to be true, we can assume that the normal curve is a fairly good approximation of the average number of kayakers on the Ottawa River. This allows us to apply what we know about the normal curve to our kayaking example.

Knowing the standard deviation allows us to estimate the proportion of all hours where mean values are above and/or below the grand sample mean and ±1, ±2, and ±3 standard deviations. Now, instead of only knowing whether any par-

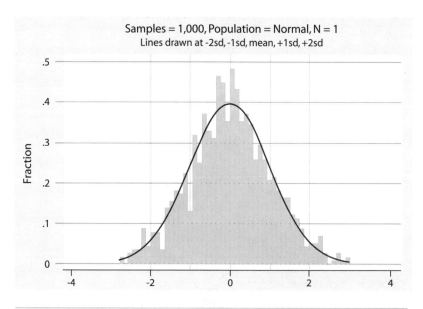

Figure 7.2 Kayakers on the Ottawa River: A Hypothetical Example

ticular hour is above or below average, we can also begin to determine the *distance* a particular observation is from the mean. From this, we can determine where any particular hour is positioned relative to all other hours.

We know a lot about normal distributions. We know, for example, that about 99 per cent of all observations are between ±3 standard deviations from the mean. So approximately 1 per cent of all cases are outside of this range, because 100 per cent – 99 per cent = 1 per cent. We also know that roughly 68 per cent of all observations are within ±1 standard deviation from the mean, and that 32 per cent of all observations are likely to differ from the mean by at least 1 standard deviation (100 per cent – 68 per cent = 32 per cent). Finally, the same procedure applies for 2 standard deviations (100 per cent – 95 per cent = 5 per cent).

With the standard deviation, it is easy to determine the proportion of people above or below the standard deviation cut-points. This is done by subtracting the number of standard deviations of the cut-point you are interested in from 100.

In our kayaking example, we know that there will probably be between 22.1 and 42.5 kayakers for 68 per cent of all days in June through August (mean of 32.3 ±1 standard deviation of 10.2), between 11.9 and 52.7 kayakers on 95 per cent of all days (mean of 32.3 ± 2 standard deviations of 10.2), and between 1.7 and 62.9 kayakers on just about any given day (mean of 32.3 ±3 standard deviations of 10.2).

This captures the observations that are on the centre portion of the normal distribution (it ignores the tails), but what if we're only interested in the left or right tail? This is a one-tailed assessment, and can be found by dividing the values by two. For example, if we want to know the number of cases *below* –3 standard deviations, we divide 1 per cent by two. We now know that roughly 1 per cent of all cases lie above or below 3 standard deviations from the mean, which means that half of 1 per cent, or 0.5 per cent, must lie below –3 standard deviations from the mean. Returning to our example, for 0.5 per cent of hours there are less than 1.7 kayakers on the river. We find this by using the '68-95-99 rule', which refers to the proportion of observations between 1, 2, and 3 standard deviations from the mean.

An Extension of the Standard Deviation: The Standard Score

The standard deviation is a great way to determine how many observations are on either side of ±1σ, ±2σ, and ±3σ, but what if you want to set your own cut-point, such as the value that separates the bottom 10 per cent of your observations from the top 90 per cent? Suppose you wanted to study the characteristics of the lowest achievers in elementary school, and decided to look at the lowest 10 per cent. Or that you wanted to study the world's most volatile nation-states, and you chose to identify them by how many years of peace they've had. Maybe you're interested in understanding the regularity of the gestation period of rabbits, using the number of days of pregnancy. Whether you're interested in

 BOX 7.1 IT'S YOUR TURN: DETERMINING THE PROPORTION OF OBSERVATIONS AT VARIOUS STANDARD DEVIATION CUT-POINTS

Now that you know the '68-95-99 rule', can you determine approximately what percentage of all observations lie at the following cut-points?

1. Below –2 standard deviations?
2. Above +3 standard deviations?
3. Above the mean?
4. Above +1 standard deviation?
5. Below +2 standard deviation?

The solution for box 7.1 can be found on page 196.

low blood pressure, high earnings, large families, small insects, or high mortality rates, the standard score allows you to compare a single score with those of the population of interest.

The equation for the standard score is:

$$z = \frac{X - \mu}{\sigma}$$

z = the z or standard score (expressed in standard deviations)
X = an individual's raw score
μ = the sample mean
σ = the sample standard deviation

The standard score, or z-score, is interpreted as a standard deviation that doesn't need to be stated as an integer. Since z-scores are standardized, the sum and mean are zero. The formula for the z-score will convert the score of any individual observation into a z-value. The value is directly related to that of the standard deviation. A z-score of +1.0 is equivalent to 1 standard deviation above the mean. A z-score of –2.0 is the same as 2 standard deviations below the mean, etc. The difference is that it is possible to have a z-score of 1.5, but not a non-integer standard deviation.

Converting raw scores (test averages, heart beats per minute, etc.) to z-scores makes it possible to determine the rank of *any* score. This rank is expressed in **percentiles**. Like standard deviations, the standard score lets you place an observation on the normal curve so that you can express the proportion of the sample, or population, above or below a particular value. Unlike the standard deviation, there are more scores to remember than the 68-95-99 rule, so you might not remember all of the critical cut-point values. Appendix A has a table for converting z-scores to percentile ranks.

Table 7.1 is a primer, containing a few z-scores.

The first column in table 7.1 lists the z-score, followed by the proportion of all observations that lie between the mean and the z-score. The third column lists the proportion of observations that are beyond the calculated z-score (the percentage of all observations in a tail). Since the z-score is a standardized measure, these values remain true for any normally distributed variable.

There will be times when you will need to determine the area between two z-scores. Continu-

ing the kayaking example, if you wanted to know how many days you might see between 20 and 40 kayakers, you would need to calculate two z-scores, one to establish a lower bound, and one for the upper bound. The mean number of kayakers is 32.3, and the standard deviation is 10.2. Calculate the lower bound first:

$$z = \frac{X - \mu}{\sigma}$$

$$= \frac{20 - 32.3}{10.2}$$

$$= \frac{-12.3}{10.2}$$

$$= -1.21$$

Table 7.1 The z-Table (area under the normal curve)

A	B	C
	Area between	Area
z-score	z and mean	beyond z
0.0	0.000	0.500
0.1	0.040	0.460
0.2	0.079	0.421
0.3	0.118	0.382
0.4	0.155	0.345
0.5	0.192	0.309
0.6	0.226	0.274
0.7	0.258	0.242
0.8	0.288	0.292
0.9	0.316	0.184
1.0	0.342	0.159
1.1	0.364	0.136
1.2	0.385	0.115
•	•	•
•	•	•
•	•	•
1.96	**0.475**	**0.025**
2.0	0.477	0.023
2.1	0.482	0.018
2.2	0.486	0.014
2.3	0.489	0.011
2.4	0.492	0.008
2.5	0.494	0.006

Next, the upper bound:

$$z = \frac{X - \mu}{\sigma}$$

$$= \frac{40 - 32.3}{10.2}$$

$$= \frac{7.7}{10.2}$$

$$= 0.75$$

Next, find these scores on the z-table. Usually only positive values can be found on a z-table, so look for the nearest absolute value; –1.21 becomes 1.21. You'll need to subtract the value for 1.21 from 1.

For 1.21, the closest z-value is 1.2, and for 0.75 the closest value is 0.8. Since we want to know the number of days *between* the two scores, we need to use information from column B. The value for 1.2 is 0.387, and for 0.8 it is 0.291. The first value tells us that there will be a z-score number of kayakers between 1.2 and 0 (the mean) for 38.7 per cent of all days. The value of 0.291 tells us that 29.1 per cent of all days will have a z-score of between 0 and 0.8. Adding these two values together yields 0.678, which means that roughly 68 per cent of days will have a z-score between –1.2 and 0.8, or between 20 and 40 kayakers, assuming that the number of kayakers on the Ottawa River follows a normal distribution.

A z-score can also be translated back into its actual value (such as the number of kayakers per hour). Suppose that we wanted to determine, with 95 per cent confidence, how many kayakers we would see in an hour. To determine this, work backwards from the formula. Instead of calculating z, which is unknown in the example above, we would calculate the upper and lower values of X, the cut-points that 95 per cent of observations are found in.

First, look at the z-table. Use the value where 47.5 per cent of all observations lie between z and the mean (column B). This table represents the absolute values of z. If you want to know the area both above and below the mean, you'll have to place a negative sign in front of the lower value. Since we want the z-value for the point where 47.5 per cent of all cases fall between z and the mean, we find it in column B: 1.96. We find the value for 47.5 per cent because it's half of 95 per

cent, the number we want to capture. By ensuring that 47.5 per cent of our cases are above the mean, and that 47.5 per cent are below, we get a total of 95 per cent of all cases. We can insert the known values into our equation for the z-statistic, focusing first on the lower bound (where we assign a negative value to the z-statistic):

$$z = \frac{X - \mu}{\sigma}$$

$$-1.96 = \frac{X - 32.3}{10.2}$$

$$-1.96 * 10.2 = X - 32.3$$

$$-19.99 + 32.3 = X$$

$$12.31 = X$$

For the upper bound:

$$z = \frac{X - \mu}{\sigma}$$

$$1.96 = \frac{X - 32.3}{10.2}$$

$$1.96 * 10.2 = X - 32.3$$

$$19.99 + 32.3 = X$$

$$52.29 = X$$

We can be 95 per cent confident that in any given hour between June and August, from the Champlain Bridge we'll see between 12.31 and 52.29 kayakers on the Ottawa River.

One-Tailed Assessments

So far, we have been finding ranges where we know the upper and lower points. We've been looking at the proportion of observations *between* two known values, as in figure 7.3.

While the information in figure 7.3 is useful, it is also useful to know the percentage of observations above or below a specified point. To use our kayaking example, we might want to know the number of hours when we would see 20 or fewer kayakers. Or maybe we want to know when we'd see over 50 kayakers. In either case, we are only interested in observations above or below a specified point, as shown in figure 7.4.

When performing a one-tailed assessment we must look at a different column on the z-table than for a two-tailed assessment. Instead of column B, we must now focus on column C. The

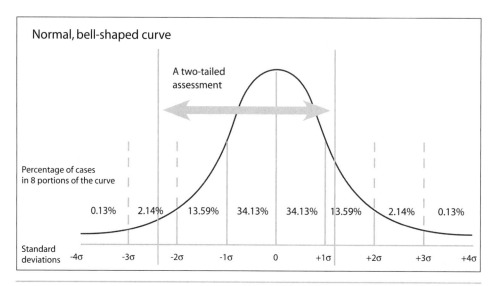

Figure 7.3 A Two-Tailed Assessment

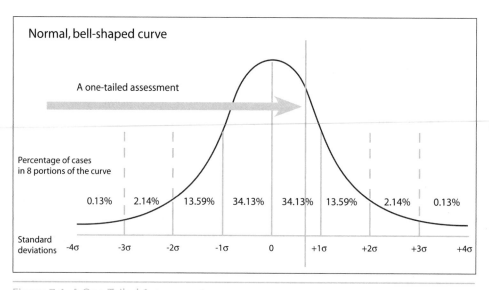

Figure 7.4 A One-Tailed Assessment

change is very subtle, particularly since the number in column B plus the number in column C always captures exactly half of the normal distribution, and is always equal to 0.5, representing half of all observations.

To illustrate a one-tailed assessment, let's continue with our kayaking example. Suppose that we were starting a parasailing club, and wanted to determine whether the Champlain Bridge area of the Ottawa River was sufficiently traffic-free (which we define as fewer than 10 kayakers per hour) to have our club there. What we need to know is what percentage of all summer hours have low kayaking traffic.

We'd need to calculate the z-statistic for 10 kayakers. We can use the same equation as before:

$$z = \frac{X - \mu}{\sigma}$$

$$= \frac{10 - 32.3}{10.2}$$

$$= \frac{-22.3}{10.2}$$

$$= -2.19$$

Instead of looking for how this corresponds with column B, which contains the area *between* the mean and z, we need to look at the area *beyond z* (as always, treat the z-statistic as an absolute value). We see the number 0.0143, which is very low, suggesting that we're likely to see fewer than 10 kayakers per hour 1.4 per cent of the time. We may want to consider another location for our club.

What if you wanted to find a high traffic area, and see how many hours we could expect to see more than 40 kayakers. The calculation would be the same:

$$z = \frac{X - \mu}{\sigma}$$

$$= \frac{40 - 32.3}{10.2}$$

$$= \frac{7.7}{10.2}$$

$$= 0.75$$

Looking at column C of the z-table for 0.75 gives us a value of 0.2266. We could expect to see at least 40 kayakers per hour 22.7 per cent of the time.

So far we have assumed that we are always looking for low values when the cut-off is below the mean or high values when the cut-off is above the mean. The final scenario is one in which we want to know the percentage of all observations above a value when that value is below the mean, or the percentage of all observations below a value when that value is above the mean. To do that, we need to modify the values in the z-table slightly. Let's suppose that we want to know what percentage of all hours we would expect to see *fewer* than 40 kayakers. The z-value would remain the same, at 0.75, and we would still need to look at the value in column C, but we'd need to subtract that value from 100, yielding 77.3 per cent of all observations. The difference between this calculation and the previous one is that 22.7 per cent refers to all values above a z-value of 0.75, or 40 kayakers. There we were interested in the information to the right of the cut-off point. Here we are interested in the information to the left of the cut-off point, which is everything except 22.7 per cent. Since we begin with 100 per cent of all observations, we need only to subtract the portion we're not interested in.

Instead of subtracting the z-value from 100, one could get the same answer by taking the number in column B (0.2734), and adding 0.50. This is possible because 50 per cent of all observations lie on each side of the mean, so column B refers to the proportion of all observations between a specified value and the mean. If you are conducting a one-tailed assessment and will be dealing with more than half of all observations, this is the procedure that you'll have to use. If you are using less than half of all observations, the simple technique will work.

To help keep all of this straight, it is useful to draw a histogram like the one in figure 7.5.

Probabilities and the Normal Distribution

The normal curve can be used to determine the probability that a person will have a trait, characteristic, or quality. Everything we learned up to now applies, except that we're dealing with probabilities, instead of sample means, scattered across the normal distribution.

Suppose we want to know the probability of randomly selecting someone who earns between $23,000 and $50,000 from the population of Québec. According to the 2001 census, the mean income in Québec is $25,171, with a standard deviation of $24,495 (this number is probably low; public use census data collapse extreme values). The first thing we need to do is calculate two z-statistics, one for $25,000:

$$z = \frac{X - \mu}{\sigma}$$

$$= \frac{23000 - 25171}{24495}$$

$$= \frac{-2171}{24495}$$

$$= -0.09$$

And one for $50,000:

$$z = \frac{X - \mu}{\sigma}$$

$$= \frac{50000 - 25171}{24495}$$

$$= \frac{24829}{24495}$$

$$= 1.01$$

Next, we need to look the values up on the z-table (using column B because we're interested in a

BOX 7.2 HOW TO CONVERT THE STANDARD SCORE TO A RANKING: AN EXAMPLE

Between 1980 and 2004, Canada admitted over 4.5 million immigrants. The average years of schooling for this group is 11.42, with a standard deviation of 4.8 years. Suppose that a person has 10 years of education, and we want to know the proportion of people with more than 10 years of education.

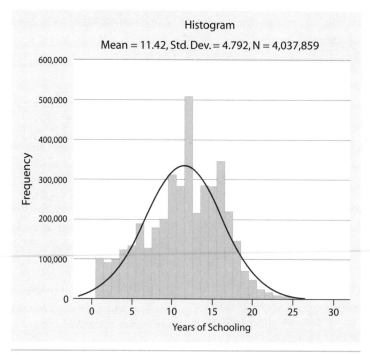

Figure 7.5   Average Years of Schooling of Canadian Immigrants, 1980–2004

Source: Landed Immigrant Data Survey

Since the distance between our observed value and the mean is less than one standard deviation, we need to convert our score with the following equation:

$$z = \frac{X - \mu}{\sigma} \text{, or } z = \frac{10 - 11.42}{4.8} \text{, or roughly } \mathbf{-0.296}$$

Plunking this number into our table gives us the value 0.386, meaning that **61.4 per cent** (100–38.6) of all immigrants to Canada have more than 10 years of education.

BOX 7.3 IT'S YOUR TURN: CONVERTING STANDARD SCORES TO PERCENTILE RANKS

Emily loved to eat out and go to movies with her friends, but her parents thought these activities were a waste of time and money. She was sure that everyone her age went out at least three times a week. Her parents did not agree—they were convinced the majority of people only go out for special occasions, maybe once a month. Using the public use microdata files collected as part of the 2004 General Social Survey, Emily looked for the number of evenings per month that Canadians between the ages of 18 and 29 reported they went to restaurants, movies, or theaters. She recoded people who went out 'less than once a month' as going out once a month, as she did not want to exclude these people just because their response was not a whole number. She found the following:

The mean number of nights per month people went out was 5.7. The standard deviation was 5.1. (Weighted n = 5,183,000 [rounded to thousands], excludes residents of the Yukon, Northwest Territories, and Nunavut, and full-time residents of institutions.)

Using the chart in Appendix A and the equation for the standard score, determine the following:

1. The range of values ±1 standard deviation from the mean.
2. The value that the lowest 10 per cent of all observations fall below.
3. The value that the highest 40 per cent of all observations are above.
4. The percentage of cases that fall between the values of 4 and 9.
5. The value that 75 per cent of all observations fall below.

The solution for box 7.3 can be found on page 196.

---

range). We find that the values are 0.0359 and 0.3438. Adding the scores together yields 0.3797, so there's about a 38 per cent chance of randomly selecting someone who earns between $23,000 and $50,000 from the Québec population.

That number probably seems a bit high because income is not a normally distributed variable. It is difficult to earn less than zero dollars, although some do (such as the self-employed). It is also difficult to earn a lot of money, although some do that too. Using techniques for normal distributions on income will probably introduce a lot of errors into our estimates.

Look at the comparison of the ways to describe scores on a normal distribution. To get a better sense of how the normal curve relates to standard deviation, cumulative percentages, and percentiles, consider figure 7.6.

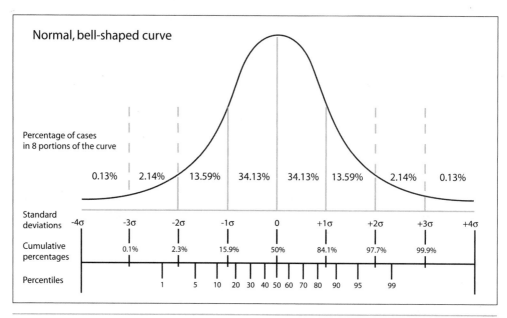

Figure 7.6 Standard Deviations, Cumulative Percentages, Percentiles, and the Normal Curve

PRACTICE QUESTIONS

1. For the numbers below find the area between the mean and the z:

   a. $z = -1.18$
   b. $z = 0.84$
   c. $z = -2.06$
   d. $z = 1.36$

2. For the numbers below find the percentile rank (the percentage of individuals scoring below z).

   a. $z = 2.25$
   b. $z = -1.67$
   c. $z = 1.43$
   d. $z = -0.44$

3. For the numbers below find the per cent of cases falling above the z.

   a. $z = 0.25$
   b. $z = -1.21$
   c. $z = 1.21$
   d. $z = -2.01$

4. For the numbers below find percent of cases falling between the two z-scores.

   a. $z = -0.38 \ \& \ z = 1.63$
   b. $z = 0.88 \ \& \ z = 1.55$
   c. $z = -1.93 \ \& \ z = 1.09$
   d. $z = -2.22 \ \& \ z = -1.34$

5. Sigmund wrote a statistics exam and scored 45 (mean = 52, standard deviation of 5). What is his percentile rank?

6. Lesley wrote the same test and scored 54. What percent of individuals received a higher score?

7. You believe that your child is a genius and decide to have him write a standardized achievement test. To your delight, he scores a 148 (mean = 125, S = 15). What is your child's percentile rank?

8. Feng and Lucy both took a spatial abilities test (mean = 80, S = 8). Feng scored a 76 and Lucy scored a 94. What percentage of individuals would score between Feng and Lucy?

Answers to the practice questions for chapter 7 can be found on page 187.

CHAPTER 8

Sampling

Learning Objectives

Up to this point, we've only worked with entire **populations**. Including all relevant observations is beneficial because it allows you to be certain that your results accurately describe your population. In reality you are likely to be working with **samples** most of the time, which requires some background information. Consequently, in this chapter you'll:

- learn how to identify a sample
- examine the main sampling types of probability and non-probability samples

Introduction

There are times when including the entire population is costly, cumbersome, or otherwise problematic. In 2001 the population of Canada was just over 30 million. If the entire population was retained, the 2001 Census of Canada file would have over 30 million observations. Even with the speed of today's computers, it would take a long time to perform even basic analysis on such a large group. Using all of the data would also make it possible to identify persons, breaching Statistics Canada's assurance of **confidentiality**.

In these situations, it makes more sense to use a **sample**. We're more alike than we are differ-

ent, so it would be unnecessary to include everyone every time we do any analysis. For example, if you wanted to know how much the average university student earns, you would not need to ask every single student because most students probably earn about the same amount of money. But since they're not identical we can't reduce the sample size to one. In these circumstances it is useful to look at a sample, or portion, of the population, because we can capture most of the information about the entire population without analyzing everyone.

A sample that is accurately and carefully selected, without a lot of **sampling error**, allows a precise analysis without including the full population.

We're going to look at some of the challenges and potential pitfalls of using samples in quantitative research, by examining methods for deriving samples, and identifying the strengths and weaknesses of each method. Then we'll cover the sources and consequences of bias in the sample.

Probability Samples

There are two types of sampling techniques: **probability** and **non-probability**. In a probability sample, each unit has a known chance of being selected. In a random sample, we can select 10 observations out of a population of 100. Each observation has a 10 per cent chance of being included. If we wanted to sample 100 people on a university campus, 50 students and 50 professors, and there were 100 professors and 5,000 students, the probability of inclusion would be different for the two subpopulations. For professors, the selection probability would be 50/100, or 50 per cent, and for students the chance of being selected would only be 50/5,000, or 1 per cent.

Probability samples have several desirable qualities. They are representative, allowing for generalization from sample to population. This means that:

1. Sample means can be used to estimate population means.
2. If the population is normally distributed, the sample will be normally distributed too.
3. It is possible to estimate the discrepancy between sample mean and population mean. This measurement is the sampling error.
4. It is possible to test how well our results resemble what we could expect to see in the population using **inferential statistical tests.**
5. Once a sample is selected, a variety of methods may be used to contact respondents, including mail, telephone, and internet surveys.

In the next section, the four most popular types of probability samples are described. Keep in mind that each of the examples below is an ideal type. Any sample used by a statistical agency, such as Statistics Canada, is likely a combination of these types.

Simple Random Sample

Simple random samples are probably the most basic probability samples. To select one, list all possible units, number them consecutively, and then use a random number chart (like the one in Appendix F) to select a certain number, or percentage, of units. In a simple random sample, every unit has an equal probability of selection. The probability of selection is n/N, where n = sample size and N = population size.

Suppose that we have a population of 100 and we want to derive a sample of 10 observations. Each observation in a random sample would have a 10/100, or 1 in 10, chance of being selected in the sample. This means that the probability of selection is 10 per cent.

Systematic Random Sample

Instead of choosing units using a random number chart, for a **systematic random sample** units are chosen from a **sampling frame**. The person deriving the sample can use a chart to select a random starting point or choose their own. Then they consistently choose every nth unit (such as every 10th observation). As long as there is no inherent ordering in the data set, a systematic random sample will represent the population fairly accurately, though not as well as a simple random sample, since it is not quite as random. Imagine that you were selecting every third person for your sample and for some reason they were more likely to be female. Your sample would have a disproportionate number of females, and not be truly random. However, systematic random samples are a quick and accurate approximation of a simple random sample.

Stratified/Hierarchical Random Sample

A stratified sample can be best described as a series of two or more simple random samples operating within the same population. If you wanted to compile a representative sample of the population of Montréal by age, you would need to ensure that your sample contained a representative ratio of people within each predefined age grouping (0 to15, 16 to 30, 31 to 45, 46 to 60, etc.). To do this, find the proportionate number of people in each age stratum, then stratify the population by appropriate criteria (age), and randomly select the appropriate number of people from each category. Suppose you had six age groupings, and wanted to ensure that you had a good number of people from each. With a stratified sample you would take a simple random sample of people *within* each age group, instead of taking one simple random sample and hoping that each age group was equally represented.

Cluster Sample

Cluster sampling is an easy way of gathering a large sample. It is used when researchers cannot get a complete list of the population they wish to study, but can get a complete list of groups, or 'clusters', of the population. Rather than select individuals at random, this technique randomly chooses clusters. Usually, everyone in a cluster is included in the sample.

Suppose you wanted to investigate the use of lawn pesticides by residents of Kelowna, but didn't have the resources to randomly sample the entire city. A cluster sample could be taken by identifying every street as a cluster. A random sampling of streets could be taken, and all residents of each chosen street could be included in the sample. It is easier to visit several streets in Kelowna than it is to bounce around the city in a random sample, observing the use of pesticides.

The main advantage of cluster sampling is that it is cost-effective. As long as the samples were chosen at random, researchers don't have to travel all over to get a representative sample. The disadvantage is there is a higher, and more difficult to quantify, risk of sampling error.

Non-probability/Non-random Sampling Strategies

There is also a set of non-random techniques used to gather samples. They are less common, but you are still likely to encounter them, usually when dealing with research done by polling firms or market research agencies.

Non-probability samples differ from probability samples in a few ways. They are not supposed to be representative of the population, and are likely to somewhat biased. Non-probability samples are often used when researchers aren't concerned with representing an entire population. Here are some of the more common types of non-probability samples:

Convenience Sample

A **convenience sample** only targets individuals who possess characteristics that make them more accessible to the researcher. For example, if you live in Edmonton it is easiest for you to derive a sample that only contains people living in Edmonton. Depending on the nature of your study, that might be okay, but you couldn't make generalizations about all of Canada by only researching in Edmonton. Convenience samples are useful for **pilot testing** a research instrument, like a questionnaire, because accuracy isn't a concern, but finding unclear questions and non-mutually exclusive response categories is.

Snowball Sample

Typically, snowball sampling techniques are used for populations that are not easily identified, resistant to being studied, or otherwise hard to reach. The term 'snowball' is used because the sample increases in size as it rolls away from its source—just like a snowball. The sample will grow in size until it reaches the researcher's ideal. Researchers will make contact with a small group, asking members of that group to identify others who might be interested in participating in the study. Initial group members become informants, leading to others in their network.

Quota Sample

Quota samples are the non-probability counterpart to stratified samples. Often used in market research and opinion polls, they are a relatively cheap and quick way to get an adequate sample. As with a stratified sample, researchers decide on strata (such as levels of income), and then try to ensure that the sample is proportionately representative of the population in the categories of interest. Unlike a stratified sample there is non-random sampling of each stratum's units. Since this is essentially a convenience sample, under-representation of less accessible groups is still a problem.

Sampling Error

Population samples rarely match the population perfectly. No matter how carefully a probability or non-probability sample is selected, there will be some degree of 'mismatch' between the sample and the population. This is called sampling error. To differentiate between samples and population, different symbols are used to represent mean and standard deviation for a sample, versus mean and standard deviation for the population. The text will continue to use μ and σ to describe the mean and the standard deviation of the population. $\overline{X}$ and s will be used to describe the mean and the standard deviation of a sample.

Tips for Reducing Sampling Error

Sampling error and standard error are tied to one another. Reducing sampling error will usually reduce standard error too, so every good social statistician who collects his or her own samples aims to reduce sampling error, thereby reducing standard error.

Some error is to be expected in any sample that is smaller than the population. This bias may not be problematic for your research, as long as it is random. Non-random sources of bias are more serious, but there are some ways to avoid them when you are trying to derive a representative sample. Remember that **probability samples** are more representative than non-probability samples. When samples are not randomly selected, certain types of people are selected more often—the most agreeable, available, or even attractive—which affects the accuracy of your results.

An inadequate sampling frame is another potential problem. If certain members of your population are forgotten or excluded when the sampling frame is calculated, it will introduce bias in your research. Statistics Canada encounters difficulties when it is trying to enumerate Aboriginal and homeless populations. Not including these people will result in a misrepresentation of the Canadian population, biasing any results that come from these data. Statistics Canada tries to make its sampling frames as complete as possible in an effort to represent the entire population.

Finally, there is the problem of non-response. Potential respondents will sometimes refuse to answer questions, either because they don't want to or because they fear the consequences. If the non-response is random (e.g., if respondents were all equally unlikely to answer a question) this would not be much of a problem. Unfortunately, most studies find regularities around non-response, suggesting that certain people (men, those who are single, those with low education, etc.) are more likely to non-respond than are others.

PRACTICE QUESTIONS

1. You need to derive a sample of writing samples from a collection of grade six grammar classes. You have a list of all children in the population, and your primary concern is with representativeness. Which sampling strategy would you use? Why?

2. The University of Alberta has 21 faculties, schools, and colleges. If you wanted to draw a representative sample of the entire student body, but wanted to be sure that you had a sufficient number of observations from each faculty, school, and college, which sampling strategy would you use, and why?

3. You're working with a vulnerable, hard-to-reach population, and would like to administer a questionnaire. Your primary concern is obtaining a sufficient sample size, even if representativeness is limited. Which sampling technique would you use, and why?

4. Frieda is having trouble choosing people to join her new orchestra, not because of a lack of interest, but because she is getting too much interest. She decides that she'll sample her population to find suitable people. She feels that everyone has equal talent, but she needs to ensure that each instrument is adequately represented. She approaches you for advice on how to randomly select the right mix of musicians. Which sampling technique would you tell her to use? Why?

5. Draw a 10 per cent simple random sample (use the random numbers in Appendix F) and a 10 per cent stratified random sample from the numbers below. Think about the strengths and weaknesses of each approach.

37	93	43	35	77	99
55	52	12	86	32	12
43	16	57	3	95	52
39	99	24	17	36	36
34	65	28	72	48	33
66	82	60	50	57	2
66	78	8	35	53	44
61	62	93	35	6	83
63	36	28	42	3	26
81	3	92	99	17	64

Answers to the practice questions for chapter 8 can be found on page 188.

CHAPTER 9

Generalizing from Samples to Populations

Learning Objectives

In this chapter we'll continue to move from discussing populations to discussing samples, by studying:

- the sampling distribution of means
- confidence intervals, and how to calculate them
- how *t*-distributions can be used for small samples

Introduction

Using the distribution of variables from the normal curve within a population, it is possible to estimate how closely a sample approximates the population. To do this, we will use the **sampling distribution of means**.

The easiest way to explain the sample distribution of means is to use an example. Suppose that you wanted to identify the average body mass index (BMI) of all Canadian adolescents. You could measure all of the 4.2 million people between the ages of 10 and 19 and get an accurate measure of the average BMI, but it would be prohibitively expensive and time-consuming to do so. Instead, you can use what you know about probability sampling, and get the same results in a more cost-efficient way. Instead of taking 4.2 million measurements, you could take a random subset of that group.

When choosing the subset, there would be a few things to consider: How many people will you want to measure? A bigger sample size will give a more accurate approximation, but too big a sample will have the same problems as studying the entire population, defeating the purpose of sampling. You could take a series of samples and average them together to find the sampling distribution of means. Repeatedly re-sampling from the adolescent population and calculating the average BMI from each sample will provide you with a list of means, like the coin-tossing

BOX 9.1 FROM POPULATIONS TO SAMPLES: RELEVANT SYMBOLS FOR DESCRIBING SAMPLE CHARACTERISTICS

Luckily, moving from samples to populations usually doesn't result in substantial changes to any equations. But there are some new symbols that you'll need to be familiar with. These are listed below:

	Sample	Population
Mean	$\overline{X}$	μ
Standard deviation	s	σ
Variance	s^2	σ^2

means in chapter 4. On their own, each of these means will be close to the population mean for BMI, but if you were to present the means as a histogram, you would get—you guessed it—an approximation of the normal curve.

The sampling distribution of means has two other notable qualities: First, the mean of (sample) means will be equal to the population mean: μ. So a mean BMI calculated using a series of population subset means (say, random samples of 1,000 of the adolescent population, taken 1,000 times) will be equal to the mean BMI for the whole population.

Second, the distribution of means will be tightly clustered around the true population mean. The variance and standard deviation of the sampling distribution of means is small, so we can be fairly confident that the mean of any random sample will be very close to the true population mean. Instead of taking numerous samples to approximate the population, this characteristic of the sampling distribution of means ensures that one random sample should be close enough to the population sample.

Since it's unusual to take more than one sample, it's unlikely that we will know much about the sampling distribution of means for our samples (we don't know the mean of means, or the standard deviation of means). If we assume that our population is normally distributed, we

can estimate how closely the mean of our sample approximates the population mean by using the following equation:

$$\sigma_{\overline{X}} = \frac{\sigma_X}{\sqrt{N}}$$

This equation gives us the **standard error of the sample mean ($\sigma_{\overline{X}}$)** when the population standard deviation (σ_X) is known. The standard error is described as the standard deviation of the population, divided by the square root of the sample size. As you can see by the denominator $\sqrt{N}$, the larger the sample size is, the smaller the standard error. This makes sense, because we expect the mean to become more accurate as the sample size approaches the population. As sample size increases, the standard error should approach, but until the sample and population are one and the same never reach, zero.

In reality, we will rarely have a sample that is close to our population size, so we need to attach a measure of how confident we are in our measurement of the mean. This is known as the **confidence interval**.

Confidence Intervals

Because it is difficult to be certain that the mean we draw from a sample is exactly the same as the mean of the population we're interested in, we can be certain that there is a chance of error (called the standard error) in the estimate. Ideally, we could attach a specific probability to the mean to give a more complete picture of the accuracy of the score.

To indicate level of confidence, we need to employ the standard error. Because the standard error is derived from the standard deviation, it can be used in almost the same way as the standard deviation. Instead of determining what proportion of observations lie between one, two, and three deviations from the mean, we are determining how much confidence we have in the accuracy of the mean taken from as sample.

Think of the sample mean as one of many in the sampling distribution of means. Each mean can be treated as an observation. Just as we can be certain that 68 per cent of all observations lie between ±1 standard deviation from the mean in a normal distribution, we can be certain that roughly 68 per cent of sample means lie between ±1 standard error from the population mean. Extending this, we can construct a 'confidence interval' by providing the upper and lower ranges (or **confidence limits**) of the standard error calculations. We can also construct a 95 per cent confidence interval by postulating that our population mean is within ±2 $\sigma_{\overline{X}}$ of the sample mean, or a 99 per cent confidence interval by postulating that our population mean is within ±3 $\sigma\overline{X}$ of the sample mean. This translates to 1.96 $\sigma\overline{X}$ and 2.58 $\sigma\overline{X}$ from the sample mean. To understand where we got 1.96 and 2.58 from, we need to look at the z-distribution (see box 9.2).

Looking at the equation for the standard error, you will notice that the standard error will differ, based on both sample size and the size of

BOX 9.2 THE STEPS: CALCULATING THE z-SCORE AND USING IT TO ESTIMATE A POPULATION MEAN WITH A KNOWN CONFIDENCE INTERVAL

1. Calculate the sample mean.

2. Assuming that the population standard deviation (σ_X) is known, calculate the standard error of the sample mean using the following equation:

$$\sigma_{\overline{X}} = \frac{\sigma_X}{\sqrt{N}}$$

Otherwise, you'll need to rely on the sample standard deviation and this equation:

$$s_{\overline{X}} = \frac{s_X}{\sqrt{n-1}}$$

3. Find the relevant value of $z_{critical}$ in the z-table in Appendix A that corresponds with a 95 per cent confidence interval (1.96 for 95 per cent, 2.57 for 99 per cent).

4. Insert the relevant values into the following equation:

$$\text{Confidence Interval} = \overline{X} \pm z_{critical} * \sigma_{\overline{X}}$$

Or

$$\text{Confidence Interval} = \overline{X} \pm z_{critical} * s_{\overline{X}}$$

5. Note that it will be necessary to do this for both upper and lower bounds, which means that you will need to solve the equation for a positive and negative value of $z_{critical}$.

the standard deviation. If a standard deviation is large, the standard error is likely to be large. Calculating confidence intervals requires multiplying the standard error by the appropriate *z*-value (1.96 for a 95 per cent confidence interval, and 2.58 for a 99 per cent confidence interval).

The *t*-Distribution

William Gosset was a mathematician and chemist who graduated from Oxford in 1899. At that time, Arthur Guinness Son & Co. Ltd. were looking for new ways to make a beer of consistent quality, and decided that Gosset was the person to ask for help. There was considerable variability in brewing quality across batches, making it difficult for Guinness to establish regularity in taste and standards. Guinness wanted to improve on its consistency, but didn't know how, and had neither the budget nor the inclination to botch large batches of brew to attain consistency. Gosset was limited to working with a few small batches. At that time, most statistical work focused on very large samples. Gosset had to forgo traditional methods and develop techniques for assessing small samples.

The histograms in chapter 5 showed that small samples tend to produce distributions that deviate from the normal distribution. Most importantly, the tails in small samples are larger, and the kurtosis value is often lower, even though the variable might have a normal distribution. Gosset's problem—and, often, our problem—was that the sample size was too small to accommo-date the normal curve, leading to an underestimation of the standard error. This led him to the **student's *t*-distribution**.

Prior to Gosset, statisticians knew that their standard error estimates were slightly too small, but they surmised (correctly) that the difference would be very slight in samples that were greater than 50. Gosset determined the exact relationship between small samples and the normal curve with his discovery of the *t*-distribution.

The *t*-distribution is actually an infinite number of curves, one for every sample size greater than or equal to two. As sample size increases, the *t*-distribution increasingly resembles the standard normal distribution. By the time sample size reaches 50, the differences between the two are difficult to detect.

Values for the *t*-distribution can be derived by using the following equation (when mean = 0 and the variance is greater than one)

$$t = \frac{\overline{X} - \mu}{s_{\overline{X}}}$$

Or

$$t = \frac{\overline{X} - \mu}{s_X / \sqrt{n-1}}$$

Or

$$t = \frac{\overline{X} - \mu}{\sigma_{\overline{X}}}$$

Or

$$t = \frac{\overline{X} - \mu}{\sigma_{\overline{X}} / \sqrt{N}}$$

BOX 9.3 WHY IS IT CALLED THE STUDENT'S *t*-DISTRIBUTION?

Prior to Gosset's arrival at the Guinness Brewery, a paper had been published by a Guinness employee revealing some of the company's brewing secrets. Consequently, the Guinness Company made the heavy-handed move of forbidding all of its employees from publishing articles of any kind!

When Gosset developed the *t*-distribution as an employee of Guinness, he couldn't share his discovery with the world (at least, not unless he wanted to lose his job), and selected the pseudonym 'Student' to protect his anonymity. Since that time, the distribution that he discovered has been known as the Student's *t*-distribution.

In the numerator for each equation we subtract the population mean from the sample mean, and divide that number by the denominator, which is the standard error estimate of the sample mean. The second equation is the same, except that the denominator is expressed as the standard deviation of the sample, divided by the square root of the sample size minus one, instead of the standard error. If you recall the earlier equation for standard error, you will recognize that the four equations produce essentially the same result, and depend on the information at our disposal.

The equations are often useless, because we don't know the population mean or standard deviation. In fact, we usually know very little about the population, which is what got us into this mess in the first place!

The best we can strive for is a range where we're fairly certain our population mean will fall. For example, if we derived a sample of 1,000 and determined that the average number of drinks that the average person in the sample has per day is 2.3, it would be helpful to know how confident we could be that the mean for the Canadian population is ±0.2 drinks; say, 90 per cent, 95 per cent, or 99 per cent confident. Even though we don't know the population mean, we could use the t-distribution and say that we are 95 per cent certain that the average Canadian has between 2.1 and 2.5 drinks per day. In the equations it is the population mean that we are trying to estimate. To do this we have to find the t-value. Finding the t-value requires an understanding of **degrees of freedom**.

What Is a Degree of Freedom?

Imagine that you live with five roommates, and split the bills according to usage (don't worry about how we calculate who owes what for now). This month the total is $500, and your roommates claim $435 of the bill. You don't need to know what each of the others owes to know that your share is $65, because what you owe is constrained by the amount that your roommates owe. Any combination of values could be assigned to what your roommates owe. As long as the sum equals $435, the amount that you owe does not change. You have the freedom to assign values (within reason) to everyone in the sample *except* the last observation. This is the

main principle behind degrees of freedom. In this instance, there are six minus one, or five, degrees of freedom.

Typically when working with the mean, the degrees of freedom (df) are equal to the number of observations in a sample, minus one ($n - 1$).

$$df = n - 1$$

Using the t-statistic, instead of z, is suitable when sample sizes are small, and you want to construct confidence intervals. When constructing intervals, knowing t and the degrees of freedom allows you to account for the slight differences between the distribution of a variable with small n, and a distribution taken from a larger sample. When should you use t instead of z? Look at the values in Appendix B (the t-table) and notice that t-values converge upon those for z as degrees of freedom increase. At $df = 120$ they are identical; t should only be used when the sample size is less than 120.

One-Tailed versus Two-Tailed Estimates

Looking at Appendix B, you'll notice a distinction between one- and two-tailed tests. In order to correctly estimate the confidence intervals for the population mean, you will have to know which chart to use.

One-tailed tests determine how likely it is that an observation is above or below a specific threshold value. For instance, if we used sample data to find the probability of someone living below the poverty line we would use a one-tailed test. Because we have a hypothesis about the direction of the relationship (that is, the person is expected to be towards the bottom of the income distribution), we can focus our attention on one end of the distribution.

To estimate a population mean from a sample mean, a two-tailed test is used. If the sample is a representative sample, there is no reason to hypothesize that the value of the sample mean should be above or below the population mean. If the sample is random there is an equal likelihood of being above or below the population mean. There is no way to specify which direction we expect the difference to fall in, so both ends of the distribution have to be included. Two-tailed tests are more common, so they are the

BOX 9.4 EQUATIONS FOR MOVING FROM POPULATIONS TO SAMPLES

Luckily, moving from samples to populations doesn't usually result in substantial changes to the equations. There are some new symbols that you'll need to be familiar with listed below:

	Sample	Population
Standard error	$s_{\overline{X}} = \dfrac{s_X}{\sqrt{n-1}}$	$\sigma_{\overline{X}} = \dfrac{\sigma_X}{\sqrt{N}}$
Standard deviation	$s = \sqrt{\dfrac{\sum (X - \overline{X})^2}{n-1}}$	$\sigma = \sqrt{\dfrac{\sum (X - \overline{X})^2}{N}}$
t-statistic	$t = \dfrac{\overline{X} - \mu}{s_X / \sqrt{n-1}}$	$t = \dfrac{\overline{X} - \mu}{\sigma_X / \sqrt{N}}$

only kind shown in the z-table in Appendix A. If you need to conduct a one-tailed test using z, use the t-table with $df = 120$.

Using Degrees of Freedom and the t-Distribution to Estimate Population Proportions

To estimate population proportions, a measurement commonly used for opinion polls, we use a slightly different equation for the standard error:

$$S_p = \sqrt{\frac{P(1-P)}{n}}$$

The difference is in the numerator, where the proportion in a certain category is multiplied by one, minus that proportion. The denominator only includes n, even though, technically, $n - 1$ would be appropriate, because the equation deals with a sample.

Once the standard error of the sample proportion has been calculated, the confidence interval remains the same, except that $\overline{X}$ is replaced by P:

$$\text{Confidence Interval} = P \pm z_{\text{critical}} * S_{\overline{X}}$$

Everything else is the same, but let's look at an example anyway. Suppose that you wanted to gauge Canadian Aboriginal opinion about the 2006 protests in Caledonia, southwestern Ontario, over land issues. You polled 500 Aboriginal people (composed of First Nations, Métis, and Inuit peoples). In your sample, you found that 62 per cent of all respondents believed that the protests were warranted. As interesting as this percentage is, what you really want to know is the attitude of the *entire* Aboriginal population of Canada, not just the sample. Since there are roughly one million Aboriginal people living in Canada, any claim you make from only 500 respondents will be suspect. Researchers try to put these kinds of doubts to rest by reporting confidence intervals. Using the information we have, let's construct a confidence interval.

First, we need to estimate the standard error of the sample proportion, using the following equation:

$$S_p = \sqrt{\frac{P(1-P)}{n}}$$

$$= \sqrt{\frac{0.62(1 - 0.62)}{500}}$$

$$= \sqrt{\frac{0.236}{500}}$$

$$= 0.022$$

To find the 95 per cent confidence interval for the population, we need to know the margin of error (z times the standard error). To find it, we need to find the value of 1.96 from the z chart. Why 1.96? Because it is the cut-point (in standard deviations) from which 95 per cent of all cases lie. We calculate the degrees of freedom to be n minus one, or 499. To be 95 per cent confident that our estimate is correct, we need to provide the range that 95 per cent of all observations fall into. If the sample was smaller, we would need to look up the value of t using the degrees of freedom, instead of z.

Second, multiply the standard error by 1.96 to find the margin of error.

$$\text{Margin of error} = 1.96 * S_p$$
$$= 1.96 * 0.022$$
$$= 0.043$$

Third, add and subtract the margin of error from the sample proportion, to find the values of the confidence interval.

$$95\% \text{ confidence interval} = \overline{X} \pm 1.96 S_{\overline{X}}$$
$$= 0.62 \pm 0.043$$
$$= 0.577 \text{ to } 0.663$$

Now we can say that we are 95 per cent confident that between 57.7 per cent and 66.3 per cent of Aboriginal peoples in Canada believe that the protests in Caledon were warranted.

This concludes our discussion of univariate statistics. The coming chapters will explore methods of analysis using more than one variable. Most of what's been covered is foundational, but without knowing what's been covered, performing any statistical analysis is nearly impossible.

Now the focus will shift to analysis with more than one variable, and how to measure relationships between variables.

BOX 9.5 THE STEPS: HOW TO ESTIMATE POPULATION PROPORTIONS USING ONLY SAMPLE CHARACTERISTICS

1. Estimate the standard error of the sample mean: $S_p = \sqrt{\dfrac{P(1-P)}{n}}$

2. Use $df = n - 1$ to calculate the degrees of freedom to find the critical value of z, or t, to find the desired confidence interval: $= P \pm z_{critical} * S_p$

3. It will be necessary to do this for both upper and lower bounds (which explains why $\pm$ appears in the equation), meaning that you will have to solve the equation for a positive and negative value of $z_{critical}$.

PRACTICE QUESTIONS

1. A research study was conducted, examining the differences between perceived life satisfaction of men and women. Ten men and 10 women were given a life satisfaction test (known to have high reliability and validity). Scores on the measure range from 0 to 60, with high scores indicating high life satisfaction and low scores implying the opposite. The data are presented below:

Men	Women
45	34
38	22
52	15
48	27
25	37
39	41
51	24
46	19
55	26
46	36

a. Calculate the mean, variance, and standard deviation for both men and women.

b. Calculate the standard errors for each mean estimate.

c. Estimate the 95 per cent confidence interval for each sample mean.

2. Professor Smart recently returned a lab assignment to his students. Before doing this, he polled them on the number of hours they spent on the assignments. There were 24 individuals in the lab, and the data were used to make inferences about subsequent classes. The data are presented below:

4.5	20	19	9
22	8	7	8.5
7.5	2.5	14.5	3.5
9	5	9	8
11	10.5	9	18
7.5	15	14	20

Compute and interpret the 95 per cent confidence interval. What does the interval mean?

3. In a sample of 50 individuals, 34 per cent prefer soft drink A to soft drink B. In the population, we could be 99 per cent confident that the real proportion lies between _____ per cent and _____ per cent.

Answers to the practice questions for chapter 9 can be found on page 189.

PART TWO

Bivariate Statistics

Using the *t*-Distribution to Compare the Means of Population Subgroups to Population Means

Learning Objectives

This chapter will examine ways to assess the relationship between two variables. Topics will include:

- a review of the student's *t*-distribution
- sample *t*-tests
- calculating confidence intervals
- *t*-tests for the same group measured twice

Introduction

In chapter 9 we examined some techniques for studying populations when the only data available comes from samples. This is an important skill because it becomes possible to learn about a large group of people, such as all Canadians, without having to talk to every one of them.

The next step is to compare groups *within* a sample (men and women; left-handed, right-handed, and ambidextrous people; immigrants and non-immigrants; university graduates and non-university graduates; etc.), to determine if the differences we observe in the sample exist in the population. It is possible to do that using the

t-distribution, which it turns out is not just useful for comparing samples to populations.

Chapter 10 will primarily focus on the *t*-test, one of the common applications of the *t*-distribution.[1] The *t*-test is used to compare the value of an interval/ratio variable across two values of another variable. For example, a *t*-test could be used to look at differences in the income of males and females.

---

[1]Remember that the *t*-distribution is similar to the *z*-distribution, except that it has modifications in the tails and the peak for sample size. As sample size increases, the *t*-distribution increasingly resembles the *z*-distribution.

Measuring Association between Dummy and Interval/Ratio Variables: The One-Sample *t*-Test

In statistical analysis, we often have information about samples, but not populations. Unfortunately, we're usually only interested in populations. How can we talk about populations when we only know about samples?

The solution is often to assume that the sample is fairly (but not perfectly) representative of the population, and build the 'uncertainty' into our estimates. We acknowledge that our sample is not a perfect representation of our population, and that there's a possibility that any differences we observe are due to chance. However, if there are clear trends in the sample, they probably exist in the population. To present the differences between sample and population, acknowledge the uncertainty by reporting the values (e.g., means) for the sample as a range, or **confidence interval**.

Let's try using this for a sample mean. Engineering students at Queen's University have been accused of consuming too much alcohol. Their average number of drinks per week is 12 (taken from a random sample of 150 engineers), compared to 8 for the entire university population. The standard deviation for the university as a whole is 4.6. Obviously, there is a difference between the sample and the population, but is it significant? There are two possibilities:

1. The mean of 12 taken from the sample of engineers is the same as the university mean (8), and the difference is caused by random chance or sampling error (H_0).
2. The difference is real (significant), and engineers are different from other students (H_1).

What we've done here is cast the possibilities as a set of competing hypotheses. The first (labelled H_0) states that there is no true relationship between being an engineer and alcohol consumption. This is known as the null hypothesis, because it predicts that the relationship between two variables is null. The second (labelled H_1) is our research hypothesis, and it asserts that a connection does indeed exist between the two variables.

Although it would be ideal to be able to prove that the research hypothesis is true, in scientific research the best that we can do is reject or fail to reject the null hypothesis. This is because we can never be sure whether our relationships are actually causal, or if they are instead 'merely' correlative. Imagine that males tend to drink more than females and that males are more likely to be engineers. The differences above would be significant, but it wouldn't be because engineers outdrink others. It would instead be because males outdrink females. By rejecting the null hypothesis instead of accepting the research hypothesis, we give ourselves room for such possibilities.

To choose between these possibilities, identify the probability of getting a sample mean of 12 for the engineers when their true mean is 8. The convention dictates that a probability of less than 5 per cent indicates that the differences between the sample means will represent an actual difference.

If we treat the entire university as our population, and engineering students as our sample, we get values of 8 for μ, 12 for $\overline{X}$, 150 for n, and 4.6 for σ. To calculate z, we use the following equation:

$$z_{obtained} = \frac{\overline{X} - \mu}{\sigma / \sqrt{N}}$$

Why are we calculating z instead of t? It probably doesn't matter which one we calculate, since our sample is big enough that z and t will be very close. The variable z is easier to calculate, but can only be used when the population parameters are known. If you prefer, you can calculate t, using the methods introduced later in the chapter. You should get the same answer.

The next step is to figure out how big the difference between the mean of the sample and the mean of the population is, using what we know about the normal distribution—particularly the **central limit theorem**. The normal distribution also tells us the probability of finding differences between samples and populations. We want to know if the probability of finding a difference of 4 drinks per week is less than 0.05 (or 5 per cent). So:

$$z_{obtained} = \frac{\overline{X} - \mu}{\sigma / \sqrt{N}}$$

$$= \frac{12 - 8}{4.6 / \sqrt{150}}$$

$$= \frac{4}{.376}$$

$$= 10.64$$

The equation places the difference between population mean and sample mean into a common metric (that's why the standard deviation appears in the denominator), so that the value can be assessed with the normal distribution, like any other variable. If we multiply the population mean, sample mean, and standard deviation by 100, 1,000, or even 100,000, we could use the same table (z or t) to assess the significance of the differences. It's often useful to think of z- or t-statistics as techniques for translating values measured in different units—be it drinks, dollars, or donkey rides—into a common unit of measurement, or standard score, as discussed in chapter 7.

One characteristic of the equation is that there is a term in the denominator ($\sqrt{n}$) that 'penalizes' z if it's calculated using a small sample. The reason is that sampling error tends to *increase* as sample size *decreases*, so there is less certainty about the representativeness of a sample when it contains a smaller proportion of the population. However, representativeness does not increase proportionally with sample size, which is why the square root of n is used. For example, if n was 200, the z-value would increase to 12.30.

Column C in the chart of critical z-values in Appendix A reveals that the area beyond z is < 0.0001. Most z-score tables only go up to 4 because anything above that has approximately the same value, so don't worry if you don't find your particular z-value (unless it's below 4!). This tells us that there is less than a 0.01 per cent chance that the value we obtained from the sample of engineers is a fluke. Since we set a threshold of 5 per cent, we can be confident (though not certain) that overall differences between our samples of engineers and university students exist. In fact, for the differences to be significant, our z value only needed to exceed ±1.96, a value referred to as the **critical value of z**, or **z(critical)**, or $z_{critical}$.

The Return of Gossett: The Student's t-Distribution

In the engineer example we used a combination of sample and population characteristics to determine whether the differences between a sample of 150 engineering students and the entire university reflect actual differences between all engineering students and the university population. Since there are more than 150 engineering students at Queen's, we cannot be certain of the significance of the differences in drinking behaviour. How-

ever, given the calculated z-value of 10.64, we can be 95 per cent confident that the differences between the two groups are significant.

Of course, this exercise is of little use in the real world, because there isn't usually that much information available. There are rarely values for σ or μ, the population standard deviation and population mean, but a value for s, the sample standard deviation, will always be available, or can be calculated. Unfortunately s is a biased estimator of σ; and there's no way to tell how big the difference is. We do know that the difference between s and σ shrinks as sample size increases. The closer the sample size comes to the population size, the more acceptable it is to use s as a 'stand-in' for σ when calculating z-values.

Once a sample size of about 120 is reached, the differences are negligible (see for yourself: look at how minimal the differences between z-values and t-values are when df = 120 in the z- and t-distributions at the back of the book), and we can consider s to be a decent approximation of σ. Substitute the sample standard deviation for the population standard deviation, and use the techniques above, to get the equation:

$$t_{obtained} = \frac{\overline{X} - \mu}{s/\sqrt{n}}$$

This looks a lot like the equation for z, except that s replaces σ in the denominator. Like z, t is a standardized unit that tells us how far $\overline{X}$ is from μ in standard deviations. Unlike z, which has only one distribution (the normal distribution), remember that t is a family of distributions, each differing slightly based on sample size. For smaller samples (<120), the t-distribution can differ substantially from the z-distribution.

Since we need to calculate degrees of freedom to use the t-distribution, it would be helpful to briefly review the concept. Recall that the degrees of freedom are the number of values in a set of scores that are free to vary. Using the example of determining how much money each of your five roommates has contributed to the household expenses, the degrees of freedom would be equal to the number of values you don't know minus one. Suppose that instead of calculating bills you're going to dinner with four friends. The meal costs $100, and you and your friend Marcie each contribute $20. This would leave you with two degrees of freedom, because you know that there is $60 unaccounted for. Once you know how much two of your three friends who have not yet paid need to contribute, the final contribution will also be determined. Only two of the values are uncertain, or free, because the final value is always known by subtracting the cumulative total of contributions from the total bill.

In the current example, when we are trying to calculate the sample mean $\overline{X}$, and don't know any of the individual scores, the degrees of freedom will be equal to the number of observations minus one, reflecting that the final score will be determined by the score of other individuals. Substituting $t_{obtained}$ for $z_{obtained}$, s for σ, and n–1 for n, the formula for the obtained *t*-score becomes:

$$t_{obtained} = \frac{\overline{X} - \mu}{s / \sqrt{n - 1}}$$

Calculating Confidence Intervals in the One-Sample Case

The variables t and z are also important for approximating the mean for a population when there is only one sample available. Samples do not perfectly represent populations because of sampling error, so we can *never* be 100 per cent sure that any sample statistic equals the true population parameter. As a partial solution, we express uncertainty about estimates by lowering the confidence interval from 100 per cent, and providing a range of values for the mean.

To analyze samples of normal populations with an unknown mean (μ), attach a range of plausible values to the sample mean ($\overline{X}$), using the following equation:

$$CI = \overline{X} \pm t * \frac{s}{\sqrt{n}}$$

The appropriate value of t can be found in the *t*-distribution at the back of the book, at n – 1 degrees of freedom.

Suppose that we have a sample of 15 refugees to Canada, and we want to look at the civic participation rates of refugees after one year in Canada. We ask respondents how many social organizations they belong to. Below are the data:

3	7	4	0	2
1	4	4	5	2
7	6	3	5	7

From these data it is possible to estimate the average number of organizations that members of the entire refugee population belong to. First, calculate the mean:

$$\overline{X} = \frac{\sum X}{n}$$

$$= \frac{60}{15}$$

$$= 4$$

Next, calculate the sample standard deviation, using the following equation:

$$s = \sqrt{\frac{\sum (X - \overline{X})^2}{n - 1}}$$

$$= \sqrt{\frac{68}{14}}$$

$$= 2.20$$

Use these values for the mean and standard deviation, and the critical value of t, to find the interval where we can be 95 per cent confident the mean falls. To find the value of t, use the degrees of freedom (n – 1 = 14) and a 95 per cent confidence interval, to retrieve the critical value of t of 2.145 (this number is found in Appendix B), leaving us with the confidence interval:

$$CI = \overline{X} \pm t * \frac{s}{\sqrt{n}}$$

$$= 4 \pm 2.145 * \frac{2.20}{\sqrt{15}}$$

$$= 4 \pm 1.22$$

$$= 2.78, 5.22 \text{ organizations per individual}$$

We can be 95 per cent confident that the mean number of social organizations for all refugees to Canada is between 2.78 and 5.22. If you wanted to be more confident of the range, say 99 per cent, go back to the *t*-table and find the critical value for a *df* of 14 and the 0.01 column. Now the critical value is 2.98, yielding a range of 2.31 to 5.69 social organizations. Now we're more confident, but the range is larger.

Single Sample Proportions

One requirement for generalizing from samples to populations is measuring variables at the interval/ratio level. However, it is possible to assess proportions instead of means in a single sample, using the normal distribution, and applying most of the same logic and techniques. For example, you could determine if the same proportion of people with a certain characteristic in a sample is likely to exist in the population. The three things you need to calculate $z_{obtained}$ are: sample proportions, population proportion, and sample size.

Let's illustrate $z_{obtained}$ with an example: A random sample of 120 individuals whose mothers put salt on their food during pregnancy reveals that 50 per cent of those people also put salt on their food. In the whole population the proportion of people who salt their food is about 40 per cent. Are individuals with mothers who salted their food different from the rest of the population in this regard?

The proportion for the population is 40 per cent, or 0.4, and the sample proportion is 50 per cent, or 0.5. Using a 95 per cent confidence interval from the z table at the back of the book, we get a critical value of 1.96 (remember that 95 per cent is on both tails, so you will look for 95/2, or 47.5 per cent, or 0.475 on the table).

To calculate z with proportions, use the following equation:

$$z_{obtained} = \frac{P_{sample} - P_{population}}{\sqrt{P_{population}(1 - P_{population})/n}}$$

This is essentially the same equation as the one we used before, except the population standard deviation in the denominator (which can't exist with nominal data) is replaced by the population probability of eating salt, multiplied by the probability of not eating salt. Otherwise, the equations are the same.

Inserting our values gives us the following:

$$z_{obtained} = \frac{P_{sample} - P_{population}}{\sqrt{P_{population}(1 - P_{population})/n}}$$

$$= \frac{0.5 - 0.4}{\sqrt{0.41(1 - 0.4)/120}}$$

$$= \frac{0.1}{\sqrt{0.002}}$$

$$= 2.24$$

Since 2.24 exceeds 1.96 (the critical value of z at 95 per cent confidence interval), we can say that there are differences at the 0.05 level be-

tween people whose mothers put salt on their food and the overall population. This suggests that whether or not your mother salted her food during pregnancy is a significant predictor of whether you will do the same.

Measuring Association between Dummy and Interval/Ratio Variables with the Same Group Measured Twice

So far the focus has been on comparing samples and the populations that they're drawn from. Recently, Canadian researchers have become more interested in following people over a longer period of time. Since the early 1990s, Statistics Canada has launched a series of **longitudinal surveys**. One of the challenges of using this type of data source is comparing the same sample at two points in time. The procedure for doing that has several names, **paired samples *t*-tests**, **repeated measures *t*-tests**, or **t-tests for dependent samples**.

To use the same sample at each point in time, we only focus on the *difference* between scores for the first and second times. As with sample means, assume that the difference between means is normally distributed, and rely on the *t*-distribution to reflect the possibility of a small sample size.

Despite the introduction of several new equations, the process is almost identical to a one-sample *t*-test. The new equations use new symbols, since they deal with differences between dependent observations.

The first equation calculates the differences between observations:

$$d_i = x_{i1} - x_{i2}$$

Where x_{i1} is the score at time one, x_{i2} is the score at time two, and d_i is equal to the difference between them.

The next equation is for the mean of the differences between time points:

$$\overline{X}_d = \frac{\sum d_i}{n}$$

The standard deviation is defined as:

$$s_d = \sqrt{\frac{\sum (d - \overline{x}_d)^2}{n - 1}}$$

BOX 10.1 IT'S YOUR TURN: *t*-TEST FOR THE SAME SAMPLE MEASURED TWICE

Joshua surveyed a number of his friends and acquaintances about how many sexual partners they had during the year they were 18 and how many partners they had during the year they were 21. How can he use the data to calculate whether the number of partners people have per year is significantly different between the two time points?

Individual	# of partners per year at age 18	# of partners per year at age 21	$d_i = x_{i1} - x_{i2}$	d^2
1	2	1		
2	0	0		
3	3	2		
4	1	2		
5	8	1		
6	1	1		
7	2	1		
8	0	2		
9	0	4		
10	3	1		
	$\overline{X}_1$	$\overline{X}_2$	d_i	Σd^2

1. For each age (column), calculate the average ($\overline{X}_1$ and $\overline{X}_2$).

2. For each individual, calculate the difference between the number of partners at ages 18 and 21 ($d_i = xi_1 - xi_2$), then sum that value (Σd_i). Square the difference for each person and sum the values.

3. Use the formula $s_d = \sqrt{\dfrac{\Sigma d^2}{n-1} - (\overline{X}_1 - \overline{X}_2)^2}$ to calculate the standard deviation.

4. Use the standard deviation to calculate the standard error of difference between means
$$s_{\overline{d}} = \dfrac{s_d}{\sqrt{n-1}}$$

5. Use those values to calculate the *t*-value using $t = \dfrac{\overline{X}_1 - \overline{X}_2}{s_{\overline{d}}}$

6. Compare the *t*-value to the critical value from the *t*-table for 9 degrees of freedom at a 95 per cent confidence level. Is there a significant difference in number of sexual partners at the two ages?

The solution for box 10.1 can be found on page 198.

Or, if you want to avoid calculating $\overline{x}_d$:

$$s_d = \sqrt{\frac{\sum d^2}{n-1} - (\overline{X}_1 - \overline{X}_2)^2}$$

To calculate the standard error of the difference between means:

$$s_{\overline{d}} = \frac{s_d}{\sqrt{n-1}}$$

Finally, the *t*-value for dependent samples is the difference between means, divided by the standard error of that difference:

$$t = \frac{\overline{X}_1 - \overline{X}_2}{s_{\overline{d}}}$$

The *t*-value is compared to the critical values, as with one-sample cases, to see if the change within individuals is statistically significant.

You should see some overlap with the material in the last chapter. The difference is that chapter 9 was about determining how closely a sample resembles a population. Now we want to know whether certain segments of a population differ significantly from the entire population.

PRACTICE QUESTIONS

1. For the past few years, Amber's drive to work has taken an average of 75 minutes (σ = 8 minutes). She thinks she's found a shorter way, and wants to see if the average time for the new route is significantly different from that of the old route. Last week she tried the new route 5 times, and got an average of 73 minutes. Help her determine whether or not the new way is significantly faster.

   a. Calculate $z_{observed}$.
   b. Compare this value to $z_{critical}$, using a 95 per cent level of confidence.

2. From 1990 to 2005 (inclusive), Jasper earned approximately $31,000 per year ($\sigma$ = 27,000). He wants to know if his earnings were significantly different from the Canadian population. Across this period, the average wage was roughly $29,000/year. Help Jasper determine whether or not his income was significantly different from that of the Canadian population. All income is stated in 2005 dollars.

3. In a recent Ipsos-Reid poll (http://www.ipsos-na.com/news/pressrelease.cfm?id=3809), of a random sample of 3,219 Canadian adults, 52 per cent thought that the price of food is too high. The 95 per cent confidence interval that Ipsos-Reid provides is 1.7 percentage points. What range is the population average 95 per cent likely to lie between?

Answers to the practice questions for chapter 10 can be found on page 189.

CHAPTER 11

Measuring Association between Dummy and Interval/Ratio Variables: *t*-Tests with Two Samples

Learning Objectives

Now that we're working with two samples, there are two sources of sampling error to account for. This chapter will introduce ways of dealing with them:

- standard error of the difference between means
- two-sample *t*-tests
- one- and two-tailed tests
- comparing proportions with two samples

Introduction

Until now we've dealt with simple random population samples, either comparing each sample to its population, or itself, at different points in time. We've more or less assumed that our samples and/or populations had roughly equal variances, which requires a lot of information about the population. To use the *z*-distribution for one-sample cases, you need to have both the population mean and standard deviation. To use the *t*-distribution the only population characteristic needed is the mean. However, both cases require at least some population information. Although

t-tests for dependent samples don't need population characteristics, we have to assume that the samples contain the same sampling error.

Situations where there are variances in what's being compared are common. For example, if we wanted to compare men and women, Hondas and Toyotas, or even dogs and cats, it wouldn't be surprising to discover that the variances between the groups are different on most characteristics. Why would they be the same?

This chapter will focus on comparing the means of two distinct groups, or independent samples. When comparing two values, what we're typically looking for is the central tendency (usually the mean) and the variation (the standard deviation) of the population. The mean for group one would be calculated as:

$$\overline{X}_1 = \frac{\sum X_1}{n_1}$$

For group two:

$$\overline{X}_2 = \frac{\sum X_2}{n_2}$$

Similarly, the sample standard deviation can be calculated as:

$$s_1 = \sqrt{\frac{\sum (X_1 - \overline{X}_1)^2}{n_1}}$$

For group two:

$$s_2 = \sqrt{\frac{\sum (X_2 - \overline{X}_2)^2}{n_2}}$$

To calculate the distance between a sample mean and a population mean (when we know μ and σ), calculate the z-value for the difference between sample means as:

$$x = \frac{\overline{X}_1 - \overline{X}_2}{s_{\overline{X}_1 - \overline{X}_2}}$$

The z-test is used because it's assumed that we have big enough samples (we'll discuss small samples momentarily). The symbols should be familiar now, except for the denominator term

$$s_{\overline{X}_1 - \overline{X}_2}$$

It is the standard error of the difference between means, or the anticipated level of error between the measurements of the two-sample means, which can be found using the following equation:

$$s_{\overline{X}_1 - \overline{X}_2} = \sqrt{\left[\frac{s_1^2}{n_1 - 1} + \frac{s_2^2}{n_2 - 1} \right]}$$

The standard error is the degree of certainty about how closely our calculated means (calculated from two samples) resemble the means of the two respective populations. A wider variance (the s^2 values in the numerator) results in higher calculations, as does a reduction in sample size (seen in the denominator).

Once the standard error is determined, the z-value can be calculated:

$$z = \frac{(\overline{X}_1 - \overline{X}_2)}{s_{\overline{X}_1 - \overline{X}_2}}$$

A larger standard error value (the denominator), or a smaller difference between means, will result in a lower z figure, reflecting waning confidence in whether the observed differences would also be found in the population.

Using small samples (< 120) complicates things further, relies on the t-distribution instead of the z-distribution (due to the differences in distributions), and involves a more complicated calculation of the standard error of the difference between means:

$$s_{\overline{X}_1 - \overline{X}_2} = \sqrt{\left(\frac{n_1 s_1^2 + n_2 s_2^2}{n_1 + n_2 - 2} \right) \left(\frac{n_1 + n_2}{n_1 n_2} \right)}$$

Substituting t for z requires the following equation:

$$t = \frac{\overline{X}_1 - \overline{X}_2}{s_{\overline{X}_1 - \overline{X}_2}}$$

The t-distribution is actually a family of distributions, making it necessary to identify which distribution to use by calculating the degrees of freedom:

$$df = (n_1 + n_2 - 2)$$

If the calculated z- or t-statistics exceed the critical value (1.96 for z, approaching 1.96 for t) for both the z- and t-distributions, you can be 95 per cent confident that differences exist. Since the null hypothesis is *always* to assume that groups are the same, reject the null whenever z exceeds $z_{critical}$ or t exceeds $t_{critical}$. Once again, as sample size increases, the t-statistics and the t-distribution increasingly resemble the z-statistic and the z-distribution.

Comparing Proportions with Two Samples

As with the one-sample case, you can compare proportions of a dichotomous nominal variable across samples. To find the value of $z_{obtained}$ or $t_{obtained}$, there are, again, several equations needed. Take a closer look and you'll see that most of these resemble the one-sample case.

Let's revisit the equation for $z_{obtained}$ in the one-sample case:

$$z_{obtained} = \frac{P_{sample} - P_{population}}{\sqrt{P_{population} (1 - P_{population})/n}}$$

BOX 11.1 IT'S YOUR TURN: THE TWO-SAMPLE *t*-TEST

Sophia is enrolled in a Sociology course examining ethnicity in Canada. For her term paper she is interested in the extent to which people who grew up in Canada feel that they 'fit into' Canadian society. Using data collected in 2002 for the Ethic Diversity Survey (Public Use Microdata File), she selected people who were either second generation (they were born in Canada, but one or both parents were not) or third generation or more (both the respondent and their parents were born in Canada). The dependent variable was a response to the question 'Up until you were age 15, how often did you feel uncomfortable or out of place because of your ethnicity, culture, race, skin colour, language, accent, or religion?', and ranged from 1 (all of the time) to 5 (never). Although the responses were ordinal, she treated them as interval.

Sophia found the following:

	Generation status – 2nd or 3rd	N	Mean	Standard deviation	Standard error mean
Felt uncomfortable before age 15	2nd – parents born outside Canada	6,799	4.59	.776	.009
	3rd or more – respondent and parents in Canada	23,237	4.78	.593	.004

Source: Ethnic Diversity Survey Public Microdata File, 2002
Note: Rescaled weights for data have been used (weight/average weight for sample selected). Target population was people aged 15 and older living in private dwellings in the 10 Canadian provinces. Sample excludes those under age 15, people living in collective dwellings, Indian reserves, people who declared an Aboriginal ethic origin or identity on the 2001 census, and people living in the territories and remote areas (Statistics Canada User's Guide, p. 4, Catalogue no. 89M0019GPE).

1. What would Sophia's null hypothesis be?

2. Use the information in the table to calculate the *z*-score (this will require you to calculate the standard error of the difference between means).

3. Comparing the *z*-score to the critical value for 95 per cent confidence, would you reject or fail to reject the null hypothesis?

The solution for box 11.1 can be found on page 199.

Now, let's compare it to the formula for $z_{obtained}$ in the two-sample case:

$$z_{obtained} = \frac{(P_{sample1} - P_{sample2})}{s_{\bar{x}_1 - \bar{x}_2}}$$

The similarities in the numerator are obvious: instead of $P_{population}$, which indicates the proportion of the population in a group or category, the proportion of respondents in the second sample, P_{sample}, is used. So far, so good.

The denominator for a one-sample case can be expressed as $s_{\bar{x}_s - \bar{x}_p}$, which is equivalent to:

$$\sqrt{P_{population}\ (1 - P_{population})/n}$$

Consequently:

$$z_{obtained} = \frac{P_{sample} - P_{population}}{\sqrt{P_{population}(1 - P_{population})/n}}$$

So the formula for calculating z in a one-sample case can also be stated as:

$$z_{obtained} = \frac{P_{sample} - P_{population}}{s_{\overline{X}_1 - \overline{X}_2}}$$

and looks like the previous equation for two-sample means.

Remember that one-sample and two-sample equations are not identical. Calculating the standard deviation of differences between a sample mean and a population mean is not the same as calculating the standard deviation between the means of two samples, because of differences in the source of error. When comparing a sample to a population, there will only be error in the sample mean (there cannot be error in the population parameters), so it is sufficient to include n in the denominator to acknowledge that the size of the error is partially a function of sample size.

With two samples, any errors are probably because there are two sources, so the calculation of

$$s_{\overline{X}_1 - \overline{X}_2}$$

is more complicated than

$$\sigma_{\overline{X}_1 - \overline{X}_2}$$

To calculate $s_{\overline{X}_1 - \overline{X}_2}$, we have to find P_u, an estimate of the proportion of the population in the category of interest (such as the proportion of men and women who smoke). In the social sciences, we always assume that the null hypothesis is true, and that there are no differences between groups (we assume that the proportion of male and female smokers is the same in the population). P_u can be calculated as the average of the proportions in samples one *and* two, adjusting for sample size, using the equation:

$$P_u = \frac{n_1 P_{S1} + n_2 P_{S2}}{n_1 + n_2}$$

Where P_{s1} is the proportion of people in a group in sample one, and P_{s2} is the proportion of people in a group in sample two.

On its own, P_u is of little interest (it is basically a weighted average of the two samples), but it is useful for calculating $s_{\overline{X}_1 - \overline{X}_2}$:

$$s_{\overline{X}_1 - \overline{X}_2} = \sqrt{P_u(1 - P_u)}\sqrt{\frac{n_1 + n_2}{n_1 n_2}}$$

This number ($s_{\overline{X}_1 - \overline{X}_2}$) is known as the standard deviation of the difference between sample proportions. If we assume that both samples are drawn from normally distributed populations, we can assume that the difference of means is also normally distributed.

The value for $s_{\overline{X}_1 - \overline{X}_2}$ is used in the following equation to calculate the obtained value of z:

$$z_{obtained} = \frac{(P_{sample1} - P_{sample2})}{s_{\overline{X}_1 - \overline{X}_2}}$$

One- and Two-Tailed Tests, Again

This chapter has only explained how to determine how different one group is from another group, without considering the directionality of difference, using a **two-tailed test**. Often you will be concerned with differences in one direction. For example, instead of studying whether men and women have significantly different numbers of friends, you might want to know if males have more friends than females, or vice versa.

This once again introduces the need for a **one-tailed test**, which measures the significance and direction of a relationship. There is no statistical reason for choosing a one-tailed test over a two-tailed test; the choice is theoretically driven. If you are trying to determine whether or not groups are equal, use a two-tailed test. If you believe that a group has more, or less, of a quality than another group, use a one-tailed test.

To use a one-tailed test, a slight modification of the two-tailed case is needed. The modification is the use of a different value from the z- or t-table. Let's illustrate using the 95 per cent confidence interval from the z-table in Appendix A. As you know, $z_{critical}$ must exceed ±1.96 to be considered significant. In column C of the table, the area beyond z is listed as 0.025, so when both tails are included we will have a 95 per cent confidence interval. However, the one-tailed case needs to have 5 per cent of all values falling in only one of the two tails, pointing to a $z_{critical}$ value of roughly 1.65. If we hypothesize that one group will have a higher score than another (i.e., that males have more friends than females), we use a value of +1.65. For a lower score (males have fewer friends), we use –1.65. Follow the same process for *t*-scores.

Look at the *z*-table and find the one-tailed values for 90 per cent and 99 per cent confidence intervals.

BOX 11.2 IT'S YOUR TURN: THE TWO-SAMPLE PROPORTION

Using data from the Aboriginal Peoples Survey 2001 (Public Use Microdata File), you've decided to study whether women or men who consider themselves to be very, moderately, or not very religious or spiritual people are more likely to engage in prayer to maintain their religious/spiritual well-being. You've recoded the variable for prayer so that if a person responded yes, their value is one. If this was not a way they maintain their spirituality, they were coded zero (therefore the means reflect the proportion who do pray). You expect that the women will be significantly *more likely* to use prayer to maintain their spirituality than the men, and use SPSS to find the weighted *n* (or the population frequencies), the mean, and the standard deviation:

Group Statistics

	Male or female	N	Mean	Standard deviation	Standard error mean
Prayer	Male	114,734	.381	.486	.001
	Female	143,013	.516	.500	.001

Source: 2001 Aboriginal Peoples Survey, Public Use Microdata File
Note: APS is a post-censal survey, with selection based on responses to four questions examining aboriginal identity (e.g., self-report, list of Aboriginal group in list of ethnic or cultural group(s) they belong to. Includes residents of 10 provinces and three territories, only off-reserve adults are included in the PUMF. Individuals were excluded if they resided in a collective dwelling (Statistics Canada 2001, 6-9).

1. Calculate P_u, the estimate of the proportion of the population in the category of interest (the proportion of somewhat spiritual men and women who use prayer) using the equation:

$$P_u = \frac{n_1 P_{S1} + n_2 P_{S2}}{n_1 + n_2}$$

2. Use this value to calculate the standard deviation of the difference between sample proportions:

$$S_{\overline{X}_1 - \overline{X}_2} = \sqrt{P_u (1 - P_u)} \sqrt{\frac{n_1 + n_2}{n_1 n_2}}$$

3. Calculate the value of $z_{obtained}$ using: $z_{obtained} = \dfrac{(P_{sample1} - P_{sample2})}{S_{\overline{X}_1 - \overline{X}_2}}$

4. Compare the value of $z_{obtained}$ to the critical value (Hint: remember that your hypothesis had direction).

The solution for box 11.2 can be found on page 199.

PRACTICE QUESTIONS

1. Leslie wants to write her doctoral dissertation in a year; Dayle wants to do it 350 days. Each dissertation will be 175,000 words. In their first 10 days of writing, these are the word counts:

Leslie	Dayle
530	340
650	750
720	210
380	200
370	905
510	1,015
520	600
580	400
440	300
490	200

Will there be a 95 per cent significant difference in time to completion?

2. A research study was conducted to examine the differences between men and women on perceived life satisfaction. In total, 200 men and 200 women were given life satisfaction tests. Scores on the measure range from 0 to 60, with high scores indicating high life satisfaction. Men scored an average of 48 ($s = 7$), and women scored 45 ($s = 5$). From these data, can you conclude that there is a significant difference between the means of these two groups?

3. In a recent Genworth Financial survey of the housing experiences of recent immigrants to Canada (www.genworth.com), 76 per cent of recent immigrant non-homeowners ($n = 201$) said that distance to work was very important for them, compared to 68 per cent of homeowners ($n = 218$). Are the differences in the proportion of these groups significant at the 95 per cent confidence level?

Answers to the practice questions for chapter 11 can be found on page 189.

CHAPTER 12

Bivariate Statistics for Nominal Data

Learning Objectives

Although what's been covered so far in this text is useful, it is foundational information—you need to know these things in order to do statistics in the social sciences, but what you now know probably won't form the analytical centerpiece of any research projects. This chapter will continue to focus on bivariate analysis by:

- examining some of the reasons why it is useful to study more than one variable at a time
- learning what independent and dependent variables are
- studying chi-square tests of independence
- learning some popular techniques for measuring the association between two nominal variables

Introduction

Typically, social scientists are interested in uncovering the **associations** or **relationships** between several variables. Some examples of relationships that social scientists might be interested in are:

- How the introduction of a child into a household affects the number of hours worked by members of that household (particularly whether it differs for men and women).
- Differences in budgetary spending between majority and minority governments.

- Differences in family size, by religion.
- Whether members of particular visible minority groups are more susceptible to certain diseases.
- Whether marital status affects the number of hours spent at clubs, discos, malls, churches, synagogues, etc.

In each example there are two variables of interest. Although we might be interested in the characteristics of each particular variable, what is central for the investigation is identifying the relationship *between* the two. Nothing that's been covered so far helps with this; we need to learn new methods.

To simultaneously analyze two variables that cannot be ranked or ordered, you'll need to learn **bivariate analysis** for nominal variables. You'll learn to deal with ordinal and interval/ratio variables using contingency tables, which help researchers 'visualize' the relationship between two variables, how to measure the existence and strength of two nominal variables, and how to identify some techniques for assessing the relationship between two continuous variables.

Analysis with Two Nominal Variables

The first step for performing bivariate analysis is organizing the data so that patterns can be easily discerned. Suppose a researcher wants to identify connections between exposure to television commercials for a pizza restaurant and the behaviour of 1,000 people watching television. What would be a useful way of identifying and assessing the nature of this relationship?

For nominal data like these, it is useful to create a frequency table, like the one in table 12.1.

The information is organized into two columns. The left column indicates the possibilities or response categories, the right indicates the number of people in each category and the total number of people in the study (the cell in the bottom right corner).

Using table 12.1 it is possible to draw some conclusions from the sample: The overwhelming majority of the people in the study had no reaction to the pizza commercial. The next two most popular alternatives are 'Grab Food from the Refrigerator' and 'Change Channels'. A minority (40 people) actually engaged in the behaviour that the pizza companies sought—they ordered a pizza (let's assume that they called the company advertised). It is difficult to determine whether 40 people in 1,000 is a sufficient number to warrant the huge advertising costs—that is a decision that only the pizza company can make—but we can see that for most people the advertisement had very little effect.

The relationship could be expanded by comparing the responses of any two population subgroups—say, men and women. This is done by subdividing the column on the right by the sex of the respondent, then determining which of the variables is affecting the value of the other; often referred to as 'determining the order of causality'. The variable that we think is modifying the outcome is an **independent variable**, and the outcome of interest is the **dependent variable**. Note: these two terms are important, because they apply to all relationships and are used often.

In the example, we hypothesize that sex of respondent will relate to reaction to the commercial. To determine if this hypothesis is correct, the first task is to determine how the data can be best presented.

Adding sex to the table (see table 12.2) makes interpretation more difficult, but also more interesting. Conventionally, independent variables are shown as columns, and dependent

Table 12.1 Response of 1,000 Television Viewers to a Pizza Commercial

Response of respondent to television commercial	F
Order a pizza	40
Grab food from the refrigerator	100
Change channels	110
No reaction	750
Total	1,000

Table 12.2 Response of 1,000 Television Viewers to a Pizza Commercial by Sex

Response of respondent to television commercial	Sex of respondent	
	Female	Male
Order a pizza	10	30
Grab food from the refrigerator	60	40
Change channels	60	50
No reaction	490	260
Total	620	380

BOX 12.1 CROSS TABULATIONS: HISTORY OF A TERM

In the second half of the seventeenth century, the German Empire was fractured, suffering from balkanization, and the resulting social ills of poverty and civil disruption. In response, administrative bureaucracies occupied themselves with the task of defining and cataloguing the micro-states. German authorities sought to not only describe, but to organize, hierarchize, and classify them. Though they called this a 'statistical' analysis, they were not using the quantitative method used today. Officials used, among other things, an early version of what is called a cross-table. The countries constituting the Empire were put into the rows of a cross-table, and state characteristics were used as columns. Rulers could compare states based on the presence of a particular characteristic, from art and culture to agriculture, and the total character of any state could be read across the rows. Using the table, it was possible to sum up a state, and compare it to other states using nominal features.

This new method of comparative taxonomy was met with resistance. Critics saw the tables as 'vulgar' statistics. They allowed qualitative equivalence and conceptual reduction, which was at odds with what the critics valued as 'subtle and distinguished' statistical analysis—an

analysis that did not employ tables at all. Both forms of schematic qualitative analysis are no longer used, having been replaced by quantitative analysis, which has also been historically driven by nations' desires to organize and understand their populations (Desrosières, 1998).

Statistician Karl Pearson (1857–1936), following in the footsteps of Francis Galton (1822–1911), argued that contingency tables allow one to schematize 'the *partial relationship* between two phenomena, midway between two limits—absolute independence and absolute dependence—or *correlation*, synonymous with association' (Desrosières, 1998: 110). The emphasis on 'contingence' is important. Pearson believed absolute unilinear causation to be rare to non-existent. Philosophical understandings of the nature of what was being described lie behind the table's schematization. Pearson described them as contingency tables because he considered each event in the observable world to be unique to itself; the human process of observation and classification is what allows for predictability. Regularity is a consequence of human conceptualization and abstraction, not an inherent feature of an external world.

---

variables as rows. These tables are called **contingency tables**, or cross-tabulations. Obviously most people had no reaction to the pizza commercial, but that is true for women more often than men. This is determined by looking at the ratio of total women in the study to the number of women who had no reaction to the pizza commercial (490 out of 620, or roughly 79 per cent). On the other hand, of the 380 men in the study only 260, or 68 per cent, of them did not react to the commercial (260/380 = 68 per cent).

What is more interesting (at least to the pizza company) is not who does *not* respond to the pizza commercial, but who actually does. Only 10 women out of 620 ordered a pizza after viewing

the commercial, compared to 30 out of 380 men. There are several ways to explain these results, including: 1) men like pizza more than women; 2) men and women like pizza equally, but the pizza commercial resonates with men more than women; or 3) women like pizza more than men, but TV is not an effective way to target women.

We don't know if any of these explanations is true. Before we can explore the alternatives, it is necessary to determine whether the results, which are based on a sample of 1,000 men and women, can be generalized for the population. This brings us back to our recurring question about the degree to which we can be certain that our sample accurately reflects the population. To assess for any **bivariate** association, we need to learn about the chi-square test of significance.

The Chi-Square Test of Significance

The chi-square, introduced by Karl Pearson in 1900, is a widely used method for determining the level of agreement between the frequencies in a distribution of observed data and the frequencies calculated on the assumption of a normal distribution. Pearson wanted to determine the frequency with which trends derived from a sample would also be seen in the population. He developed the chi-square to serve that purpose. Since then, it has become an important part of statistical theory and practice.

The chi-square can be used for all levels of measurement, not just nominal data, and for combinations of levels—nominal/ordinal, ordinal/interval, nominal/ratio, etc.—making it extremely useful. It is **non-parametric**, so you don't have to make assumptions about the shape or distribution of a sample and/or population (it doesn't need to be normally distributed, for example). Using the chi-square makes it easy to identify statistically significant relationships between characteristics, without worrying about whether the variables are normally distributed until after a relationship has been identified.

Perhaps the most compelling aspect of the chi-square is that it can be directly calculated from bivariate tables, such as table 12.2, by comparing the discrepancies between observed values and expected values. It determines whether the observed differences in data come from random sampling error, or if they exist in the data.

In order to calculate the chi-square, it is necessary to:

1. Compute row and column totals, or **marginals**.
2. Divide the marginals by the total number of possible variable values in order to determine the distribution of highest probability. These are the expected values.

For example, there are 400 students and 20 classes at a high school. With no other information about the distribution of students (that is, there are no independent variables predicting allocation across classes), we would expect each class to have 20 students. If there were discrepancies

between the expected class sizes and the observed class sizes, we might suspect that there are factors other than random allocation (popularity of teachers, subject matter, location of friends, etc.) behind classroom designation. Chi-square measures the magnitude of that discrepancy, and tells us whether we should pursue further analysis.

To further illustrate the calculation of chi-square, let's imagine that there are two soccer teams, A and B, each made up of 11 people (there are 22 people in total). Of these, 12 are female, and 10 are male. If we guessed at the distribution of men and women across teams A and B, assuming that there were no factors influencing their distribution, we would guess that each team has 6 females and 5 males.

To calculate the numbers (shown in parentheses in table 12.3) we must derive the expected frequencies for *each cell*. The expected frequency is the number of observations in each cell, if the independent variable has no impact on them. It can be calculated using the equation:

$$f_e = \frac{\Sigma column * \Sigma row}{n}$$

The expected frequency f_e is equal to the column marginal, multiplied by the row marginal, divided by the total number of observations. There are a total of 12 women and 10 men, with 11 people on each soccer team. Let's calculate the expected frequency for each of the four cells:

Upper left:

$$f_e = \frac{\Sigma column * \Sigma row}{n} = \frac{12 * 11}{22} = \frac{132}{22} = 6$$

Upper right:

$$f_e = \frac{10 * 11}{22} = 5$$

Lower left:

$$f_e = \frac{12 * 11}{22} = 6$$

Lower right:

$$f_e = \frac{10 * 11}{22} = 5$$

The numbers are the most likely distribution of men and women across the two teams, assuming a random distribution with no other explanatory

Table 12.3 Sex Composition of Two Hypothetical Soccer Teams

	Female	Male	Total
A	7(6)	4(5)	11
B	5(6)	6(5)	11
Total	12	10	22

factors or independent variables involved. In the event of a non-integer, it is acceptable to have an expected frequency that is not a whole number (e.g., 5.3) even though it is not likely to occur in reality (it is not possible to have part-persons on soccer teams).

The numbers that represent the expected distribution (typically expressed as f_e for expected frequencies) are used with the numbers you have observed (f_o for observed frequencies) to calculate chi-square (χ^2) using the following formula:

$$\chi^2 = \Sigma \frac{(f_o - f_e)^2}{f_e}$$

To reduce the possibility of calculation errors, it is useful to organize the data in a table, like table 12.4. In the left-most column, each of the four cells is identified by its team name (A or B), and whether the cell refers to females or males (F or M). 'AF' refers to the cell containing the frequency of females on team A. The observed frequencies, f_o, appear in the second column,

Table 12.4 Sex Composition of Two Hypothetical Soccer Teams

Group	f_o	f_e	$(f_o - f_e)^2$	$\dfrac{(f_o - f_e)^2}{f_e}$
AF	7	6	1	0.17
AM	4	5	1	0.20
BF	5	6	1	0.17
BM	6	5	1	0.20
Total	22	22		$\chi^2 = 0.74$

followed by expected frequencies, f_e, in column three. Column four is $(f_o - f_e)^2$, the solution for the numerator of the chi-square equation, and column five solves the equation for each row. The summation of values appears in the bottom right cell, and represents the value of chi-square in this example.

Now that we have the chi-square value, we need to assess it using a chi-square table. Like other distributions (normal distribution, t-distribution, etc.), chi-square has a known distribution (the table is shown in Appendix C), which means that we can determine if there are significant differences between observed and expected values. To do this, we need to revisit **degrees of freedom**, but with a slightly different calculation to reflect that two variables that are being used.

When we looked at the t-distribution to assess sample means, we calculated the degrees of freedom to be equal to sample size minus one. We subtracted one from the sample size because the individual values of any particular set of numbers can be determined using $n - 1$ values. Since there was one variable, only one value was determined by the others.

Now we are looking at two variables, but the same logic applies. Remember that it is possible to determine the value of any cell by knowing the table total and the value of all other cells. Now there are two values that are determined entirely by other values. In this case, degrees of freedom can be defined as the number of rows, minus one, times the number of columns, minus one:

$$degrees\ of\ freedom = (r - 1)(c - 1)$$

In the example, there are two rows and two columns in table 12.3 (we never count the totals columns), so the degrees of freedom: $(2 - 1)(2 - 1) = (1)(1) = 1$. Using Appendix C, we can choose level of significance (also often called α or p-value) of either 0.05 or 0.01. Next, find the correct number for the degrees of freedom that we calculated (1). For our example, with level of significance of 0.05, the critical chi-square value is 3.841. To determine whether our observed values differ significantly from the expected values, we need to compare the calculated chi-square value of 0.74 to 3.841. If the calculated value exceeds the critical value, we can conclude that the observed values differ significantly from expected values.

BOX 12.2 CHI-SQUARE: THE STEPS

1. Compute row and column totals, or marginals.

2. Divide marginals by the total number of possible variable values to determine the distribution of highest probability. These are the expected values.

3. Subtract expected cell frequencies from observed cell frequencies.

4. Square that number and divide it by the expected frequency.

5. Sum the product of these calculations. This is your observed chi-square value.

6. Assess the statistical significance of this number using the chi-square chart in Appendix C; $df = (r - 1)(c - 1)$.

Our calculated value is well *below* the critical value, suggesting that a respondent's sex is not a significant factor in determining which team they will be on.

Further analysis on this association is probably unnecessary, since chi-square suggests that the observed trends could have easily appeared at random. An important point to make about the chi-square is that it depends on both the strength of the relationship *and* the sample size. The difference in sex composition across teams may be too slight to be certain about its existence. It is also possible that the relationship is not significant because our sample of 22 is too small to determine if a significant association exists. With our pizza commercial example, we could express the same doubts. Sample size is not as important for the measures that we'll discuss in the next section.

Measures of Association for Nominal Data

As you know by now, researchers are not only interested in identifying the significance of relationships between variables, but also the strength of those relationships. Before the pizza company revamps its advertising strategy to more effectively target women, it would be useful to know if sex is associated with reaction to television commercials, or if the study was a fluke. For various reasons (perhaps a non-probability sample was used), it is possible that the 1,000 people in the study do not accurately reflect the pizza company's target audience. If that was the case, the patterns in tables 12.1 and 12.2 would not be an accurate representation of the pizza company's customer base.

To solve this problem, a measure of **statistical significance** between sex and the reactions of the study members is needed. This measure will allow us to determine whether the observed patterns actually exist, or if they were due to chance or bias. This we have with chi-square. What we don't have, but need, is a measure of the strength of the association.

The level of measurement of a particular variable determines which measures of association are suitable. For nominal data, we'll learn about phi, Cramer's V, and lambda.

Phi

Phi is a chi-square-based measure of association used only for tables where both independent variable and dependent variable can have two response categories (2 by 2 tables). The chi-square coefficient depends on the strength of the relationship and sample size, but phi eliminates the influence of sample size by dividing chi-square by the sample size, n, and taking the square root.

$$\phi = \sqrt{\frac{\chi^2}{n}}$$

Since phi is a **symmetrical** measure, it doesn't matter which of the two variables you believe to be the independent variable (although it's good practice to keep them straight). Phi is the per cent of difference between a product of the diagonal cells to the product of the non-diagonal cells. It is the magnitude of difference between observed and expected values, adjusting for sample size. Phi defines a perfect association as one with complete statistical dependence, for example if all members of a certain category of the independent variable (e.g., all women) are also all members of one response of the dependent variable (e.g., all grabbed food from the fridge). Phi defines a null relationship as statistical independence (e.g., there is no difference between what men and women did after seeing the pizza ad).

Let's suppose that you were interested in the relationship between owning a gun to protect personal property and being a victim of a crime. You want to determine if people who are victims of crime are more likely to take extreme measures to protect themselves and their property. Since both gun ownership and victim data are nominal variables, having only two possible categories (yes/no), using phi is a good way of determining whether an association exists. Let's use the 2004 Victimization Survey (GSS cycle 18) as a data source (see table 12.5).

The first thing we need to do is create a table to calculate chi-square, like we did in table 12.4 (see table 12.6).

Table 12.5 Gun Ownership and Victims of Crimes

	Have you been a victim of a crime in the past 12 months?		
Owns gun	Yes	No	Total
Yes	21,400 (17,994)	234,900 (238,306)	256,300
No	1,793,400 (1,796,806)	23,799,000 (23,795,594)	25,592,400
Total	1,814,800	24,033,900	25,848,700

Source: 2004 Victimization Survey (GSS cycle 18)

Table 12.6 Computing Chi-Square for Gun Ownership and Victims of Crimes

Group	f_o	f_e	$(f_o-f_e)^2$	$\dfrac{(f_o-f_e)^2}{f_e}$
YY	21,400	17,994	11,600,836	644.71
YN	234,900	238,306	11,600,836	48.68
NY	1,793,400	1,796,806	11,600,836	6.46
NN	23,799,000	23,795,594	11,600,836	0.49
Total	25,848,700	25,848,700		$\chi^2=700.34$

Looking at Appendix C, we can see that chi-square is significant. Now that we have chi-square, the calculation of phi is relatively straightforward:

$$\phi = \sqrt{\frac{\chi^2}{n}} = \sqrt{\frac{700.34}{25848700}} = 0.005$$

The interpretation of 0.005 is complicated and beyond the scope of this text, but suffice it to say that there is a significant association between gun ownership and victimization (700.34 is much higher than the critical value of 3.841 found in Appendix C). Turning to the phi value of 0.005, researchers typically regard values between zero and 0.10 as a weak association, 0.10 and 0.30 as a moderate association, and values between 0.30 and 1.0 as a strong association. Since phi is a symmetric measure there isn't a distinction made between independent and dependent variables, so we don't know if victimization results in gun ownership, or vice versa. When two values are completely dependent on one another, phi will take the value of one. When there is no dependence, phi will take the value of zero. Each observation has a specific value for one variable (for example, a respondent reports owning a gun) whenever they report a value on the other variable (that they've been a victim of a crime in the past 12 months). The results point to a weak association.

Despite having some undesirable qualities, phi is a popular measure for 2 by 2 tables. It is not possible to analyze the pattern of the relationship

BOX 12.3 IT'S YOUR TURN: PHI – DRINKING AND DAILY EXERCISE

A student was thinking about the different guys she knows: the guys who were always exercising and the guys who were always drinking. It seemed like none of them liked to both exercise and drink, but she thought that maybe this was just among her friends. Using data from the Canadian Community Health Survey (CCHS, wave 2.1) she randomly selected 20 cases to test her null hypothesis that men who exercise at least 15 minutes a day are as likely as those who exercise less to regularly consume 12 or more drinks in a week (these cases were selected only from males who were not missing on either question). If she rejects her null hypothesis, she'll be able to conclude that there is a significant relationship between exercise and drinking for males.

Table 12.7 Drinking and Exercise, 20 Cases from the Canadian Community Health Survey, Wave 2.1

Case	Regularly has more than 12 drinks a week (1 = yes, 0 = no)	Participates in at least 15 minutes of exercise daily (1 = yes, 0 = no)	Case	Regularly has more than 12 drinks a week (1 = yes, 0 = no)	Participates in at least 15 minutes of exercise daily (1 = yes, 0 = no)
1	1	0	11	0	1
2	0	0	12	0	0
3	1	0	13	0	0
4	1	1	14	1	1
5	0	1	15	0	0
6	0	0	16	1	0
7	1	1	17	0	0
8	1	0	18	0	0
9	0	0	19	1	0
10	0	0	20	1	1

1. Create a table (like table 12.7) that compares your dependent (as rows) and independent (as columns) variables. Include column and row totals. (In this example, because we are not testing a causal relationship, either variable can be the independent or dependent).

2. Compute the expected values for each cell and add values to the table in question 1.

$$f_e = \frac{\Sigma_{column} * \Sigma_{row}}{N}$$

3. Create a chi-square table (like table 12.6). To do this you will: 1) subtract the expected from the observed value in each cell, and square the number, and 2) divide it by the expected value ($\frac{(f_o - f_e)^2}{f_e}$). Once that is done for each cell, compute the totals to find the χ^2 value.

4. Calculate phi $\phi = \sqrt{\frac{\chi^2}{N}}$. Is there a strong or weak association between the variables?

The solution for box 12.3 can be found on page 200.

without looking at the contingency table, so trends in the data cannot be determined from the measure of association alone. Phi is only useful for measuring the strength of the relationship, but there is no easy way to measure that strength.

Another limitation of phi is that it is sensitive to shifts in marginal distributions. Phi does not necessarily vary from zero to one. For tables larger than 2 by 2, the maximum value of phi is the square root of $k - 1$, where k is the number of response categories in the variable with a smaller number of categories. Phi can be greater than 1.0 for larger tables, with a theoretical maximum of infinity, differing depending on table size. Because of this, phi is typically only used with 2 by 2 tables. For tables larger than 2 by 2, the appropriate chi-square-based measure is **Cramer's V**.

Cramer's V

Cramer's V is an elaboration of phi, except that it always assumes a value between zero and one. Calculating Cramer's V is simple, using the following equation:

$$V = \sqrt{\frac{\chi^2}{(n)(\min(r - 1) \mid (c - 1))}}$$

Although the equation seems more daunting than the one for phi, they are actually similar. The difference is in the denominator, which is the number of observations multiplied by the lesser of the number of rows – 1, or the number of columns – 1.

If we calculated Cramer's V for city of residence and favourite Canadian NHL hockey team from a sample of 1,000 people, we would have 26 different cities and six hockey teams. The denomina-

tor for the Cramer's V equation would be 1,000 * (6 – 1), or 5,000, because the hockey teams variable has 6 values, considerably less than the 26 values for city of residence. For a 2 by 2 table, the denominator would be n (2 – 1), which equals n, and reduces the equation for Cramer's V to that of phi.

Since Cramer's V is so similar to phi, they share almost all of the same properties and weaknesses.

The Proportional Reduction of Error: Lambda

The final measure of association for nominal data that we will study is lambda. Like phi and Cramer's V, lambda is used to measure the strength of a relationship between two nominal variables. It is non-directional, and since it relies on a **proportional reduction of error**, its numbers are interpreted more straightforwardly than either phi or Cramer's V. Lambda allows us to answer the following question: How much is our ability to predict one variable improved by taking another variable into account?

To get lambda, calculate the extreme possibilities, then calculate the total classification error by comparing the extreme predictions with the actual distribution of observations across response categories.

Like the other measures, the mechanics of calculating lambda are better illustrated with an example. Suppose we wanted to determine if there is a relationship between smoking and sex of respondent, and saw the trends found in table 12.9 in our hypothetical data.

From table 12.9 we see that a higher proportion of females in our sample are smoking. From this, we might conclude that knowing the sex of

BOX 12.4 PHI AND CRAMER'S V: THE STEPS

1. Calculate the observed chi-square value (box 12.2).
2. For phi, divide chi-square by the number of observations.
3. For Cramer's V, divide chi-square by the number of observations, multiplied by *either* the number of rows *or* the number of columns (use the smaller of the two values).
4. To get either phi or Cramer's V, take the square root of the calculation you create in step three.

BOX 12.5 IT'S YOUR TURN: CRAMER'S V

Based on readings that Jeff had done for his Sociology of the Family course, he wondered if women were more or less likely to have worked full-, rather than part-, time in the last year if they were married, divorced, or single. Using data from the 2001 Census of Canada, he selected only women who answered both the questions on full vs part time work and marital status, and recoded marital status to combine divorced and separated (people who were widowed were excluded). He found the following observed and expected (in brackets) values for the Canadian population:

Table 12.8 Chi-Square for Women's Relationship between Work Status and Marital Status in 2000

| Work status in 2000 | Marital Status | | | Total |
	Married	Divorced/separated	Single	
Worked mainly full-time weeks	3,485,748 (1,624,006)	604,011 (257,131.1)	1,193,175 (701,797.2)	2,582,934
Worked mainly part-time weeks	1,291,201 (1,455,333.0)	152,330 (230,424.9)	871,134 (628,907.1)	2,314,665
Total	4,776,949	756,341	2,064,309	7,597,599

1. Using the observed and expected frequencies for each cell, compute chi-square.

2. Instead of computing phi, compute Cramer's V (because there is more than one degree of freedom) using this equation:

$$V = \sqrt{\frac{\chi^2}{(n)(\min(r-1)\,|\,(c-1))}}$$

The solution for box 12.5 can be found on page 201.

 BOX 12.6 WHY DOES NON-DIRECTIONALITY MATTER?

Because variables that are measured at the nominal level cannot be ranked or ordered, it's not surprising that these measures are non-directional. A non-directional measure is the best we can hope for.

Table 12.9   Smoking and Sex of Respondent (fictional data)

	Female	Male	Row total
Smokes	42	21	63
Does not smoke	10	30	40
Column total	52	51	103

a respondent increases the accuracy of our prediction about whether or not they are a smoker. However, what we don't know yet is whether the difference is big enough that we would see a similar trend in the population. To determine if that is the case, we need to make two predictions, and ignore the influence of the independent variable (sex). The first prediction is that everyone is a smoker (S = 103, NS = 0), and the second is that nobody smokes (S = 0, NS = 103). Then we calculate the classification error in both cases, which is the number of observations minus the number of misclassified cases.

For smokers, it would be equal to:

103 (the total number of observations) – 63 (the number of correctly classified cases) = a total of 40 misclassifications.

For non-smokers, the misclassification would be equal to 103 – 40 = 63.

To calculate lambda, we keep the lower of the two misclassifications (40). This is because we are interested in making the best possible prediction with no additional information from any independent variable. We will call this number E_1. For this example, $E_1 = 40$.

The next step is to determine how much better we can do by using the values of our independent variable, sex of respondent. Like last time, calculate the extreme possibilities for each value of the independent variable first, except now we predict that all females smoke first, then do not smoke second, and then do the same for males, calculating the classification error each time.

Predicting that all females smoke yields a classification error of 10 (52 – 42 = 10), and predicting that they do not smoke misclassifies 42 people

BOX 12.7 CALCULATING LAMBDA: THE STEPS

1. What are the extreme possibilities? Make two predictions, ignoring the independent variable for now:

   a. Everyone is in one category of the dependent variable.
   b. Everyone is in the other category of the dependent variable.

2. Calculate classification errors (total minus number in one category, total minus number in the other category).

3. Keep the smaller of the two classification errors. This is the best possible prediction that can be made without information from an explanatory (independent) variable. Call it E_1.

4. What are the extreme possibilities for each value of the independent variable?

   a. Repeat step two for each category of the independent variable.
   b. Sum the lowest classification errors of each category of the independent variable. This is E_2.

5. Calculate lambda as $\lambda = \dfrac{E_1 - E_2}{E_1}$

(52 – 10 = 42). For males, predicting that all males smoke yields a classification error of 30 (51 – 21 = 30), and that they do not smoke misclassifies 21 people (51 – 30 = 21).

Choose the lowest classification error for each sex, and sum those numbers to produce E_2, which is the total classification error that can be made with the information provided for the independent variable. Since the fewest errors come from guessing that all women smoke (10), and that all men do not (21), we sum those numbers to get a classification error of 31. This is the second error, and it represents the best possible prediction that can be made by including the independent variable, sex.

Finally, we define lambda (λ) as the per cent improvement from knowing a person's sex, using the following equation:

$$\lambda = \frac{E_1 - E_2}{E_1}$$

$$= \frac{40 - 31}{40}$$

$$= 0.225$$

The number tells us the change in the number of correct predictions between knowing the value for the independent variable and not knowing that value. The accuracy of the smoking prediction improves by 22.5 per cent when the value of the independent variable (sex of respondent) is known.

 BOX 12.8 IT'S YOUR TURN: LAMBDA

Jose and his girlfriend Vanessa have been arguing about whether women are more safety-conscious than men when they play sports. Vanessa is sure that they are, but Jose is sure they are just as likely as men to take safety risks. To test if there is any difference between the two,

Vanessa and Jose randomly select 100 individuals from the second wave of the CCHS who had gone in-line skating during the previous three months, and had responded to a question about whether they use protective gear when skating. They found the following:

Wears all protective equipment for in-line skating	Female	Male	Row total
Yes	9	2	11
No	42	47	89
Column total	51	49	100

1. Make the two extreme predictions for the dependent variable. The lower prediction will be E_1.

2. Calculate the extreme predictions using the independent variable to determine E_2.

3. Calculate lambda (or the percentage increase in predictive accuracy): $\lambda = \dfrac{E_1 - E_2}{E_1}$

The solution for box 12.8 can be found on page 202.

PRACTICE QUESTIONS

We're interested in the relationship between religion and city of choice. Here are the data from a selected sample from the 1901 census:

Religion	City		
	Saint John	Toronto	Quebec City
Roman Catholic	98	329	641
Church of England	73	552	30
Methodist	26	414	8
Presbyterian	55	403	5

1. Why are these variables nominal?
2. Calculate chi-square for each of the cells.
3. How many degrees of freedom are there in the table?
4. Calculate phi and Cramer's V. Which of the two measures would you use? Why?

Answers to the practice questions for chapter 12 can be found on page 190.

CHAPTER 13

Bivariate Statistics for Ordinal Data

Learning Objectives

This chapter will continue our overview of the various measures of association for the different levels of measurement. We'll cover several measures for ordinal data, specifically:

- Kruskal's gamma (γ)
- Spearman's rho (ρ)
- Somer's d
- Kendall's tau-b

Introduction

In chapter 12 we looked at some of the tests of significance and measures of association frequently used for nominal variables. Some of the measures (phi, Cramer's V) are based on the Chi-Square, while the other (lambda) relies on a 'proportional reduction in error'. Since nominal data cannot be ranked or ordered, we did not discuss any statistics that assess the *direction* of a relationship between two variables. So we cannot determine what happens to the value of the dependent variable as the value of the independent variable changes. The best we can do with these data is figure out how knowing the value of one

nominal variable (the independent variable) will help us to accurately predict the value of another nominal variable (the dependent variable).

In this chapter we will look at tests of significance and measures of association for ordinal variables. Since ordinal variables have more desirable statistical properties than nominal variables (notably, the ability to rank response categories), after completing chapter 13, not only will you be able to assess the significance of difference and the proportional reduction of errors, but you will also be able to measure the **direction** of any relationship.

There are at least four popular measures of association for variables measured at the ordinal level: Kruskal's gamma (γ), Spearman's rho (ρ), Somer's *d*, and Kendall's tau-*b*. As with nominal variables, one of the most useful ways to understand the relationships between ordinal variables is to look at a contingency table.

Contingency Tables/Crosstabulations

To illustrate measures of association between ordinal variables, consider an example from mental health research. Suppose you want to determine if there are differences in self-perceived mental health by level of education. You hypothesize that people with higher education levels are likely to report higher mental health levels, because you believe that a critical component of mental health is self-fulfillment and life satisfaction, two things that you think are related to education. What would you need to determine whether that relationship actually exists? In Canada, this inquiry can be made using the Canadian Community Health Survey, a longitudinal survey conducted by Statistics Canada. We'll use wave 2.1.

The first thing to do is some univariate analysis; look at the distribution of each of the variables, identify **outliers** and/or **missing data**, etc. We'd want to make sure that there are enough observations in each possible category (you'll see why this is important in a minute), and that there are no outliers, or observations with scores that lie far outside the area under the normal curve. Once that is done, we confidently look at the relationship.

First, let's look at education, which we believe is the independent variable.

Using table 13.1, we can see that approximately one-quarter of the total population has less than a secondary school education. Another 17.8 per cent have achieved a secondary school diploma, 7.5 per cent of all respondents have attained at least some post-secondary training, and the remaining 46.4 per cent claim to have successfully completed post-secondary training. Although it is not possible to assess the accuracy of these results without comparing them with those from another data set (such as the census), it is not unreasonable to believe that approximately half of all Canadians have completed post-secondary training. Similarly, that 26.1 per cent of all Canadians have less than secondary school training probably fits with what we would see in the census data. If we saw that 80 per cent of all people in Canada didn't have post-secondary training that should raise a red flag for us!

Since these values make sense to us, they have **face validity**. Therefore, we can be fairly confident about using them in our analysis. Notice that there are a number of people who, for whatever reason, did not answer the question. Treat these instances as missing data, meaning that they will not add any useful information to the analysis. In fact, they might obscure our investigation of the relationship between education and

Table 13.1   Educational Attainment Levels of the Canadian Population, Canadian Community Health Survey, Wave 2.1, All Observations

| | Highest level - respond. 4 levels - (*D*) | | | |
	Frequency	%	Valid %	Cumulative %
Valid	< than secondary	6,923,116	26.1	26.6	26.6
	Secondary grad.	4,726,816	17.8	18.2	44.8
	Other post sec.	1,996,934	7.5	7.7	52.5
	Post-sec. grad.	12,333,484	46.4	47.5	100.0
	Total	25,980,349	97.8	100.0	
Missing	Not stated	575,081	2.2		
Total		26,555,430	100.0		

Source: Canadian Community Health Survey Public Use Data, Wave 2.1

mental health, because most software packages will treat the missing cases as another response category (unless we tell it to do otherwise, or it has already been defined as missing).

Looking at table 13.2, again we see that there are several missing responses in our mental health measure. Before we perform any bivariate analyses, we want to eliminate these cases from our investigation. More importantly, since we are analyzing two variables at a time, we want all observations to have available data for both variables.

For now, we'll skip over how to select or exclude cases (please consult your lab manual to learn how to exclude cases in the package that you are using for your course), since it is done differently in each statistical package. The 575,081 cases that were missing in table 13.1 have been excluded from table 13.3, leaving only observations with valid values for each variable.

All of the 'don't know', 'refusal', and 'not stated' responses have been eliminated in table 13.4.

Now that the data is in shape, we can look at **contingency tables**.

Table 13.2   Self-perceived Mental Health of the Canadian Population, Canadian Community Health Survey, Wave 2.1, All Observations

| | | **Self-perceived mental health** | | | |
		Frequency	**%**	**Valid %**	**Cumulative %**
Valid	Excellent	9,941,583	38.4	38.4	38.4
	Very good	9,068,745	34.2	35.0	73.4
	Good	5,666,929	21.3	21.9	95.3
	Fair	997,559	3.8	3.9	99.2
	Poor	210,984	0.8	0.8	100.0
	Total	25,885,801	98.5	100.0	
Missing	Don't know	35,749	0.1		
	Refusal	8,105	0.0		
	Not stated	625,774	2.4		
	Total	669,629	2.5		
Total		26,555,430	100.0		

Source: Canadian Community Health Survey Public Use Data, Wave 2.1

Table 13.3   Educational Attainment Levels of the Canadian Population, Canadian Community Health Survey, Wave 2.1, Valid Observations Only

| | | **Highest level - respond. 4 levels - (D)** | | | |
		Frequency	**%**	**Valid %**	**Cumulative %**
Valid	< than secondary	6,923,116	26.6	26.6	26.6
	Secondary grad.	4,726,816	18.2	18.2	44.8
	Other post-sec.	1,996,934	7.7	7.7	52.5
	Post-sec. grad.	12,333,484	47.5	47.5	100.0
	Total	25,980,349	100.0	100.0	

Source: Canadian Community Health Survey Public Use Data, Wave 2.1

Table 13.4   Self-perceived Mental Health of the Canadian Population, Canadian Community Health Survey, Wave 2.1, Valid Observations Only

| | | **Self-perceived mental health** | | | |
		Frequency	**%**	**Valid %**	**Cumulative %**
Valid	Excellent	9,923,648	38.4	38.4	38.4
	Very good	9,055,679	35.0	35.0	73.5
	Good	5,652,134	21.9	21.9	95.3
	Fair	994,779	3.9	3.9	99.2
	Poor	210,764	0.8	0.8	100.0
	Total	25,837,004	100.0	100.0	

Source: Canadian Community Health Survey Public Use Data, Wave 2.1

In table 13.5, the distribution of self-rated mental health is presented, contingent on education. When looking at them, pay particular attention to how the data are 'clustered' in certain cells. Notice that in table 13.5, every cell has a fairly high number of observations, so we needn't worry about **sparsity** affecting our results. Other than that, it is difficult to glean any useful information. For this reason when working with large data sets it is easier to identify trends by looking at the percentages of observations in each cell, rather than the number of observations.

By doing this we start to see that a relationship exists between the two variables. Looking at the percentage gradually increases as education levels get higher. Similarly, poor mental health appears to be negatively related to education. Beyond identifying the direction of the relationship between the two variables, it is difficult to identify the strength of the relationship. We need to rely on measures of association partly for this reason.

Kruskal's Gamma (γ)

Like lambda does for nominal variables, gamma (γ) relies on a proportional reduction of error—meaning that using it improves the odds of correctly predicting a score. By calculating gamma

Table 13.5   Observed Counts of Education by Self-perceived Mental Health Status, Canadian Community Health Survey, Wave 2.1, Valid Observations Only

Highest level - respond. 4 levels - (D) * Self-perceived mental health crosstabulation							
		Self-perceived mental health					
		Excellent	**Very good**	**Good**	**Fair**	**Poor**	**Total**
Highest level - respond. 4 levels - (D)	< than secondary	2,158,456	2,237,899	1,789,087	331,363	70,770	6,587,575
	Secondary grad.	1,725,723	1,639,759	1,028,018	181,424	41,202	4,616,126
	Other post-sec.	768,166	685,646	413,825	87,898	18,494	1,974,029
	Post-sec. grad.	5,103,471	4,327,080	2,299,402	373,042	76,288	12,179,283
Total		9,755,816	8,890,384	5,530,332	973,727	206,754	25,357,013

Source: Canadian Community Health Survey Public Use Data, Wave 2.1

Table 13.6 Education by Self-perceived Mental Health Status Presented as Percentages, Canadian Community Health Survey, Wave 2.1, Valid Observations Only

Highest level - respond. 4 levels - (D) * Self-perceived mental health crosstabulation

		Self-perceived mental health (%)					
		Excellent	Very good	Good	Fair	Poor	Total
Highest level - respond. 4 levels - (D)	< than secondary	32.8	34.0	27.2	5.0	1.1	100.0
	Secondary grad.	37.4	35.5	22.3	3.9	0.9	100.0
	Other post-sec.	38.9	34.7	21.0	4.5	0.9	100.0
	Post-sec. grad.	41.9	35.5	18.9	3.1	0.6	100.0
Total		38.5	35.1	21.8	3.8	0.8	100.0

Source: Canadian Community Health Survey Public Use Data, Wave 2.1

we can determine by how much our ability to predict the score of Y is improved if we take the score of X into account. However, unlike lambda the values of gamma range between –1.00 and +1.00, suggesting that the measure is directional.

To compute gamma, two quantities are necessary:

1. N_{same} is the number of case pairs that are ranked in the *same* order on both variables, also known as concordant observations.
2. $N_{different}$ is the number of case pairs that are ranked in a *different* order on each variable, also known as discordant observations.

To understand what we mean by N_{same} and $N_{different}$, consider this example: Suppose that we are interested in the relationship between educational attainment and income for Aboriginal Canadians. To do this, we can use the 2001 Aboriginal Peoples Survey, which includes highly detailed information on this and many other contemporary characteristics of Canada's First Nations. Although there is more detailed information in the survey, for the purpose of this example pretend that we only have two dichotomous, ordinal measures of income and education.

Looking at table 13.7, it is easy to see that high school graduates are more likely to earn an income than people without a high school diploma. In the 'Yes' column for 'High school graduate?' there is a much larger proportion of individuals in the 'Yes' row for income (roughly 84 per cent) than the 'No' row (16 per cent). Compare this to those without a high school diploma (the column labelled 'No'). Only 71 per cent of all people in that column are earning an income, and 29 per cent of people report having no income.

Table 13.7 The Relationship between Graduation from High School and Income from Paid Employment or Self-employment

		High school graduate?		
		Yes	No	Total
Income from paid employment or self-employment	Yes	329,269	86,485	415,754
	No	62,278	35,285	97,563
Total		391,547	121,770	513,317

Source: 2001 Aboriginal Peoples Survey

Table 13.7 suggests that there is a relationship between having a high school diploma and earning some income from paid employment or self-employment. What we do not know at this point is whether the relationship is strong, moderate, or weak. We use gamma to figure that out. To calculate gamma we need two numbers. The first, N_{same}, is calculated by multiplying the number of people who have positive values on both variables (high school graduate = yes, earning income = yes) by the number of people who have negative values on both variables (high school graduate = no, earning income = no). This gives us:

$$329269 * 35285 = 11618256665$$

Next, calculate, $N_{different}$, which is equal to the number of observations with different values on each variable. In a 2 by 2 table, this is the two opposite cells of the ones used to calculate N_{same}, yielding:

$$62278 * 86485 = 5386112830$$

Now that we have N_{same} and $N_{different}$, we calculate gamma using the equation:

$$G = \frac{N_{same} - N_{different}}{N_{same} + N_{different}}$$

Inserting our numbers of interest then making the necessary calculations yields:

$$G = \frac{11618256665 - 5386112830}{11618256665 + 5386112830} = \frac{6232143835}{17004369495} = 0.367$$

The equation gives us a gamma value of 0.367. Now we know that if we guessed whether or not a person earns an income, we would make 36.7 per cent fewer errors if we knew whether or not they have a high school diploma.

The equation may look daunting, but that's only because of the big numbers. There are over 500,000 people in the study (actually, it is more accurate to say that there are over 500,000 *weighted* observations in the study). Using smaller samples would make these numbers less intimidating.

If you look at table 13.8, you can see from the rough guidelines for interpreting gamma that this value counts as a strong relationship, so now we know that there is a strong relationship between education and income in the First Nations population.

Table 13.8 Rough Guidelines for the Interpretation of Gamma Values

Value	Strength
Between 0.0 and 0.10	Weak
Higher than 0.10 and less than 0.30	Moderate
Greater than 0.30	Strong

Gamma ranges in value from –1.00 to +1.00, and, like lambda, has a proportional reduction in error interpretation. A value of –1.00 indicates that all (untied) pairs are discordant, which implies that knowing a person's score on an independent variable makes it harder to predict the score of a dependent variable. A value of +1.00 indicates the opposite; that all pairs are concordant and that knowing a person's score on an independent variable makes it easier to predict the score of a dependent variable. A discordant pair is defined as any value where values on each variable run in a different 'direction'—meaning that somebody who has a high score on the independent variable has a low score on the dependent variable, and vice versa. A concordant pair refers to any observation with scores that run in the same direction; here, a high score on the independent variable would be matched by a high score on the dependent variable. Let's use another example: the relationship between support for a smoking ban in the workplace and an individual's level of education.

In a 2 by 2 table like table 13.9, calculating concordant and discordant pairs is easy. When your contingency table is arranged properly (so that values consistently go from high to low, or low to high, on both axes), concordant pairs in a 2 by 2 table are defined as those in the top left and bottom right cells, and discordant pairs are those in the top right and bottom left cells. The top left cell of frequencies (where individuals do not support smoking bans and hold less than a university degree), represents one of the two concordant cells, because 18 people with both low support for smoking bans and lower levels

Table 13.9 How to Calculate Concordant and Discordant Pairs in a 2 x 2 Table

	No university training	At least some university training	Total
No support for ban	18	10	28
Full support for ban	10	14	24
Total	28	24	52

of educational attainment are placed there. The other concordant table is the bottom right cell of frequencies, because that is where the 14 people with high support for a smoking bans and higher levels of education are found.

In a table that is larger than 2 by 2, it is more difficult to calculate concordant and discordant pairs. This is because determining whether a pair is concordant or discordant depends on the location of a particular cell. Imagine that table 13.9 had three categories for each variable, instead of two.

A concordant pair is defined as any positive diagonal of a particular cell. A positive cell is one where responses to one variable are in the same direction as responses on another variable (always remember that ties are ignored for gamma in a table larger than 2 by 2). For example, in table 13.10 the cells concordant with the top left cell, a (less than high school diploma, no support for smoking ban), are cells e, f, h, and i. Each one is both below and to the right of cell a. Other concordant cells in table 13.10 are: f and i with b; h and i with d; and i with e. In a 3 by 3 table, these form the four concordant sets.

The next step is to sum the number of observations that are concordant to each cell, and multiply that sum by the cell frequency, giving us N_{same}. To help with that, it is useful to organize the information in the manner seen in table 13.11.

Now that we have N_{same}, we must calculate the number of discordant cells and observations ($N_{different}$). The logic is the same as for calculating concordant cells, except that we tally the number of observations operating in the *opposite* direction (to the left and below). For cell c, the discordant cells would be e, d, g, and h; for cell b it is d and g; for f it is g and h; and for e it is g.

Table 13.12 gives us N_{same} and $N_{different}$, allowing gamma to be calculated using the same formula as before:

$$G = \frac{N_{same} - N_{different}}{N_{same} + N_{different}} = \frac{1728 - 1124}{1728 + 1124} = 0.212$$

Although gamma is widely used, it has the limitation of ignoring tied pairs. A significant proportion of all observations are often not used in the calculation of a relationship, suggesting that gamma tends to overestimate the relationship between variables, especially when there are a lot of tied cases.

Table 13.10 How to Calculate Concordant and Discordant Pairs in a Table Larger than 2 x 2

	Less than high school diploma	High school diploma, no university	At least some university training	Total
No support for ban	18(a)	10(b)	10(c)	38
Some support for ban	14(d)	12(e)	11(f)	37
Full support for ban	10(g)	14(h)	14(i)	38
Total	42	36	35	113

Table 13.11 Concordant Cells of Table 13.10

Cell	# of concordant cells	# of concordant observations	Contribution to N_s
a	4 (e, f, h, i)	12 + 11 + 14 + 14 = 51	18 * 51 = 918
b	2 (f, i)	11 + 14 = 25	10 * 25 = 250
c	0		
d	2 (h, i)	14 + 14 = 28	14 * 28 = 392
e	1 (i)	14	12 * 14 = 168
f	0		
g	0		
h	0		
i	0		$N_s = 1{,}728$

Table 13.12 Discordant Cells of Table 13.10

Cell	# of discordant cells	# of discordant observations	Contribution to N_D
a	0		
b	2 (d, g)	14 + 10 = 24	10 * 24 = 240
c	4 (d, e, g, h)	14 + 12 + 10 + 14 = 50	10 * 50 = 500
d	0		
e	1 (g)	10	12 * 10 = 120
f	2 (g, h)	10 + 14 = 24	11 * 24 = 264
g	0		
h	0		
i	0		$N_d = 1{,}124$

 ## BOX 13.1 GAMMA: THE STEPS

1. Calculate N_{same} (or the number of concordant pairs).

2. Calculate $N_{different}$ (or the number of discordant pairs).

3. Calculate gamma using the following equation: $G = \dfrac{N_{same} - N_{different}}{N_{same} + N_{different}}$

4. As a rough guideline, consider values between 0 and 0.10 to be weak; greater than 0.10, up to 0.30, to be moderate; and 0.30 or higher to be strong.

BOX 13.2 IT'S YOUR TURN: CALCULATING GAMMA

Zane has recently noticed a lot of media attention on how people are afraid of walking alone in his city at night. He wonders if this fear stems from a belief that the Canadian justice system is not effective. He uses data from the 2004 General Social Survey (GSS18), which focused on victim-ization. Since the GSS is a very large survey and Zane knows he would have to compute gamma by hand (his computer is broken), he decides to select a sample of 500 people. Once the missing cases are removed, Zane has 413 observations. The contingency table is presented below.

Relationship between views of justice and frequency of walking alone at night

Count

		Courts do good job of quick justice			
		Good	Average	Poor	Total
Walk alone at night	At least once a week	40	77	86	203
	Up to once a month	18	61	51	130
	Never	16	26	38	80
Total		74	164	175	413

Source: 2004 General Social Survey

1. Compute N_{same} and $N_{different}$ (Hint: use a table to make this easier.)

2. Calculate gamma: $G = \dfrac{N_{same} - N_{different}}{N_{same} + N_{different}}$

3. Determine if there is a weak, moderate, or strong relationship between people's views on the efficiency of the courts and walking alone in neighbourhoods after dark.

The solution for box 13.2 can be found on page 203.

Spearman's Rho

As you can imagine, calculating gamma is unpleasant using any table larger than 2 by 2. Although it is possible, and most software packages do it, my humble opinion is that it is much easier to use some of the other measures of association for ordinal variables whenever a table exceeds 2 by 2. Also, given the limitations of gamma it is often useful to consider other options.

Spearman's rho is one such option. The traditional formula for calculating the rho is:

$$r_s = 1 - \frac{6 * \sum D^2}{N(N^2 - 1)}$$

Spearman's rho is a somewhat unique measure, because it relies exclusively on the *rank* of observations, rather than the value, making it a prime candidate for calculations using ordinal data. Since it is not possible to measure distances between values with ordinal data, Spearman's rho takes the approach of comparing the level of concordance between one variable and another.

To illustrate, consider an example. Suppose we suspect that there is a relationship between the number of charities a pageant contestant volunteers at, and the number of endorsements they receive. To keep it simple, let's look at five contestants: Miss Japan, Miss USA, Miss Canada, Miss Russia, and Miss Venezuela. Each has participated in a number of charities, and we believe that charity work makes a particular candidate more attractive to sponsors, leading to an increase in the number of endorsements received.

Since rho is only concerned with ranks, it is necessary to sort and rank each of the variables.

The easiest way to calculate Spearman's rho is by organizing all of the information in a table, like table 13.14.

Once we have the information organized, calculating rho is easy because we can straight-forwardly measure the discrepancy between the

Table 13.14 Spearman's Rho and the Relationship between Charity and Endorsement Participation

	# of charities	Rank	# of endorsements	Rank	D	D²
Miss Japan	5	3	4	4	-1	1
Miss USA	2	5	3	5	0	0
Miss Canada	3	4	5	3	1	1
Miss Russia	6	2	7	1	1	1
Miss Venezuela	7	1	6	2	-1	1
	$N = 5$			Σ	0	4

BOX 13.3 SPEARMAN'S RHO

Psychologist Charles Spearman (1863–1945) first proposed the measure of correlation we call *rho* in a 1904 paper titled 'The proof and measurement of association between two things'. In that initial form, he did not call the value he arrived at *rho*, nor did he give it the Greek letter ρ, which is often used today. In this early paper it was similar to, but not the same as, rho as we know it today. Calling it a 'method of rank differences', he listed some disadvantages:

1. It can be done with ranks only, not measurements.
2. The probable error we get tells us what correlation we could expect from independent variables, it doesn't tell us the error we can expect to attribute to measurement (as does Pearson's probable error).
3. Because the values of *Sd* do not follow a normal, or even symmetrical, distribution, there are problems when one takes negative values as inverse correlation.
4. This value *r* is not the same as the rho of other methods of correlation.

Spearman continued working and reflecting on formulae for assessing correlation, and took up *r* again in a 1906 paper titled 'Footrule for measuring correlation' where he advocates for it as a quick rule for determining correlation, while still being comparable to Pearson's *r*.

Spearman's motivation was apparently to establish a suitable rule for correlation in psychology that is both pragmatic and statistically meaningful. One of his supporting arguments for this measure of correlation is that it may be done in less than a minute by hand, in some cases entirely in one's head, and can provide a guideline, or footrule as he calls it, for what sort of correlation, or lack thereof, one is looking at. It is up to the reader whether the standard formula for *rho* fulfills Spearman's desire for a footrule requiring only a 'trifling expenditure' on the part of the researcher. Perhaps just as electronic calculation has supplanted the extensive need for logarithmic tables, the ease of use of statistical formulae is no longer a determining factor in their development.

BOX 13.4 IT'S YOUR TURN: CALCULATING SPEARMAN'S RHO

Andy feels that he's been doing pretty well in his statistics class. His friend Marianne is surprised—they always study together, but she doesn't do as well. What could be the difference? 'Andy does go out drinking every weekend', she thinks to herself. To figure out if drinking more might improve her grades, Marianne conducts a small study. She asks Andy and seven other friends what grade they received on the midterm, and how many drinks they usually have in a week. These are the data she collects:

Case	Number of drinks a week	Grade
1	10	60
2	2	75
3	2	52
4	0	98
5	1	45
6	5	55
7	20	70
8	3	60

At first glance there doesn't appear to be much of a pattern, but she realizes that a ranking table would be more thorough.

1. Complete the ranking table below.

   Notice that there are two people who have the same number of drinks (two drinks per week). When this happens the ranking is the average of the two ranks. If they take up the places for ranks three and four, they will each rank 3.5. When in doubt of how to handle ties, you'll know you've made the right choice when the sum of D equals zero.

Case	Number of drinks a week	Drinks rank	Grade	Grade rank	D	D^2
1	10		65			
2	2		75			
3	2		52			
4	0		98			
5	1		45			
6	5		55			
7	20		70			
8	3		60			

2. Calculate rho: $r_s = 1 - \dfrac{6 * \sum D^2}{N(N^2 - 1)}$

3. Square the value of rho.

4. How much does knowing the number of drinks a person has in a week improve your ability to estimate how well Marianne and Andy will do in their statistics class?

The solution for box 13.4 can be found on page 204.

BOX 13.5 SPEARMAN'S RHO: THE STEPS

1. Organize the observations into a chart, with columns for score on each variable of interest, their respective ranks, the differences between the two (D), and differences between the two squared (D²). D² will the most useful for calculating rho.

2. Calculate rho as $r_s = 1 - \dfrac{6 * \sum D^2}{N(N^2 - 1)}$

rank of one variable and the rank of the other. D is the difference between rankings on number of charities and number of endorsements, and D^2 is $D * D$. By summing D^2, we get $\sum D^2$, one of the numbers that we need to calculate rho.

$$r_s = 1 - \frac{6 * \sum D^2}{N(N^2 - 1)}$$

$$= 1 - \frac{6 * 4}{5(25 - 1)}$$

$$= 1 - \frac{24}{120} = 0.80$$

Squaring rho allows for a PRE-type interpretation, which means that we can calculate the reduction in our errors using the value of the independent variable. In this case it's $0.8^2 = 0.64$, so our errors of prediction will be reduced by 64 per cent.

Somer's d

Somer's d is one of several alternatives to gamma, and is quite similar except that it adjusts for tied ranks on the dependent variable. Ties occur when two pairs of scores are both concordant on

the independent variable—one ranks higher than the other—and discordant on the dependent variable—the same variable ranks higher again. This equation is used to calculate Somer's d:

$$d = \frac{N_{same} - N_{different}}{N_{same} + N_{different} + Ties_y}$$

As you can see, the equation is very similar to gamma except for the addition of a term in the denominator. Calculating the number of ties can be problematic; see table 13.17 for help.

In table 13.17 cells b and c are tied with a; c is tied with b; e and f are tied with d; f is tied with e; h and i are tied with g; and i is tied with h, yielding the following value for $Ties_y$:

$$Ties_y = 18(10 + 10) + 10(10) + 14(12 + 11) + 12(11)$$
$$+ 10(14 + 14) + 14(14)$$
$$= 360 + 100 + 322 + 132 + 280 + 196$$
$$= 1390$$

$$d = \frac{N_{same} - N_{different}}{N_{same} + N_{different} + Ties_y} = \frac{1728 - 1124}{1728 + 1124 + 1390} = 0.142$$

This is a lot lower than the gamma value of 0.212, because there is an additional term in the

Table 13.15 Levels of Education and Support for Smoking Ban

	Less than high school diploma	High school diploma, no university	At least some university training	Total
No support for ban	18(a)	10(b)	10(c)	38
Some support for ban	14(d)	12(e)	11(f)	37
Full support for ban	10(g)	14(h)	14(i)	38
Total	42	36	35	113

BOX 13.6 SOMER'S d: THE STEPS

1. Calculate N_{same}, or the number of concordant pairs.
2. Calculate $N_{different}$, or the number of discordant pairs.
3. Calculate $Ties_y$, or the number of ties.
4. Calculate Somer's d using the following equation: $d = \dfrac{N_{same} - N_{different}}{N_{same} + N_{different} + Ties_y}$

Just like when you're using gamma, consider values between 0 and 0.10 to be weak, between 0.10 and 0.30 to be moderate, and 0.30 or higher to be strong.

 BOX 13.7 IT'S YOUR TURN: CALCULATING SOMER'S d

Isa is convinced that people who study full-time have dirty homes, but she wants to test her theory using Somer's d. Using data from the 2001 Census of Canada Individual File, Isa randomly selects 250 people who had answered questions on their educational status and the number of hours they spent on housework. She recoded educational status, going from not being a student to being in school full-time. She also recoded hours of unpaid housework into three categories.

The relationship between educational status and hours spent on unpaid labour per week

Hours on unpaid household labour/week	Educational Status			
	Not studying	Part-time student	Full-time student	Total
Less than 5	52	1	20	73
5 to 14	59	2	5	66
15 or more	106	2	3	111
Total	217	5	28	250

Source: 2001 Individual Census

1. Compute N_{same} and $N_{different}$ and $Ties_y$.
2. Calculate Somer's d: $d = \dfrac{N_{same} - N_{different}}{N_{same} + N_{different} + Ties_y}$
3   Based on your calculation, what can you say about the relationship between hours of unpaid household work and being a student, using Somer's d? Is Isa's theory correct?

The solution for box 13.7 can be found on page 204.

denominator. Like gamma, values for Somer's *d* range between –1 and +1, with an approximately similar interpretation.

Kendall's Tau-*b*

Kendall's tau-*b* is conceptually similar to gamma and Somer's *d*, but it goes one step further than Somer's *d* and corrects for tied pairs on both the dependent variable and the independent variable. Its equation is:

$$tau\text{-}b = \frac{N_{same} - N_{different}}{(N_{same} + N_{different} + Ties_y)(N_{same} + N_{different} + Ties_x)}$$

Calculating $Ties_x$ is similar to calculating $Ties_y$, except instead of looking for ties on the dependent variable, it also looks for ties on the independent variable. So, for table 13.17:

$$
\begin{aligned}
Ties_x &= 18(14 + 10) + 14(10) + 10(12 + 14) + 12(14) \\
&\quad + 10(11 + 14) + 11(14) \\
&= 432 + 140 + 260 + 168 + 250 + 154 \\
&= 1404
\end{aligned}
$$

And the equation is:

$$tau\text{-}b = \frac{N_{same} - N_{different}}{(N_{same} + N_{different} + Ties_y)(N_{same} + N_{different} + Ties_x)}$$

$$= \frac{1728 - 1124}{\sqrt{(1728 + 1124 + 1390)(1728 + 1124 + 1404)}}$$

$$= \frac{604}{\sqrt{(4242)(4256)}}$$

$$= 0.142$$

In our example, Somer's *d* and tau-*b* are identical, because 1,390 and 1,404 are so close that multiplying essentially equal numbers (4,242 and 4,256) and then taking the square root has nearly no effect on the denominator.

Conclusion: Which One to Use?

In this chapter we have covered four different measures of association for ordinal data. How do you choose which of these measures to use? Unfortunately, that is a hard question to answer.

BOX 13.8 KENDALL'S TAU-*b*: THE STEPS

1. Calculate N_{same}, or the number of concordant pairs.

2. Calculate $N_{different}$, or the number of discordant pairs.

3. Calculate $Ties_y$, or the number of ties in the dependent variable.

4. Calculate $Ties_x$, or the number of ties in the independent variable.

5. Calculate Kendall's tau-*b* using the following equation:

$$tau\text{-}b = \frac{N_{same} - N_{different}}{\sqrt{(N_{same} + N_{different} + Ties_y)(N_{same} + N_{different} + Ties_x)}}$$

As with gamma and Somer's *d*, values between 0 and 0.10 are weak, higher than 0.10 and up to 0.30 are moderate, and 0.30 or higher are strong.

There are occasions when one measure is preferable to another. For example, if there are a lot of ties, it is desirable to use something other than gamma. Spearman's rho is often easiest to understand when you're more interested in ranks than scores. Some of the others can be computationally intense, and might be undesirable in certain situations. It's important to remember that although they won't give you the same numbers, most measures will yield similar results in most circumstances.

BOX 13.9 IT'S YOUR TURN: KENDALL'S TAU-b

Using the same data that Isa collected in box 13.7, can you see any changes in the relationship when you calculate Kendall's tau-b?

1. Compute the value for $Ties_x$.

2. Calculate Kendall's tau-b:

$$tau\text{-}b = \frac{N_{same} - N_{different}}{\sqrt{(N_{same} + N_{different} + Ties_y)(N_{same} + N_{different} + Ties_x)}}$$

3. Does the inclusion of the ties on the independent variable change what Isa can say about the relationship between students and hours spent on housework?

The solution to box 13.9 can be found on page 205.

PRACTICE QUESTIONS

1. Jerry is interested in the relationship between exercising every week and improvement in self-perceived health. He thinks it might be part of why older people care for themselves more closely than young people do. Here are the data he is working with:

	Changes in self-rated health	
Exercises every week	Poor	Good
No	13	11
Yes	17	25

Calculate gamma.

2. Suppose you are interested in squirrels and nuts (who isn't??), and you hypothesize that the heavier a squirrel is, the more food that squirrel will hide away for the winter. Since the data are coarse, you can only treat them as ordinal. Calculate Spearman's rho to identify the relationship between the two variables:

Weight	Nuts
7	4
5	7
8	9
9	8

Answers to the practice questions for chapter 13 can be found on page 190.

Bivariate Statistics for Interval/Ratio Data

Learning Objectives

Chapter 14 will continue to survey techniques for assessing associations between two variables. Now that we've moved through dichotomous–interval/ratio, nominal–nominal, and ordinal–ordinal relationships we will look at measures of association between two interval/ratio variables. Specifically, this chapter will focus on:

- Pearson's r
- what r tells us about explained variance
- what to do when there are mixed levels of measurement in your independent and dependent variables

Introduction

By now you probably know that when we examine associations between variables we are primarily interested in how much categories of one variable relate to categories of another variable. Interval/ratio data, which is the focus of this chapter, are unique because not only can they be used to determine whether a relationship exists between two variables, but they can also determine the *direction* and *strength* of that relationship, as well as the rate of change. Unlike the measures of association we learned for nominal and ordinal levels of measurement, it is possible to represent relationships graphically using interval/ratio variables, so we can determine the approximate *rate of change* in the dependent variable across the values of the independent variable.

Pearson's r: The Correlation Coefficient

The primary measure of association used for interval/ratio variables is another contribution of statistician Karl Pearson. Pearson's r measures the amount of change in Y produced by a unit change in X, where the units are expressed as standard deviations. Like some of the ordinal measures covered in the last chapter, r ranges between –1 and +1, with zero representing no relationship between variables. A value of –1 denotes a perfectly negative relationship (as X rises/declines in value, Y always moves in the opposite direction), and +1 represents a perfectly positive relationship (as X rises/declines in value, Y always moves in the same direction).

There are a few different formulas for Pearson's r. The first is considered an 'illustrational' formula, because it illustrates the process, but can be cumbersome to use:

$$r = \frac{\sum[(X-\overline{X})(Y-\overline{Y})]}{\sqrt{[\sum(X-\overline{X})^2 * \sum(Y-\overline{Y})^2]}}$$

The problem with this equation is that it requires you to subtract the average from each X and Y value line-by-line, which would take forever and a day in large data sets. Fortunately, the equation can be modified so that that task is unnecessary:

$$r = \frac{N\sum XY - (\sum X)(\sum Y)}{\sqrt{[N\sum X^2 - (\sum X)^2][N\sum Y^2 - (\sum Y)^2]}}$$

Most of the time you'll want to use the second equation. Even though it looks more difficult, it is actually much easier to use.

Take note of the $(\sum X)^2$ and $(\sum Y)^2$ in the denominator. According to BEDMAS, the order of operations that we discussed in chapter 2 (Brackets-Exponents-Division-Multiplication-Addition-Subtraction), it is necessary to perform the calculations within the parentheses first, then the ones outside of them. This means that it is necessary to sum the X and Y values *first*, before raising them to the power of two. People often forget to do this the first time they calculate r, and consequently calculate it incorrectly.

With a little care, you won't be one of those people. To make sure of that, we'll demonstrate the calculation of r with an example: Suppose we are interested in the relationship between a person's age and the age of their spouse in colonial Canada (or New France as it was then known) in 1665 to 1666. This data is available because Jean Talon, Intendant of Justice, Police, and Finance from 1665 to 1668 and 1670 to 1672, decided that the best way to learn about the colony was to take a numerical inventory of its inhabitants. Talon's efforts, which enumerated the 3,278 residents of New France, represent North America's

first census, which was critical to establishing New France as a self-sufficient settlement.[1]

These records, which form an interesting and important part of Canada's history, can be used to demonstrate Pearson's r. As with most other measures of association, it is helpful to arrange your data in a table first so that the values of interest can be calculated easily. Table 14.1 shows these data for five randomly selected cases from the 513 suitable for analysis (unmarried people were dropped, as were those with missing data, etc.). In the table, X represents the age of the husband and Y the age of his wife. Note that the sum at the bottom of each column pertains to ALL observations, not just those shown in the table.

Once these data are organized and each of the columns is summed, it is easy to calculate r by inserting the appropriate values.

A Rough Interpretation of r

The calculated value of +0.686 has little meaning, unless we read it with some guidelines in mind. Typically, a value between ±0.01 and ±0.30 is considered a weak correlation, ±0.31 to ±0.70

Table 14.1 Age of Married Couples in 1666 New France

Observation #	X	Y	X²	Y²	XY
1	41	40	1,681	1,600	1,640
2	36	47	1,296	2,209	1,692
3	40	30	1,600	900	1,200
4	27	18	729	324	486
...	...	...	...	...	...
513	42	28	1764	784	1,176
Sum	19,021	14,808	764,779	497,544	593,371

Source: 1881 Census of Canada 100% sample file
Note: There is only one observation per household, and only couples where both ages are listed are included. Sums reflect ALL observations, not only those shown above.

---

[1] Special thanks to Lisa Dillon of the Université de Montréal for providing me with a copy of these data.

BOX 14.1 PEARSON'S r: THE STEPS

1. Using a spreadsheet program, square each value of the independent variable X.
2. Square each value of the dependent variable Y.
3. Find X * Y for each observation.
4. Pearson's r can be solved using the following equation:

$$r = \frac{N \sum XY - (\sum X)(\sum Y)}{\sqrt{[N \sum X^2 - (\sum X)^2][N \sum Y^2 - (\sum Y)^2]}}$$

Values between ±0.001 and ±0.30 are considered weak correlations, ±0.3001 and ±0.70 are moderate correlations, and ±0.7001 to ±1 are strong.

is a moderate correlation, and ±0.71 to ±1 suggests that the variables are strongly correlated. Here, the value of 0.686 suggests a conclusion that in New France a husband's age was a moderate predictor of the age of his spouse.

You should note that r is important because it tells you what happens to one variable, X, as the value of the other variable, Y, changes. In our example the value is positive, so we can say that on average, as a person's age increases so does the age of his or her spouse. If the value was negative, we would say the opposite: on average, as a person's age increases the age of his or her spouse *decreases*.

A Visual Representation of r

To further illustrate how r describes bivariate relationships between two interval-ratio variables, let's look at a couple of graphs, each with a different set of data. In figure 14.1 the independent variable x1 is positively related to y, with a Pearson's r value of 0.25. The dots represent (simulated) values of x1 plotted against y. The straight line represents fitted, or expected, values. Although an approximate relationship between y and x1 is detectable, the fit line doesn't do a very good job of representing the relationship. Note that if Pearson's r was negative, for example –0.25, the line would slope downward.

With a stronger positive association (as r increases), we expect the average distance between

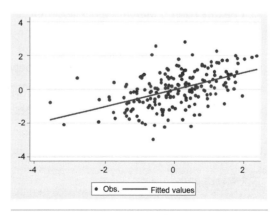

Figure 14.1 An Illustration of a Pearson's r Value of 0.25 Using Simulated Data

Figure 14.2 An Illustration of a Pearson's r Value of 0.50 Using Simulated Data

BOX 14.2 IT'S YOUR TURN: CALCULATING PEARSON'S r

Marcus has been involved with a number of student groups during his undergraduate career, and has loved that part of his life. As he nears the end of his degree he has started to wonder if he will be able to keep this up while working, especially since he expects to have a job that will demand a lot of his time. It seems to him that there won't be enough hours in the day, but he has often read about people who manage to juggle organizational involvement and successful careers. Are these people exceptional, or are they the norm? As a research question, he wonders if an increase in work hours has a negative correlation with organizational involvement.

To study this, Marcus uses the Survey on Social Engagement (GSS17) public use microdata file (target population of Canadians over 15, excluding those in the Yukon, the Northwest Territories, Nunavut, and full-time residents of institutions). Since he is concerned about his own prospects, he has decided to limit the sample to men, and only those who have completed high school. Since this is a huge data set and Marcus doesn't have a computer, he decides to take a random sample of 15 people. He is careful that none of the 15 are missing on either number of hours worked or number of civic groups belonged to, his two variables of interest. Only individuals who were involved in at least one civic group are included, since Marcus only wants people with some likelihood of involvement. He also limits the number of hours worked to 74 or less (individuals who worked over 75 were grouped together, which changed the variable from being a ratio variable). The 15 people looked like:

Respondent	Hours of work/week	Number of civic groups
1	38	2
2	40	2
3	60	2
4	50	2
5	60	2
6	50	4
7	35	1
8	50	2
9	36	2
10	30	3
11	65	1
12	45	1
13	48	3
14	40	2
15	55	3

Source: Survey on Social Engagement (GSS17)

1. Construct and complete a table like table 14.1.

2. Calculate the value of r.

3. What can you say about the relationship between the variables based on your calculation?

4. Marcus was able to borrow a friend's computer. He re-ran the analysis with the full weighted sample (with the same exclusions described above). The Pearson's r value was 0.058. How does this compare to yours?

The solution for box 14.2 can be found on page 206.

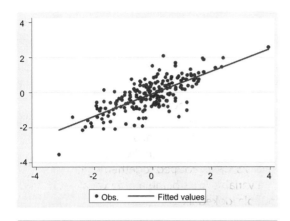

Figure 14.3 An Illustration of a Pearson's *r* Value of 0.75 Using Simulated Data

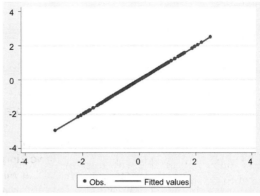

Figure 14.4 An Illustration of a Pearson's *r* Value of 1.0 Using Simulated Data

a particular observation and the line to shrink, indicating a reduction in estimation error. To determine if this is the case, consider figure 14.2, where a Pearson's *r* value of 0.50 is illustrated.

A close examination of figure 14.2 suggests that the observations are closer to the line than in figure 14.1. The convergence becomes more obvious when Pearson's *r* increases to 0.75, which happens between $x3$ and y in figure 14.3.

Variable $x4$ finally has a perfect positive relationship to y. This demonstrates that by knowing a person's score on an independent variable ($x4$) their score on the dependent variable (y) can be predicted. Thus *all* of the observed values perfectly lie on the line of best fit.

BOX 14.3 PEARSON'S CORRELATION COEFFICIENT: HISTORY OF A TERM

Pearson's *r* is an indicator of how closely two variables are related, and designates the degree of a linear relationship. Pearson called his method for calculating this coefficient the product, which he derived in 1896, 'moment method' (Porter, 1989). He developed it while working on regression analysis and by taking up Galton's work, for it was Galton who first posited the indicator, and did so in the context of heredity. Although Pearson published it in an 1895 paper, it was not received with much fanfare. Francis Galton himself was one of the paper's reviewers, and thought it should be published rather than read out loud in a lecture. In Galton's words, 'It would be too dull to *read*' (Stigler, 1986: 344).

The attribution for this coefficient brings up important issues about who gets crediting with developing statistical methods. Although Pearson can be credited with much of the work, he did not operate in a vacuum. As I mentioned before, *r* also stems from Galton's research. Further, Pearson and statistician Francis Edgeworth corresponded and reviewed each other's work. Though Pearson did credit the work Edgeworth did early on, referring to it as 'Edgeworth's theorem', in Pearson's later work he did not do so.

Explained Variance

Using Pearson's r it is possible to determine how much of the variation in a variable can be explained with the use of other variables. The value of zero does not reflect a relationship between two variables, but a value of +1 indicates a perfect positive relationship, and a value of –1 indicates a perfect negative relationship. Values between –1 and +1 do not have a direct interpretation, unless you're comfortable with interpreting values in terms of standard deviations.

To determine the variation, find the coefficient of determination by squaring r, yielding r^2. The coefficient of determination is the percentage of all variation in the dependent variable that can be explained by the values of the independent variable. The variable r^2 is the percentage that errors are reduced by, when the information found in the independent variable is incorporated into the prediction.

This introduces **explained variation** and **unexplained variation** in the dependent variable. Explained variation is how much more accurate a prediction becomes when the independent variable, X, is taken into account. Unsurprisingly, unexplained variation is the remaining prediction error, which could be due to variables that weren't included as predictors, measurement error, or random error. The sum of the explained variation and unexplained variation of a variable is equal to its **total variation**.

A More Precise Interpretation of r

Looking at what the calculation of r achieves makes it possible to move beyond examining rough patterns between variable relationships. The calculation for r standardizes the values of each variable, allowing comparison between correlation coefficients without worrying about how many values each variable has, or what their standard deviation is. When each variable is standardized, r refers to the degree of correspondence between a person's z-score on one variable (X) and their z-score on another variable (Y), measuring the relationship between the average person's score in standard deviation units on one variable to their standard deviation score on a second variable. In an instance where $r = 1$, a person with a variable that has a change in the z-score from zero to two on one variable of interest will see a corresponding increase of a z-score of two on the other variable of interest. Conversely, an r value of –1 will translate to a z-score of +1 on one variable and a score of –1 on another. Remember, r is a measure of what happens to one variable as the value of another variable changes.

The Correlation Matrix

A **correlation matrix** is used to show correlations between variables and all of the possible relationships between variables in a grid.

Suppose that we wanted to study the relationship between incidents of domestic violence and unwanted sexual acts perpetrated by an ex-spouse/domestic partner, because we want to know if violence and sexual acts are interchangeable techniques for asserting dominance, or if they are qualitatively different. To determine this, we could use the 18th wave of the General Social Survey, Public-Use Microdata File (the Victimization Survey) to construct a correlation matrix between the occurrence and frequency of violent and sexual acts (see table 14.3).

A typical correlation matrix presents a series of numbers in a triangular pattern. Each cell represents the correlation between the variables that are listed above, and to the left of, the number. For example, the number 0.2391 refers is the correlation between the number of unwanted sexual acts and the number of violent acts. In a cor-

Table 14.2 Correlation between Violent and Sexual Activities between Spouses/Partners

	# violent acts	# sexual acts
# violent acts	1.0000	
# sexual acts	0.2391	1.0000

Source: 2004 General Social Survey, Public Use Microdata File
Note: Includes persons aged 15 or older in Canada, excluding residents of the three territories and full-time residents of institutions (Statistics Canada, 2005).

relation matrix, the diagonal that runs from the top left cell to the bottom right cell will always be one, which refers to the correlation between a variable and itself. Using table 14.3, we can see that there is a weak relationship between violent acts and sexual acts committed by and against domestic partners. The weak relationship suggests that there are other factors involved with both of those phenomena.

Although the primary focus of this chapter is bivariate relationships, a correlation matrix can be used for more than two variables. A correlation matrix can contain as many relevant variables as you can imagine.

Using a *t*-Test to Assess the Significance of *r*

When using *r* it is usually necessary to determine if we can assume that the relationships we observe in the sample also exist in the population. If a sample that we drew from the population had high sampling error, that would make it impossible to be confident about the inferential capacity of the *r* value we calculate.

By mathematically manipulating *r*, we can use *t*-distributions to assess its representativity. Remember that *t*-distributions are closely related to the *z*-distribution, except that *t*-distributions make adjustments for sample size. The first step is to select the appropriate *t*-distribution. Because there are two known parameters (two variables we know the values for), the degrees of freedom are equal to $(N - 2)$, where N is equal to the sample size. If, for example, we had a sample of 22 people and we wanted to be 95 per cent confident of the generalizability of our results, we would need a *t*-value of at least 2.086. To get this value, we look at the row for $df=20$ (remember to look at $n - 2$ degrees of freedom) in Appendix B, and look for a 0.05 level of significance in a two-tailed test (remember that levels of significance are usually stated as alpha values in a *t*-distribution, and can be calculated as one minus your desired confidence interval). This value is known as $t_{critical}$.

The other value we need to calculate is $t_{observed}$, which is done using this formula:

$$t_{observed} = r \sqrt{\frac{n - 2}{1 - r^2}}$$

Using the same example we used to calculate the correlation matrix, and a hypothetical sample size of 22 observations:

$$t_{observed} = r \sqrt{\frac{n - 2}{1 - r^2}}$$

$$= 0.2391 \sqrt{\frac{22 - 2}{1 - 0.2391^2}}$$

$$= 0.2391 \sqrt{\frac{20}{1 - 0.572}}$$

$$= 0.2391 * 4.6058$$

$$= 1.101$$

Since the $t_{observed}$ value of 1.101 is below the critical value of 2.086, we cannot be 95 per cent confident that the sample *r* value of 0.2391 did not occur by chance. Based on our sample of 22 respondents, we cannot be certain that there is a correlation between violent and sexual activities between ex-spouses/domestic partners.

Assumptions of Linearity

Pearson's *r* provides a rough and ready measure of the relationship between two interval/ratio variables. The variable *r* assumes that the relationship between two variables is the same, regardless of what the values of either of these variables is. This is called linearity.

Imagine that we wanted to identify the relationship between age and amount of time spent on entertainment. We expect that teenagers have more time than their parents do to go to the movies, dance clubs, or malls. We also assume that retirees also have a high proportion of spare time. This suggests that the relationship between age and time spent on entertainment is not linear; the rate at which available time to spend for entertainment increases is not consistent across the range of ages. There could be a very strong and positive relationship across the teenage years, after which the relationship begins to decline as many Canadians buy houses, get married, have children, develop their careers, etc. Finally, as people get older, their children might leave home, they might begin to work less, etc., and they have more spare time again, impacting the relationship between entertainment and age. To consider how this relationship might look, consider figure 14.5.

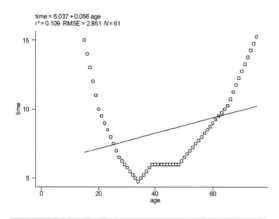

time = 6.037 + 0.056 age
r² = 0.109 RMSE = 2.851 N = 61

Figure 14.5 A Graphical Representation of the Relationship between Age and the Proportion of Time Spent on Entertainment

The curvilinear pattern of circles represents the actual relationship between age and time, and the straight line represents the relationship described by *r* (actually, this is known as the least squares regression line, but we'll talk about that later). Without manipulating one or both of the variables (for example, by taking their logarithms), we must be content with summarizing the relationship with a straight line. Unfortunately, as the diagram shows, the line is not an accurate or sensitive representation of the relationship.

For our purposes, the generalization provided by that straight line will have to do. The next chapter will deepen your understanding of that line.

Before embarking on a deeper discussion of the fit line, a brief discussion about using variables measured at different levels is necessary. Most measures of association assume that both variables are measured at the same level, and that you are working with two nominal, ordinal, or interval/ratio variables. However, this is often not the case. When that happens you'll find yourself in a position where it's necessary to assess the association between variables using different levels of measurement. Don't worry, there are a few short guidelines that we can apply to help us through this added layer of complexity.

Measuring Association between Interval/Ratio and Nominal or Ordinal Variables: Using the Lowest Common Measure of Association

Although previous chapters presented the measures of association as being specifically for one level of measurement, it is possible to use the measures for other levels of measurement, under certain circumstances. The measure of association can always be used on variables measured *above* the level of complexity for which they were designed.

Recall that there are essentially three levels of measurement: nominal, ordinal, and interval-ratio. If we were working with two nominal variables, we could choose between phi, Cramer's V, or lambda, depending on the nature of the variables and the information we seek. However, if we are looking at a nominal by ordinal relationship we could use any of the three measures (remember that we only use phi for a 2 by 2 relationship). Since these measures are non-directional they can be used even if one of the two variables can be ranked. By using the measure of association for the variable at a lower level of measurement, we 'discard' the additional information in the ordinal variable.

However, the opposite is not possible—a nominal variable cannot be 'infused' with information that would allow it to be ranked. If we wanted to look for a relationship between visible minority status and attitudes about the seriousness of climate change (coded as extremely serious, very serious, not very serious, and not at all serious), we would use a nominal level of measurement, because ranking information for the ordinal variable, climate change, could be discarded to make it a nominal variable. However, it is not possible to rank visible minority categories, so we would choose a measure of association for nominal variables.

Demoting the level of measurement for particular variables is a technique that can be used for several combinations of variables. For ordinal and interval/ratio variables, it is necessary to discard the information on differences between response categories in the interval/ratio variables, and treat that variable as ordinal. To measure the association between attitudes towards the seriousness of climate change and income in dollars, we would have to choose from gamma, rho, Somer's d, or Kendall's tau-b.

PRACTICE QUESTIONS

1. The following data from the 1971 Census of Canada describes two pieces of information about 10 families.

Family number	Total income ($)	# People in family
1	1,330	2
2	800	4
3	1,200	5
4	1,600	4
5	900	6
6	6,144	4
7	3,490	2
8	1,310	4
9	5,670	3
10	1,330	2

Source: 1971 Census of Canada

Calculate r.

2. Calculate the value of Pearson's r for the following set of data:

X	Y
4	5
12	20
13	8
14	6
8	11
3	10
5	6
6	9

Answers to the practice questions for chapter 14 can be found on page 190.

CHAPTER 15

One-Way Analysis of Variance

Learning Objectives

Now that many of the techniques for measuring bivariate relationships have been covered, this chapter will discuss the final technique for identifying relationships between two variables in this text: one-way analysis of variance (ANOVA). Topics will include:

- what a one-way ANOVA is
- when it should be used
- how to calculate within-group sums of squares, between-groups sums of squares, and total sums of squares, the three main components of one-way ANOVAS
- how to use the F-distribution with ANOVA

Introduction

The last few chapters have been about strategies for identifying the existence and strength of a relationship between two variables. This chapter will build on what we've learned by discussing another method for identifying associations between variables measured at different levels. We'll focus on interval/ratio dependent variables, and nominal or ordinal independent variables that have more than two categories by discussing a procedure known as ANOVA, or the ANalysis Of VAriance.[1]

What Is ANOVA?

ANOVA is a little like a t-test. The t-test can be used in any situation where a comparison between two groups on a continuous variable is desired. The t-test is useful, but what if we want to compare more than two groups?

---

[1] Throughout this chapter, we'll only discuss one-way ANOVA, even though there are multiple ANOVA techniques. For brevity, ANOVA here will be used as shorthand to refer to one-way ANOVA.

For example, say we want to compare the level of control an individual feels he or she has over his or her own life, using Statistics Canada's 2003 Social Engagement Survey, checking to see if it differs by religion. Specifically, we want to compare the differences across Roman Catholics, Protestants, members of the United Church, and people with no religious affiliation.

Table 15.1 shows the average levels of mastery for each group.

Higher scores indicate superior mastery. A glance at the columns suggests that there are differences across religious groups, but we do not know if the differences are the result of chance, sampling error (most of the time, we can't distinguish between the two), or differences that exist across groups. How can we find this out?

One way is to conduct a series of *t*-tests, comparing two groups at a time. How many *t*-tests would we have to do?

For **No Religion** there would be three: NR-RC, NR-UC, and NR-P.

For **Roman Catholics** there would be two: RC-UC, and RC-P (there are only two comparisons because Roman Catholics have already been compared with no religion).

For the **United Church**, there would be one: UC-P (the only remaining comparison to be made).

That's six *t*-tests. What's wrong with that? First, it's a computational nightmare. Can you imagine wrestling with the results of six *t*-tests? With that many calculations, the chance of making an error increases dramatically—or it does for me, anyway.

Even if you were precise with your calculator, the bad news is that conducting multiple *t*-tests (or any other analysis conducted repeatedly) increases **type one error**—rejecting the null hypothesis when it should be retained—increasing the risk of making a bad judgment about your hypothesis. The more statistical tests conducted, the higher the likelihood of sampling error.

Recall that a 0.05 level of significance is used to assess hypotheses, meaning that we accept that 5 per cent of the time we will mistakenly conclude that the differences we observe in our sample actually exist in the population. If each of the *t*-tests in the sample containing six *t*-tests has a 5 per cent chance of yielding significant results by mistake, our 95 per cent significance level decreases to about 73.5 per cent (to get this number, multiply the independent probabilities, 0.95 * 0.95 * 0.95 * 0.95 * 0.95 * 0.95).

Clearly, a single statistical test to assess differences between more than two groups is necessary. That test is ANOVA, or the ANalysis Of VAriance. Think of ANOVA as an elaborated *t*-test. It compares three things:

- differences between means,
- differences in values within samples, and
- differences in values across samples.

Like a *t*-test, there is an internal logic to ANOVA. Each observation is different from the grand

Table 15.1   Average Levels of Mastery by Religious Affiliation, 2003 Social Engagement Survey

	Levels of mastery			
Observation #	No religion	Roman Catholic	United Church	Protestant
1	21	17	22	21
2	25	21	14	23
3	26	19	16	22
4	24	20	13	24
5	22	20	14	21

Source: Statistics Canada 2003 Social Engagement Survey (GSS17)

mean by some amount. There are two sources of this difference:

1. the independent variable, and
2. random, unexplained error.

ANOVA compares the variation around the mean within groups to the variation across groups. Is a Roman Catholic more likely to be similar to another Roman Catholic than they are to a person in another category? What about a Protestant to another Protestant, etc.? If the answer to these questions is yes, then we could conclude that there are religious differences in levels of personal mastery.

Although that description is oversimplified, it nicely captures what is going on with ANOVA. We need to go over several equations before we can compare variation within groups to variation between groups.

The first equation is the **sum of squares**, which is defined as the total variation of all observations from a **grand mean**. In order to determine whether there is more variation within groups than across groups, we need to identify the total variation available to be distributed between and across groups. This is the **total sum of squares**, or SS_{total}, and equals the total variation of all observations from the grand mean. The equation for SS_{total} is:

$$SS_{total} = \sum (X - \overline{X})^2$$

Stated in words, the equation is a sum of the differences between individual observations (X) and the grand mean ($\overline{X}$). The result is squared to remove the negative numbers that would result from subtracting the means from a value that is below the mean, which would equal zero. For example, if a person had a mastery score of 15, subtracting the grand mean of 18.85 would yield –3.85. On their own, negative numbers would not be a problem, but here they are because they are summed, and therefore cancelled out by positive values. Remember that we take the sum of all deviations; since the mean is the midpoint of all values the negative numbers resulting from values below the mean would cancel out all values above the mean. If deviations aren't squared, then the sum of the deviations will always equal zero.

Once the total sum of squares has been calculated, equations are used to calculate the differences within groups and the differences across groups. These terms are known as the sum of squares within groups (SS_{within}) and the sum of squares between groups ($SS_{between}$).

The equation for the sum of squares within groups is:

$$SS_{within} = \sum (X - \overline{X}_{group})^2$$

This equation is strikingly similar to the equation for the total sum of squares. The major difference between the within-groups sum of squares and the total sum of squares is that instead of trying to calculate the total variation of *all* observations, we are trying to calculate the variation that exists *within* each group (we calculate deviations of each group member from their group mean, rather than the grand mean). For the equation, the difference is that the grand mean $\overline{X}$ is replaced by the group mean $\overline{X}_{group}$.

The final equation is a little different. Since we're interested in the variation across groups, each group is treated as an observation.

$$SS_{between} = \sum N_{group}(\overline{X}_{group} - \overline{X})^2$$

To find the sum of squares between groups, subtract the grand mean from each group mean, square the difference, multiply it by the number of observations in each group, and add the results across all groups.

The Sum of Squares: An Easier Way

While it's possible to use those equations, they are a lot of work. You have to subtract the mean from each observation, which involves going through your data set line-by-line and calculating deviations. In a sample of 100,000 observations, that would be incredibly tedious and time-consuming, even with a spreadsheet program.

Luckily, there's an easier way: summing variables *before* taking differences. Since the mean is the midpoint of all values of a particular variable, it can be multiplied by the number of observations and squared, speeding up the calculation of the sums of squares. Unfortunately, you'll still need to calculate the sum of all observations and square it, but the following equations are still easy to work with:

$$SS_{total} = \sum X^2_{total} - N_{total}\overline{X}^2_{total}$$

$$SS_{within} = \sum X^2_{total} - \sum N_{group}\overline{X}^2_{group}$$

$$SS_{between} = \sum N_{group}\overline{X}^2_{group} - N_{total}\overline{X}^2_{total}$$

A few words of caution: First, for the total sum of squares and within-groups sum of squares, it is important to square the value of the observations (in each case, this first term in the equation) *before* summing them. The mean value in both of the second terms needs to be squared before being multiplied by either N_{total} or N_{group}. Second, when finding the sum of squares between-groups, the group average and the grand mean need to be squared *before* being multiplied by N_{group} or N_{total}. Skipping either of these steps will result in the wrong value.

So what exactly is the sum of squares and why is it useful? The sum of squares is defined as the squared and summed measures of variance that exist between observations. They are a standardized measure of deviance from a measure of central tendency, which is why they periodically pop-up in statistics. When two samples of the same size are being compared, a higher sum of squares indicates greater variation between observations.

The sum of squares is useful in certain circumstances, but like the *t*-statistic, deviations depend on sample size. A higher sum of squares is more likely in an analysis of 100,000 observations than with a sample size of 10, suggesting that the sum of squares (total, within, and between) increases with either greater variation between scores, or sample size. When measuring variation between scores, the sum of squares must be standardized so that values can be compared regardless of sample size. This creates a standardized measure called the **mean square**.

The equation for the mean square within groups is:

$$MS_{within} = \frac{SS_{within}}{df_{within}}$$

The equation for mean square between groups is:

$$MS_{between} = \frac{SS_{between}}{df_{between}}$$

You should recognize the sum of squares within-groups and between-groups in the numerator

of the equation. The denominator is new. The symbols refer to the degrees of freedom within groups (df_{within}) and between groups ($df_{between}$).

Calculating these values is fairly simple:

$$df_{within} = N_{total} - k$$

and

$$df_{between} = k - 1$$

Where k = the number of groups you are comparing.

Remember that for the *t*-distribution the degrees of freedom are defined as the number of values that are free to vary. Although the equations for degrees of freedom differ slightly, the logic is the same.

First, since we're estimating group means within the population using sample means, only the number of observations in each group minus one can assume any value. Consequently, in each group there is one pre-determined value. We define df_{within} as $N_{total} - k$, since one value of each group is perfectly determined by all other values within that group, when the group mean is known.

Second, since we're calculating the observed variation between groups, we don't need to know the means for every group. If the grand mean is known, then the values for $k - 1$ groups will determine the value of the last group . Therefore, only $k - 1$ values for $df_{between}$ can vary freely.

The *F*-Distribution

By now you should know that when statistical equations seek standardized numbers, it means that they're going to be assessed against a pre-established benchmark. These equations are no different, but now, instead of using the *t*- or *z*-distribution, we're going to use the *F*-distribution.

To assess values against the *F*-distribution, a test statistic must be calculated first. This test statistic is known as the *F*-ratio, and is calculated using the following equation:

$$F_{observed} = \frac{MS_{between}}{MS_{within}}$$

Since $MS_{between}$ and MS_{within} are the only variables needed, we won't bother with MS_{total}. (I'm

Table 15.2 The *F*-Distribution for 95 Per Cent Level of Significance

$df_{between}$	2	3	4	5	6	7	8
df_{within}							
1	199.50	215.71	224.58	230.16	233.99	236.77	238.88
2	19.00	19.16	19.25	19.30	19.33	19.35	19.37
3	9.55	9.28	9.12	9.01	8.94	8.89	8.85
4	6.94	6.59	6.39	6.26	6.16	6.09	6.04
5	5.79	5.41	5.19	5.05	4.95	4.88	4.82
6	5.14	4.76	4.53	4.39	4.28	4.21	4.15
7	4.74	4.35	4.12	3.97	3.87	3.79	3.73
8	4.46	4.07	3.84	3.69	3.58	3.50	3.44
9	4.26	3.86	3.63	3.48	3.37	3.29	3.23
10	4.10	3.71	3.48	3.33	3.22	3.14	3.07
11	3.98	3.59	3.36	3.20	3.10	3.01	2.95
12	3.89	3.49	3.26	3.11	3.00	2.91	2.85
13	3.81	3.41	3.18	3.03	2.92	2.83	2.77
14	3.74	3.34	3.11	2.96	2.85	2.76	2.70
15	3.68	3.29	3.06	2.90	2.79	2.71	2.64
16	3.63	3.24	3.01	2.85	2.74	2.66	2.59
17	3.59	3.20	2.97	2.81	2.70	2.61	2.55
18	3.56	3.16	2.93	2.77	2.66	2.58	2.51
19	3.52	3.13	2.90	2.74	2.63	2.54	2.48
20	3.49	3.10	2.87	2.71	2.60	2.51	2.45
30	3.32	2.92	2.69	2.53	2.42	2.33	2.27
40	3.23	2.84	2.61	2.45	2.34	2.25	2.18
50	3.18	2.79	2.56	2.40	2.29	2.20	2.13
60	3.15	2.76	2.53	2.37	2.25	2.17	2.10
70	3.13	2.74	2.50	2.35	2.23	2.14	2.07
80	3.11	2.72	2.49	2.33	2.21	2.13	2.06
90	3.10	2.71	2.47	2.32	2.20	2.11	2.04
100	3.09	2.70	2.46	2.31	2.19	2.10	2.03
120	3.07	2.68	2.45	2.29	2.18	2.09	2.02
∞	3.00	2.61	2.37	2.22	2.10	2.01	1.94

sure you'll agree that enough equations have already been covered in this chapter!)

Finally, we have enough information to assess our observed test statistic against the *F*-distribution, our predetermined benchmark. Like the *t*-distribution, the shape of the *F*-distribution depends on sample size. Unlike the *t*-distribution, the *F*-distribution depends on the number of groups. You need to look at both the within-group and between-group degrees of freedom. Table 15.2 is an abbreviated version of a table that lists the critical values of the *F*-distribution (the same table can also be found in Appendix D).

If you encounter degrees of freedom values that do not perfectly coincide with the provided values, always use the higher value. This will give you a more conservative basis for assessing your calculated *F*-statistic. For example, if you have a $df_{between}$ of 1 and a df_{within} of 118 (reflecting an independent variable with two categories, the equivalent of an independent samples t-test), choose a $df_{between}$ of 2 and a df_{within} of 120.

To help this congeal, let's keep using the example from before. Remember that we were comparing levels of mastery by four religious groups. For ease of reference, the earlier table is replicated in table 15.3.

To work through the necessary equations, the first thing we want to do is square the individual X values; see table 15.4.

Here are the equations again:

$$SS_{total} = \sum X^2_{total} - N_{total}\overline{X}^2_{total}$$

$$SS_{within} = \sum X^2_{total} - \sum N_{group}\overline{X}^2_{group}$$

$$SS_{between} = \sum N_{group}\overline{X}^2_{group} - N_{total}\overline{X}^2_{total}$$

The X^2 values in table 15.4 are useful for calculating the total sum of squares and the within-groups sum of squares (the sum of these values represents the first part of each equation). We also need the grand mean and the group means, so we'll have to calculate a few more numbers before using the equations.

Now that we have all of the information we need, let's calculate the sums of squares, starting first with the total sum of squares.

$$SS_{total} = \sum X^2_{total} - N_{total}\overline{X}^2_{total}$$

$$= (2802 + 1891 + 1301 + 2471) - 20(20.25)^2$$

$$= 8465 - 20(410.06)$$

$$= 263.8$$

This calculation is fairly straightforward. The only thing you need to watch for is the order of

Table 15.3 Average Levels of Mastery by Religious Affiliation, 2003 Social Engagement Survey

Observation #	Levels of mastery			
	No religion	Roman Catholic	United Church	Protestant
1	21	17	22	21
2	25	21	14	23
3	26	19	16	22
4	24	20	13	24
5	22	20	14	21

Source: Statistics Canada 2003 Social Engagement Survey (GSS17)

Table 15.4 Average Levels of Mastery by Religious Affiliation, 2003 Social Engagement Survey

Observation #	Levels of mastery							
	No Religion		Roman Catholic		United Church		Protestant	
	X	X^2	X	X^2	X	X^2	X	X^2
1	21	441	17	289	22	484	21	441
2	25	625	21	441	14	196	23	529
3	26	676	19	361	16	256	22	484
4	24	576	20	400	13	169	24	576
5	22	484	20	400	14	196	21	441

Source: Statistics Canada 2003 Social Engagement Survey (GSS17)

Table 15.5 Average Levels of Mastery by Religious Affiliation, 2003 Social Engagement Survey

Observation #	No religion		Roman Catholic		United Church		Protestant	
	X	X^2	X	X^2	X	X^2	X	X^2
1	21	441	17	289	22	484	21	441
2	25	625	21	441	14	196	23	529
3	26	676	19	361	16	256	22	484
4	24	576	20	400	13	169	24	576
5	22	484	20	400	14	196	21	441
Σ	118	2,802	97	1,891	79	1,301	111	2,471
$\overline{X}$	23.6		19.4		15.8		22.2	
N	20		Grand Mean		20.25			

Source: Statistics Canada 2003 Social Engagement Survey (GSS17)

operations in the second part of the equation. Remember to exponentiate the grand mean before multiplying it by the number of observations. Failing to do so will result in a calculation error. The total sum of squares represents the total amount of variation within our sample that can be explained by the sample's characteristics.

The next calculation is the within-group sum of squares. We can take a shortcut here, since we already calculated it.

$$SS_{within} = \sum X^2_{total} - \sum N_{group}\overline{X}^2_{group}$$

$$= 8465 - [5(23.6)^2 + 5(19.4)^2 + 5(15.8)^2 + 5(22.2)^2]$$

$$= 8465 - [2784.8 + 1881.8 + 1248.2 + 2464.2]$$

$$= 8465 - 8379$$

$$= 86$$

For the between-group sum of squares we can either use the equation, or we can subtract the within-group sum of squares from the total sum of squares. Recall that the total sum of squares represents the total amount of variation within the sample, and the within-group sum of squares represents the total variation within each group. The between-group sum of squares should be the difference between the two, but let's make sure.

The first part of the equation for the between-group sum of squares is the same as the last part of the equation for the within-group sum of squares. The second part is the same as the second part of the equation for total sum of squares. We can insert those values.

$$SS_{between} = \sum N_{group}\overline{X}^2_{group} - N_{total}\overline{X}^2_{total}$$

$$= 8379 - 8201.2$$

$$= 177.8$$

The answer should be the same as what we would get by subtracting the within-group sum of squares from the total sum of squares:

$$SS_{between} = SS_{total} - SS_{within}$$

$$= 263.8 - 86$$

$$= 177.8$$

It is, so we can be fairly certain that our calculations are correct. To be even more certain, we could choose not to borrow $\sum N_{group}\overline{X}^2_{group}$ and $N_{total}\overline{X}^2_{total}$ from our previous equations, since any errors we made before will be embedded in them.

Now that we have our sums of squares, the next thing to do is calculate the mean squares. To do so, we need the two degrees of freedom values:

$$df_{within} = N_{total} - k$$

$$= 20 - 4$$

$$= 16$$

and

$$df_{between} = k - 1$$
$$= 4 - 1$$
$$= 3$$

We can put these values into our equations for the mean square. First, for within-groups:

$$MS_{within} = \frac{SS_{within}}{df_{within}}$$
$$= \frac{86}{16}$$
$$= 5.38$$

And then for between-groups:

$$MS_{between} = \frac{SS_{between}}{df_{between}}$$
$$= \frac{177.8}{3}$$
$$= 59.27$$

Finally, we can calculate our F-statistic:

$$F = \frac{MS_{between}}{MS_{within}}$$
$$= \frac{59.27}{5.38}$$
$$= 11.02$$

Next, we need to compare that value with the $F_{critical}$ value on the F-table. For degrees of freedom, 3 and 16 return the critical value of 3.24, and since 11.02 greatly exceeds that number, we can be 95 per cent confident that there is at least one significant difference in levels of mastery across religions in the population. In other words, we now know with 95 per cent certainty that at least two of our groups differ significantly in terms of mastery.

Is This New?

Although a lot of material has been covered in this chapter—especially equations—there are striking similarities between the techniques we've been using and the techniques for t-tests. We have already compared variances between samples with variance within samples to determine where the greater differences lay. ANOVA is an elaboration of this technique, because it makes it possible to compare more than two groups. Think of ANOVA as a t-test for more than two groups, with a lower probability of type one error.

Limitations of ANOVA

Of course, ANOVA has limitations. Two of them in particular are of concern to us.

First, the assumption of equal variances across groups within the population; the idea is that each of the groups within a population has approximately the same distribution of values around the mean. Slight differences between groups are acceptable, but ANOVA becomes increasingly unusable when there are large differences. Therefore, it is a good idea to compare the variances prior to conducting an ANOVA.

Second is the determination of what a significant F-value means. When $F_{observed}$ exceeds $F_{critical}$, the only information provided is that the mean of at least one group in the sample is significantly different from the population as a whole. If we were interested in determining *which* group was different, we'd have to conduct a series of complicated **post-hoc tests**. These can be calculated using statistical software, but my preference is to

BOX 15.1 ANOVA: THE STEPS

1. Find the grand mean and the mean for each group.
2. Find group sums, sum of squared scores.
3. Find SS_{total}, SS_{within}, $SS_{between}$.
4. Find $df_{between}$ and df_{within}.
5. Find $MS_{between}$ and MS_{within}.
6. Obtain the F-ratio.
7. Compare $F_{observed}$ to $F_{critical}$.

BOX 15.2 ONE-WAY ANOVA: HISTORY OF A TERM

In the mid-nineteenth century, agriculturist James F. W. Johnston recognized a problem with agricultural analysis. Because of the importance of practical agricultural knowledge to individual and national economic development its importance was acknowledged, but unlike fields such as physics, where researchers can control conditions, agriculture is not easily translatable to the laboratory. For example, if there are two crops with differing methods of production, how can the cause of differences in yield be determined? Influences can't be isolated, so there is no way to discern whether the treatment of a crop had a significant contribution to its behaviour and yield.

Gigerenzer et al. (1991) relate the story of how statistician and geneticist Ronald Fisher (1890–1962) attempted to solve the problem. He aimed 'to ascertain whether a difference in means between treated population and controls indicates the causal efficacy of the treatment' (73). Specifically, he wanted to know how to evaluate the application of manure or bone meal when the yield from plots is not constant, but has a particular distribution. When there is variation among plots not treated with bone meal or manure, how can the distribution of yield of certain plots be accounted for when an independent variable is introduced (fertilizer)? Fisher developed the statistical and systematic means for comparing within-group variance and the variance between groups in order to solve this problem—the F in F-ratios and the F-test comes from him.

create a series of dummy variables and use them as predictors in a regression, which we'll discuss in the next two chapters.

Ordinary least-squares regression, covered in the next chapter, is superior to post-hoc tests because you can assess the statistical significance of differences, while holding other characteristics constant. For example, the differences in levels of mastery across religious groups that we saw could be due to differences in the average age or level of education of each group. Suppose that mastery and religion are heavily correlated with age and education, it's possible that the differences observed in an ANOVA are the result of one or both of the third or fourth variables. In a regression framework it is possible to determine if that is the case. In a one-way ANOVA, it is not.

Many social science disciplines use ANOVA frequently, testifying to its utility. There have been numerous elaborations on the simple technique described in this chapter that address the concerns. These are beyond what is necessary for an introductory statistics course.

PRACTICE QUESTIONS

1. Sarah plans to start exercising so that she can lose weight. She wonders whether she will burn the same number of calories no matter what type of activity she does. Sarah chooses 5 different exercises and asks 5 different people the number of calories they burn by doing each activity for a period of 1 hour.

Number of calories burned per hour				
Bicycling	House cleaning	Health club exercise	Yoga	Tennis
236	207	325	236	413
321	249	401	312	599
345	292	452	345	604
292	302	474	281	434
301	222	353	301	477

   a. Construct and complete a table containing X^2, N, the average time spent on each activity, the sum of all the times, and the grand mean for all activities.

   b. Calculate SS_{total}, SS_{within}, and $SS_{between}$.

   c. Calculate df_{within} and $df_{between}$.

   d. Calculate MS_{within} and $MS_{between}$.

   e. Obtain the F-ratio.

   f. Compare $F_{calculated}$ to $F_{critical}$.

2. Ann's friend Jen always tells Ann that she should buy more expensive jeans because they last longer. Ann asked 5 people how many days they wore the following 4 types of jeans before they were no longer able to wear them, to see if there are significant differences between the type of jeans and their durability.

Durability of Jeans				
Observation #	Levi's	People's Liberty	Silvers	Guess
1	182	209	1,040	260
2	130	225	780	624
3	91	156	520	416
4	200	260	340	222
5	154	101	416	85

   a. Construct and complete a table that contains the necessary information for finding $F_{calculated}$.

   b. Compare $F_{calculated}$ to $F_{critical}$.

Answers to the practice questions for chapter 15 can be found on page 191.

PART THREE

Multivariate Techniques

Regression 1—Modelling Continuous Outcomes

Learning Objectives

In this chapter, we're moving beyond bivariate techniques and focusing on analysis with more than two variables. Specifically, we'll look at:

- why and when multivariate analysis might be necessary
- ordinary least squares (OLS) regression
- how to calculate and interpret OLS coefficients
- standardized partial slopes
- dummy variables

Introduction

You probably expect your income to increase as you age, but do you know how to determine if that is a reasonable expectation? If so, can you calculate the rate at which it will increase? You could run a bivariate correlation between age and income, but what if you believe that other variables, such as education, will also have an effect? What about if you're male or female? Black or white? A resident of Winnipeg or Halifax? How can you look at the relationship between two variables and still acknowledge that other variables matter?

So far, a lot of this text has been about levels of measurement, variance, and correlations between variables. In a way, this has all been 'build-up' to the next two chapters. In this chapter, everything will come together with ordinary least squares regression, the multivariate technique of choice for continuous dependent variables. Then, chapter 17 will cover logistic regression, which is often used with binary outcomes.

Ordinary Least Squares Regression: The Idea

When two sets of numbers are plotted on a graph (say, age and income), and you think that you can see a general trend or relationship between the two sets, you might be tempted to draw a 'trend line' (like the one we used in chapter 14 to illustrate Pearson's r) to describe the relationship that you think you see. Although this can be done by eye, some quick calculations will be more accurate. If you drew several lines, how would you know which is the best one? Your goal is to find the line that best represents the relationship between individual scores on an independent variable and a dependent variable. You want the sum of the distances between the data points and the line to be as small above the line as below the line. The distance is known as the estimation error.

If all of the points were on a straight line, we could trace that line. This is rarely the case, so we must decide where to draw the line. To do that, we use regression. The shorthand term 'regression' refers to a set of techniques that allow identification and generalization of relationships between two or more variables. For now we'll only consider cases where the relationship between the variables is linear, but that isn't necessary. In the next chapter we'll look at a type of non-linear relationship, the logistic curve.

Social scientists use computers to help them with regression. However, the best practitioners are also familiar with the 'behind-the-scenes' calculations. In this chapter we'll focus on calculating regression coefficients by hand, so that when you use Excel, SAS, Stata, SPSS, or any other program, you'll understand what the numbers in the output mean and how they were calculated. Although research with more than 50 independent variables is common, because of the complexity of the calculations for regression, we'll only use examples with far fewer independent variables.

Onward from Bivariate Correlation

To understand ordinary least squares regression, it is useful to think of it as an extension of a bivariate correlation between two interval/ratio variables. Like a bivariate correlation, Pearson's correlation coefficient is used to measure the strength of the association between two variables (let's call them X and Y). However, unlike a bivariate correlation, it is possible to examine the strength of an association between Y and several variables (such as X and Z).

To illustrate, suppose that you wanted to look at the relationship between age and hours of sleep. You feel that years of schooling affects hours of sleep, but you aren't actually interested in this second relationship. Perhaps the most

BOX 16.1 WHY IS REGRESSION CALLED REGRESSION?

The term 'regression' is a bit odd. The origin of the term is an interesting one that brings us back to Francis Galton and his pea seeds.

Francis Galton (1822–1911) had a problem. He wanted to know 'How is it possible for a whole population to remain alike in its features, as a whole, during many successive generations, if the *average* produce of each couple resembles their parents?' (Walker, 1929: 103).

To answer the question, he took several hundred pea seeds, sent them to friends and asked them to grow them, keeping their soil constant, and to class the offspring according to parental size.

Then Galton asked his friends to return those peas. He weighed the parents of each pea seed and the pea seeds themselves, then divided them into classes.' The measurements ... led him to his first statement of the law of regression: the mean of every batch of progeny was displaced from the general mean in an amount proportional to the displacement of their parents. The mean displacement of the offspring, however, was always less than that of their parents; they had, on the average, "reverted" part way back to the mean for the entire race.' (Porter, 1986: 286–287). In terms of heredity, the idea that developed into what we know now as regression was described as a regression, or reversion, of attributes (such as height) towards the mean. Even if height is hereditary, heights of successive generations continue to observe a normal distribution, and appear to be 'pulled back' towards a new mean value, away from radical deviation.

important feature of regression is that each relationship can be assessed without worrying about the impact of potential explanatory variables. If you were interested in the relationship between age and hours of sleep, but acknowledge that years of schooling probably has an effect on that relationship, you can 'control' for years of schooling by entering it into the regression. The relationship that we observe between age and hours of sleep will represent the relationship after the effect of years of schooling has been removed. Regression assesses the effect of an additional variable, while holding the value of all other variables (except the dependent variable) at zero.

Regression: The Formula

A little bit of basic geometry (the relationship between points and lines) should give you a better understanding of regression.

Basically, regression takes the following form:

$$Y = a + b_1x_{1i} + b_2x_{2i} + ... + b_nx_{ni} + e_i$$

Where:

- Y = the dependent variable
- a = the Y intercept
- b_1 = the partial slope of X_1 on Y
- b_2 = the partial slope of X_2 on Y
- b_n = the partial slope of X_n on Y
- x_{1i} = the first independent variable for individual i
- x_{2i} = the second independent variable for individual i
- x_{ni} = the nth independent variable for individual i
- e_i = error for individual i

The equation represents a formalized hypothesis about the relationship between the independent variables and one dependent variable, acknowledging that each prediction is likely to carry at least some error, making the combination of the variables 'miss' the actual score of the dependent variable by some margin. This margin is represented by e_i, an error term that each individual will have a distinct value for. The addition sign between each partial slope coefficient/independent variable couplet implies an additive relationship, which means that each independent or explanatory variable has equal potential to impact the dependent variable.

For now, we assume that the relationship between independent variables and the dependent variable is linear, so it can be plotted as a straight line. The independent variables are summed to determine the slope of the line. Since each variable can contribute to the slope, they are referred to as **partial slope coefficients**. The term coefficient refers to a number or quantity that expresses the nature of the relationship between an independent variable and the dependent variable.

Let's look at a simple example: the relationship between age and income, using individuals of all ages. Since this is probably your first time using regression, we'll only look at one independent variable, age, even though it would be easy to think of numerous characteristics that shape income (gender, occupation, number of hours worked, years of education, etc.). The basic equation looks like this:

$$Income = a + b_1age_i + e_i$$

A regression takes the score of the independent variable (age) for each individual, and determines how that value relates to the dependent variable income.

The equation identifies three values: the y-intercept, the partial slope coefficient, and the individual error. We've already discussed partial slopes and errors, and you may remember from high school geometry that the y-intercept represents the value where the regression line (there you may have called it the fit line) crosses the y-axis (note: now you finally know why you had to learn geometry!). The y-intercept refers to the point on the y-axis where the regression line crosses. The interpretation here is more nuanced because it also represents our prediction of a person's income when their scores on the independent variable of age are at their lowest value. Since we are looking at people of all ages, the y-intercept will represent a person's expected income at zero years of age. The partial slope coefficient, which is actually the *only* slope coefficient in this case, represents the effect of an additional year on our income prediction. Usually, the partial slopes and y-intercepts are the values of greatest interest. Occasionally, it is interesting to look at the error, or the disparity between predicted values (our 'guess' of a person's income) and actual values (what their income actually is).

Now that we know what each of the terms in the regression equation means, let's estimate the relationship between age and income using the 2001 Census of Canada (see table 16.1). We'll restrict the sample so that a person must have valid values on both variables. For now we'll use a computer to do the calculations. We'll learn how to calculate intercepts and coefficients in the next section.

Each computer program presents results differently. This regression was calculated with Stata, and you probably won't be able to interpret table 16.1 on your own. For now, focus on the two values in the column with the heading 'Coef' (shown in bold). These are the coefficients for age (called agep in the 2001 public-use census file) and the y-intercept (called _cons in Stata), respectively. The value of 17,795.57 tells us that our regression predicts that a person with zero years of age will be earning \$17,795.57 (actually, since nobody under age 15 has valid income values on the census, this represents income at age 15), and the agep coefficient tells us that the value is expected to increase by \$218.93 for every additional year of age. Inserting these values into our equation above, a now carries a value of 17,795.57 and b is 218.93. For now, ignore the other columns, even though some of them (Std. Err., t, 95% Conf. Interval) may look familiar.

Graphing the relationship with a scatterplot can make it easier to visualize the relationship.

Although it may be difficult to see, figure 16.1 shows that our estimate of the y-intercept (17,795.57) corresponds with where the line crosses the y-axis. Equally difficult to see is how the pitch of the regression line corresponds with this partial slope coefficient value (218.93) in our equation. These numbers should be identical. The equation describes the characteristics of the regression line, and that the distance between the line and any given observation is the error.

You can probably see some similarities between regression and correlation by now. In some ways, regression is a correlation with many variables.

Regression allows you to predict the value of the dependent variable using the information provided in independent variables. For example, if somebody was 25 years old, we could estimate their income as follows:

$$Income = 17795.57 + 218.93age_i$$
$$= 17795.57 + 218.93 * 10$$
$$= 17795.57 + 2189.30$$
$$= \$19984.87$$

Based on our regression equation, we can predict that a person who is 25-years-old will earn \$19,984.87. Why did we only add 10 years of age for someone that is 25? Because we estimated our regression on those over age 15, so we need to take the difference between lowest age and our age of interest, which is 25 – 15 = 10.

How accurate is that estimate? According to the 2001 census file, the actual average income for a 25 year old is \$21,663.40. Although our guess is pretty good—we're only off by \$1,678.53—there are things we could do to get a more accurate estimate. One is to add more explanatory variables (education, gender, occupation, etc.), and another is to restrict the age range of our sam-

Table 16.1   Regression Output for a Single Independent Variable Model

Source	SS	df	MS		Number of obs	=	645961
					F(1645959)	=13748.61	
Model	9.8500e+12	1	9.8500e+12		Prob > F	=	0.0000
Residual	4.6279e+14645959		716439688		R-squared	=	0.0208
					Adj R-squared	=	0.0208
Total	4.7264e+14645960		731687274		Root MSE	=	26766

totincp	Coef.	Std. Err.	t	P>|t|	[95% Conf. Interval]	
agep	218.9251	1.867095	117.25	0.000	215.2657	222.5846
_cons	17795.57	88.38844	201.33	0.000	17622.33	17968.81

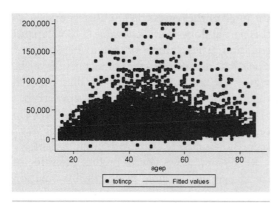

Figure 16.1   Regression of Age and Income,
2001 Canada

ples so that we are primarily looking at people in a more valid age range—say, age 25 to 55—since few 15-year-olds are likely to be working full-time. For now let's just work with what we have, and develop our understanding of the one independent variable model.

Now that we know how to estimate y using slopes and intercepts, how are the y-intercept, the partial slope coefficient, and the error terms obtained? We are kind of working backwards, but with some careful thought it is possible to imagine what some of the necessary information might be. Since the regression line is supposed to minimize errors (the average gap between observed values and predicted values should be as small as possible), we need an equation that will create a line of best fit where average distance between observations above the line are the same as, or as close as possible to, those below the line.

That makes sense: with the best fitting line, which is what the regression line is supposed to be, we want the average level of *under*estimation to be approximately equal to the average level of *over*estimation. If positive errors (those above the line) surpass negative errors, then our line will not cut midway through the data.

The line of best fit can also be stated as the sum of cross-product deviations from their means of independent variable X and dependent variable Y, divided by the sum of squared deviations from its mean of independent variable X. This is the equation:

$$b = \frac{\sum (X - \overline{X})(Y - \overline{Y})}{\sum (X - \overline{X})^2}$$

Where:

- $\overline{X}$ = the mean value of variable X
- $\overline{Y}$ = the mean value of variable Y

The numerator is the sum of the deviations of the independent variable, multiplied by the deviations of the dependent variable. Remember that we're trying to identify how strongly the scores of Y depend on the scores of X. When observations have a high value of X alongside a high value of Y, a middle value of X alongside a middle value of Y, and lower X values alongside lower Y values, the numerator will be high, resulting in a larger partial coefficient.

What's going on with the denominator? Given that the size of the numerator partially depends on the range of values of X (if X has a large variance, then the numerator will be large, and vice versa), it is necessary to standardize these values. This is done by dividing the numerator by the squared deviations of X from the mean. These values are squared because if they are not then the sum of deviations from the mean will be equal to zero. You might remember this from when we calculated variance and standard deviation.

Once the partial coefficient b is found, calculating the y-intercept and the error is easy. The y-intercept a is defined as:

$$a = \overline{Y} - b\overline{X}$$

And error e is defined as:

$$e = Y - \hat{Y}$$

Where $\hat{Y}$ is the predicted value (the value of Y on the regression line at a particular value of X).

Let's illustrate this with an example. Using the 1971 Census of Canada public use file we can use age at first marriage to predict family size, focusing on people who were 35-years-old in 1971. As with other statistical techniques, the calculations are cumbersome in large samples, so we'll restrict our analysis to 12 randomly selected observations. These observations appear in table 16.2.

Let's revisit our equation for b:

$$b = \frac{\sum (X - \overline{X})(Y - \overline{Y})}{\sum (X - \overline{X})^2}$$

The first things we'll need to find are the means of family size (Y, the dependent variable) and age at first marriage (X, the independent variable).

Table 16.2 Family Size and Age of First Marriage among 12 Randomly Selected Cases, 1971 Census of Canada

Age at first marriage (X)	Family size (Y)
21	4
32	2
21	3
25	5
24	1
17	3
22	5
21	4
22	2
22	5
28	2
26	3

For family size we get:

$(4 + 2 + 3 + 5 + 1 + 3 + 5 + 4 + 2 + 5 + 2 + 3)/12 = 3.25$

For age at first marriage we get:

$(21 + 32 + 21 + 25 + 24 + 17 + 22 + 21 + 22 + 22 + 28 + 26)/12 = 23.42$

We'll also need the sum of cross-product deviations of independent variable X and dependent variable Y from their means. This is a little harder to calculate, but a chart like the one in table 16.3 will make things easier.

We are primarily interested in two pieces of information in table 16.3. $\sum (X - \overline{X})(Y - \overline{Y})$, which is often referred to as the sum of products (SP), and $\sum (X - \overline{X})^2$, the sum of squares ($SS$).

Now that we have the sum of products, the sum of squares, and the means of the two variables, the equation for the partial slope is easy to solve:

$$b = \frac{\sum (X - \overline{X})(Y - \overline{Y})}{\sum (X - \overline{X})^2}$$

$$= \frac{-20.25}{168.92}$$

$$= -0.12$$

Table 16.3 Using Family Size and Age of First Marriage among 12 Randomly Selected Cases to Calculate Regression Coefficients, 1971 Census of Canada

Age at first marriage (X)	Family size (Y)	$X - \overline{X}$	$Y - \overline{Y}$	$(X - \overline{X})(Y - \overline{Y})$	$(X - \overline{X})^2$
21	4	-2.42	0.75	-1.82	5.86
32	2	8.58	-1.25	-10.73	73.62
21	3	-2.42	-0.25	0.61	5.86
25	5	1.58	1.75	2.77	2.50
24	1	0.58	-2.25	-1.31	0.34
17	3	-6.42	-0.25	1.61	41.22
22	5	-1.42	1.75	-2.49	2.02
21	4	-2.42	0.75	-1.82	5.86
22	2	-1.42	-1.25	1.78	2.02
22	5	-1.42	1.75	-2.49	2.02
28	2	4.58	-1.25	-5.73	20.98
26	3	2.58	-0.25	-0.65	6.66
Mean=23.42	Mean=3.25			Sum=-20.25	Sum=168.92

As is the intercept:

$$a = \overline{Y} - b\overline{X}$$
$$= 3.25 - (-0.12)*23.42$$
$$= 6.06$$

To calculate the error we need to generate **predicted values** for each observation: the predicted family size for each person, given the available information (their age at first marriage). We use our standard regression equation and the values we calculated above to find this:

$$\hat{Y} = a + bX$$
$$= 6.06 - 0.12X$$

Next, we calculate predicted values for each observation, and by substituting values for X we calculate prediction errors with the following equation $e = Y - \hat{Y}$ (see table 16.4).

Multiple Regression

In the previous example, we used models with only one independent variable and one dependent variable. Although this nicely illustrated the principle of ordinary least squares regression, such small models are rarely used in social science research. Typically, models will have more than one independent variable—in fact, analysts will usually include more than 50 independent variables in a single model. This makes for an extremely complex analysis that would be just about impossible without computers and statistical software packages.

The same equations are used for models with several independent variables, but there are more considerations. Any two independent variables will not only be correlated with the dependent variable but probably also with each other. Because of this, the independent effect of one variable cannot be isolated without looking at the impact of the other variables, and identifying the relationship between them. For example, the number of years that a Canadian immigrant has been in the country is related to his or her age. Of course, it is impossible to have been in Canada for longer than you've been alive, but older people have had the opportunity to be in Canada for much longer than young people, so we expect there to be a correlation between age and years in Canada. If we use both of these independent variables to predict a dependent variable, like the number of charities a person participates in, we would not be able to identify the independent impact of either age or years since migration without acknowledging that there is some relatedness, or **covariance**, between them.

Table 16.4 Using Age of First Marriage among 12 Randomly Selected Cases to Calculate Predicted Family Size, 1971 Census of Canada

Age at first marriage (X)	Family size (Y)	$\hat{Y}$	$e = Y - \hat{Y}$
21	4	3.54	0.46
32	2	2.22	-0.22
21	3	3.54	-0.54
25	5	3.06	1.94
24	1	3.18	-2.18
17	3	4.02	-1.02
22	5	3.42	1.58
21	4	3.54	0.46
22	2	3.42	-1.42
22	5	3.42	1.58
28	2	2.70	-0.70
26	3	2.94	0.06

BOX 16.2 REGRESSION WITH ONE INDEPENDENT VARIABLE: THE STEPS

1. Find the mean for each X and Y variable.

2. Subtract the mean from the value for each observation.

3. Square and sum these terms. Each value is known as the sum of squares.

$$SS_X = \sum (X - \overline{X})^2 \quad SS_Y = \sum (Y - \overline{Y})^2$$

4. Find the sum of products:

$$SP = \sum (X - \overline{X})(Y - \overline{Y})$$

5. Calculate b (the partial slope):

$$b = \frac{SP}{SS_X}$$

6. Calculate a (the y-intercept):

$$a = \overline{Y} - b\overline{X}$$

7. Calculate r:

$$r = \frac{SP}{\sqrt{SS_X SS_Y}}$$

Handling covariance can become complicated. Since we are dealing with correlations, we can return to bivariate correlations to help us understand regression with more than one independent variable. To remind you, here's the equation for a bivariate correlation between variables X and Y:

$$r_{xy} = \frac{N\sum XY - (\sum X)(\sum Y)}{\sqrt{[N\sum X^2 - (\sum X)^2][N\sum Y^2 - (\sum Y)^2]}}$$

We need to change the notation slightly to accommodate the new correlations we're measuring, resulting in the following three equations:

$$r_{x1y} = \frac{N\sum X1Y - (\sum X1)(\sum Y)}{\sqrt{[N\sum X1^2 - (\sum X1)^2][N\sum Y^2 - (\sum Y)^2]}}$$

$$r_{x2y} = \frac{N\sum X2Y - (\sum X2)(\sum Y)}{\sqrt{[N\sum X2^2 - (\sum X2)^2][N\sum Y^2 - (\sum Y)^2]}}$$

$$r_{x1x2} = \frac{N\sum X1X2 - (\sum X1)(\sum X2)}{\sqrt{[N\sum X1^2 - (\sum X1)^2][N\sum X2^2 - (\sum X2)^2]}}$$

These probably look daunting, but they're essentially the same equation that we used to calculate correlation in chapter 10, except that the notation has changed to indicated that we're looking at different combinations of correlations.

Let's see how this works in practice. Recall from chapter 14 that we used the 1666 census to illustrate correlation, so let's use that again to elaborate on regression with two indepen-

dent variables. This time both the age of the husband and the age of the wife will be independent variables, and we'll use that information to predict the number of children in the household. Let's suppose that we expect the age of the husband to be positively correlated with the age of the wife, and for the ages of both husband and wife to be positively associated with the number of children in the household. To get a better sense of what we're trying to do, let's take a look at the data in table 16.5 (we'll focus on only 12 observations).

We need to calculate the correlations between all of the variables (since we already did that in chapter 14, let's rely on computers here):

```
.corr spage age nchildhh
(obs=12)

|        wifage  husage  nchildhh
--------------+--------------------------
wifage  |  1.0000
husage  |  0.7073  1.0000
nchildhh|  0.1485  0.6152  1.0000
```

As you can see, our expectations are met. Each of the three correlations is positive, suggesting that age of husband is positively correlated with both age of wife and number of children in the household. Similarly, age of wife is positively correlated with age of husband and number of children in the household. Finally, we can infer from the previous two statements that number of children in the household is positively correlated with age of wife and age of husband.

Table 16.5 Age of Husband and Wife and Number of Children among 12 Households, 1666 Census of Canada

obs #	spage (X1)	Age (X2)	# child (Y)
1	40	41	0
2	47	36	0
3	30	40	5
4	18	27	0
5	37	50	7
6	50	62	4
7	32	30	3
8	40	54	6
9	41	36	1
10	20	27	1
11	36	36	2
12	32	37	5

Note: There is only one observation per household.

Now that we have the **zero-order correlations** (correlations between variables without assuming any causal order), we need the equations for the partial correlation coefficient:

$$b_1 = \left(\frac{s_y}{s_{x1}}\right)\left(\frac{r_{yx1} - r_{yx2}r_{x1x2}}{1 - r^2_{x_{1x2}}}\right)$$

$$b_2 = \left(\frac{s_y}{s_{x2}}\right)\left(\frac{r_{yx2} - r_{yx1}r_{x1x2}}{1 - r^2_{x_{1x2}}}\right)$$

Where s refers to the standard deviations of certain variables, and r denotes the correlations between them. Let's work through these equations to derive the partial correlation coefficients:

$$b_1 = \left(\frac{s_y}{s_{x1}}\right)\left(\frac{r_{yx1} - r_{yx2}r_{x1x2}}{1 - r^2_{x_{1x2}}}\right)$$

$$= \left(\frac{2.517}{9.612}\right)\left(\frac{0.1485 - 0.6152*0.7073}{1 - 0.7073^2}\right)$$

$$= (0.2618)\left(\frac{0.1485 - 0.4351}{1 - 0.5003}\right)$$

$$= (0.2618)(-0.5735)$$

$$= -0.1502$$

$$b_2 = \left(\frac{s_y}{s_{x2}}\right)\left(\frac{r_{yx2} - r_{yx1}r_{x1x2}}{1 - r^2_{x_{1x2}}}\right)$$

$$= \left(\frac{2.517}{10.765}\right)\left(\frac{0.6152 - 0.1485*0.7073}{1 - 0.7073^2}\right)$$

$$= (0.2338)\left(\frac{0.6152 - 0.1050}{1 - 0.5003}\right)$$

$$= (0.2338)(1.0210)$$

$$= 0.2387$$

When the coefficients are calculated, an interesting difference between these figures and the zero-order correlations emerges. Notice that b_2 remains positive, showing that the age of the husband remains positively correlated with the number of children in the household. At the same time, age of wife is now negatively related to the number of children in the household.

How can this be? The correlation between age of husband and age of wife was so strong that it obscured the negative relationship between the age of wife and the number of children in the household. This nicely illustrates the importance of regression analysis, and explains why it is one of the most frequently used techniques in social science data analysis.

Standardized Partial Slopes (beta-weights)

In the example, the partial slopes (b_1 and b_2) were in the original units of the independent variables. The coefficient refers to the expected increase in the dependent variable when there is a one-unit increase in the value of an independent variable. Since both independent variables were measured in years, it was easy to compare the relative impact of each variable. We know that the age of husband had a more direct impact than the age of the wife because the coefficient was greater in magnitude.

To compare the relative effects of independent variables that are not measured in the same units, a beta-weights (b^*) needs to be computed. Beta-weights show how much change there is to *standardized* scores of Y when there is a one-unit change in the *standardized* scores of each independent variable, and controls for the effects of all other independent variables. With standardized betas, the independent variables do not have to be measured in the same units. Since calculating beta-weights is really just a standardization technique that once again relies on standard deviations. The equation is simple:

$$b_{1*} = b_1 \left(\frac{s_1}{s_y} \right)$$

The Multiple Correlation Coefficient

Recall chapter 14, when r was used to identify the strength of the relationship between two variables. To get the per cent variation of one variable, we squared r. The same thing is possible using multiple regression, except that we are now able to assess the cumulative effect of several independent variables on one dependent variable.

Although we already calculated the bivariate correlations, adding them together will overestimate the per cent of explained variation because of the correlation that exists between X_1 and X_2. Both might be explaining a similar portion of the dependent variable. Think of an apple as the dependent variable, with multiple slices representing the variable's variation. Regression aims to explain as much of the total variation (the whole apple) as possible; ideally, each independent variable will remove a slice of the apple. Since independent variables are frequently correlated with one another, there will be overlap in the slices that each independent variable will remove.

Consequently, the correlation of independent variables must be accounted for in the calculation of R^2. The equation to do that is:

$$R^2 = r_y^2{}_{x1} + r_y^2{}_{x1.x2} (1 - r_y^2{}_{x1})$$

Or

$$R^2 = \frac{\sum (\hat{Y} - \overline{Y})^2}{\sum (Y - \overline{Y})^2}$$

We have most of the information we need to solve the equation. The only missing piece is $r_y^2{}_{x1.x2}$, which is calculated as:

$$r_y^2{}_{x1.x2} = \frac{r_{yx2} - (r_{yx1})(r_{x1x2})}{\sqrt{1 - r_y^2{}_{x1}} \sqrt{1 - r_x^2{}_{1x2}}}$$

Applied to our 1666 example, we get:

$$r_y^2{}_{x1.x2} = \frac{r_{yx2} - (r_{yx1})(r_{x1x2})}{\sqrt{1 - r_y^2{}_{x1}} \sqrt{1 - r_x^2{}_{1x2}}}$$

$$= \frac{0.6152 - 0.1485 * 0.7073}{\sqrt{1 - 0.1485^2} \sqrt{1 - 0.7073^2}}$$

$$= \frac{0.5102}{0.6991}$$

$$= 0.6530$$

Now, we can solve for R^2:

$$R^2 = r_y^2{}_{x1} + r_y^2{}_{x1.x2} (1 - r_y^2{}_{x1})$$

$$= 0.1485^2 + 0.6530^2 * (1 - 0.1482^2)$$

$$= 0.0221 + 0.4264 * (0.9780)$$

$$= 0.4391$$

Now we know that age of husband and age of wife together explain about 44 per cent of the variation in the number of children in a household. Notice that this result is substantially lower than when the two zero-order correlations are added together $((0.1485+0.6152)^2 = 0.5832)$. This is due to correlation between variables.

Requirements of Ordinary Least Squares Regression

There are some fundamental assumptions behind ordinary least squares regression. You'll be familiar with most of them, because they've been covered elsewhere (particularly in our discussion of correlation).

1. All variables are interval/ratio, dichotomous, or dummy (discussed below).
2. All variables, and their errors, are normally distributed.
3. There is linearity between variables. This means that the relationship between an independent variable and a dependent variable is the same across the range of both variables. For example, it is assumed that the relationship between years of schooling and number of hours worked per week is the same for a high school graduate as it is for somebody with a PhD.
4. Random samples are necessary for significance tests, otherwise there will be non-random sampling error.

Dummy Variables

The problem with ordinary least squares regression in the social sciences is that many variables of interest are measured at nominal and ordinal levels. For example, a common interest is the differences between men and women. This is problematic because it is not possible to rank respondents based on their sex, nor is it possible to measure the 'distance' between men and women. Compare this to something like age, where we can determine the difference between two respondents based on their response (we know that a ten-year-old is five years older than a five-year-old). Does this mean that we can't use regression techniques for all variables?

Fortunately, the 'distance' between response categories can be measured in a nominal or ordinal variable when there are only two response categories (typically, these variables are referred to as **dichotomous variables**, **binary variables**, or **dummy variables**). If we view the response categories of a dichotomous variable as being on two ends of a continuum (for example, males are on one end, and females are on the other), then we know that a person who identifies as male is 100 per cent more male than a female is. In this indirect way we are able to quantify the distance between two categories in a dichotomous variable so that it can be used in a regression.

In the case of variables with more than two response categories (religion, region of residence, visible minority status), a 'cheat' is possible if nominal and ordinal variables with more than two response categories are broken down into a series of dichotomous variables and then entered into a regression. This process is referred to as **dichotomization**.

Let's try an example. In the 1901 Census of Canada every respondent was asked their race. There were four allowable responses: black, red, white, and yellow. In the census file, this information exists as a single nominal variable, 'Race'. Without modification it is not possible to include this variable in a regression, because it is not possible to rank the four response categories, or to measure the distance between them, thereby violating OLS assumption one.

To get around the problem, we need to create a series of new variables. Let's call them $D1$ through $D4$. As table 16.6 illustrates, $D1$ assumes a value of one when a respondent identifies as red, and zero otherwise. $D2$ is set to one when a respondent identifies as yellow, and zero otherwise. In the same way, $D3$ and $D4$ identify white and black respondents, respectively.

We've created four new dichotomous variables out of one nominal variable. Since the new variables have only two values, zero and one, they can be used in an OLS regression. The new dummy variables use the same logic as the gender example. A person who has a value of one on variable $D1$ is 100 per cent more red than somebody with a value of zero.

Unfortunately, working with dummy variables is complicated by the necessity of having a **reference group**. The four dummy variables don't all need to be included in the regression, only three are needed. Think about it: if a respondent has a score of zero on variable $D1$ (indicating that they are not red), $D2$ (they are not yellow), and $D3$ (they are not white), by default they must be black.

If we assume that everyone responded to the original race question, then we can infer a person's race using only three variables. Only $k - 1$ dummy variables need to be included, where k equals the number of response categories in the original variable or the total number of dummy variables.

There is no hard and fast rule for choosing the reference category. Researchers often choose the most common or populous group, although any group that's big enough is acceptable.

Interpreting Dummy Variable Coefficients

Interpreting dummy variable coefficients is more complicated than interpreting regular variables. Each coefficient refers to a one-unit increase in that particular variable, with all other variables set to zero. So the coefficient for somebody who is white represents the increased or decreased value of the dependent variable, *relative to the reference group*. This can be tricky, but an example should help to clarify.

Returning to the 1666 data, imagine that we believe that families in which the parents are farmers will be larger than families in which the parents belong to other occupations. We believe

Table 16.6 Using 1901 Race Categories to Illustrate Dummy Variables

	D1	D2	D3	D4
Red	1	0	0	0
Yellow	0	1	0	0
White	0	0	1	0
Black	0	0	0	1

that farmers will have more children because children provide cheap farm labour. To assess this we create a dummy variable 'farmer' (1 = yes, 0 = no), and run the regression. This produces a coefficient with a value of 0.405, which can be interpreted this way: 'Farmers in 1666 could be expected to have an average of 0.405 more children than non-farmers.' Our suspicion is supported.

Every regression output will have a level of statistical significance and a confidence interval for each coefficient. Unless otherwise specified, the 95 per cent confidence interval will be reported by most programs.

A Final Note on OLS Regression

Although a lot has been covered, we have still barely scratched the surface of regression. We have not looked closely at statistical significance, standard errors, confidence intervals, F-statistics, ANOVA, and many other factors that are usually part of a regression analysis. However, most of these topics have been covered elsewhere in the text.

We also have not taken a look at regressions with more than two independent variables, even though these are common. This chapter is only intended to give you a basic understanding of the most basic type of regression.

You'll encounter regression with more than two independent variables in the more advanced statistics courses that you'll (hopefully) take.

PRACTICE QUESTIONS

1. The following table contains data on the number of rooms and monthly rent for 12 houses. Yan wants to know if there is a relationship between the two variables. Help Yan out by answering the following questions:

Number of rooms (X)	Monthly rent (Y)
3 *-0.67 -0.45*	890 *-118.59*
2 *- -0.33 -0.11*	568 *- -203.41*
3 *- 0.67 0.45*	860 *-88.59*
1 *- -1.33 -1.77*	625 *- -146.41*
1 *- -1.33 -1.77*	775 *-3.59*
3 *-0.67 -0.45*	900 *-128.59*
3 *-0.67 -0.45*	1,095 *- 383.59*
3 *-0.67 -0.45*	800 *- 28.59*
2 *- -0.33 -0.11*	765 *- -6.41*
3 *-0.67 -0.45*	629 *- -142.41*
1 *- -1.33 -1.77*	600 *- -171.41*
3 *-0.67 -0.45*	750 *- -21.41*

a. Find the mean for each X and Y variable.

b. Subtract the mean from the value for each observation.

c. Find the sum of squares for X and Y, and the sum of cross-products, using the following equations:

$$SS_X = \sum (X - \overline{X})^2$$

$$SS_Y = \sum (Y - \overline{Y})^2$$

$$SP = \sum (X - \overline{X})(Y - \overline{Y})$$

d. Calculate b (the partial slope):

$$b = \frac{SP}{SS_X}$$

e. Calculate a (the y-intercept):

$$a = \overline{Y} - b\overline{X}$$

f. Calculate r:

$$r = \frac{SP}{\sqrt{SS_X SS_Y}}$$

g. How much does the accuracy of your prediction of the value of the dependent variable increase if you know a person's score on the independent variable?

2. The city of Abbotsford is launching a study to identify the degree to which the number of people sharing a single dwelling affects the cost of utilities. Use the number of people living in a home to predict the amount charged per month.

Number of people (X)	Monthly charge
3	175
2	130
3	231
3	278
2	40
3	205.83
1	0
1	38.41
1	41.23
3	44.2
3	176
3	315

a. Calculate r to measure the association between the two variables above.

b. Calculate the standardized partial slope coefficient using the following equation to calculate the standard deviations of X and Y (this is the equation for standard deviation in a sample):

$$s = \sqrt{\frac{\sum (X - \overline{X})^2}{n - 1}}$$

Answers to the practice questions for chapter 16 can be found on page 193.

CHAPTER 17

Regression 2 — Modelling Discrete/Qualitative Outcomes with Logistic Regression

Learning Objectives

Ordinary least squares regression (OLS) is an excellent technique for multivariate analysis with continuous dependent variables. However, there are many situations where outcomes of interest are *not* continuous. In this chapter we'll cover:

- why OLS might be inappropriate in these instances
- logistic regression, a technique for modelling dichotomous dependent variables

Introduction

Suppose you're trying to figure out what factors determine whether or not a person gets a mortgage, and that you want to know how their earnings affect their chances. Since getting a mortgage is dichotomous—you're either approved, or you're not—you know that there is an upper limit (getting a mortgage) and a lower limit (not getting a mortgage) to your outcome of interest.

If a person earns $1 an hour, they'll probably be rejected for a mortgage (assuming they have no savings to supplement their earnings). Similarly, if they earn $2 an hour, or even $3, their application is still likely to be rejected. The re-lationship between earnings and acceptance is relatively consistent at such low wages. Compare this to a scenario where a person earns $101 an hour. That person is *much* more likely to qualify for a mortgage. A person earning $100 an hour is also likely to qualify, suggesting that the re-lationship between earnings and mortgage is constant here as well. In both cases, we could say that the relationship between earnings and get-ting a mortgage is 'flat'.

Somewhere between these two extremes lies a more direct relationship. For example, earning $18 an hour may be below a critical threshold that $19 an hour is above. Earning that extra dollar that didn't matter much in the extremes could make a big difference here.

Using the ordinary least squares regression will oversimplify the relationship between earnings and getting a mortgage, leading to inaccuracies in certain ranges of the dependent variable. This is because ordinary least squares regression assumes that the same relationship exists between both variables at all ranges, even though this is obviously not the case.

In instances where an assumption of linearity cannot be made there is a family of models that can be used to easily estimate binary outcomes. In this chapter we'll look briefly at logistic regression, one of the simpler and more commonly used techniques. Logistic regression is a counterpart to OLS for binary outcomes.

Logistic Regression: The Idea

Although ordinary least squares regression can be used to estimate a binary outcome, and it is easy to do with all software packages, introducing a dichotomous outcome may violate the assumptions of ordinary least squares. The most significant (and useful for comparing OLS, and logistic regression) are assumptions about the assumed distribution of the dependent variable.[1] For OLS the dependent variable must be continuous, and normally distributed. One of the problems with this assumption for dichotomous outcomes is that OLS coefficients will assume a normal distribution, with theoretical limits of $\pm \infty$ (plus or minus infinity), rather than a bounded or binomial distribution. With logistic regression, a dichotomous outcome variable is assumed from the outset, and coefficients are calculated with this in mind.

Another problem with using OLS regression for dichotomous variables is the assumption of a linear relationship between the outcome and other variables in the model. As the mortgage example demonstrates, this is often not the case. Results from an OLS regression could contain significant error, depending on the value of the independent variables.

Logistic regression solves these problems, and others, because:

1. Independent variables do not have to be linearly related to the dependent variable.
2. Neither the dependent variables nor the error terms need to be normally distributed (the dependent variable *does* need to resemble one of the other distributions, but that is beyond this text).
3. Logistic regression does not assume homoscedasticity in variance across levels of the independent variable.[2]

Logistic Regression: The Formula

Many principles of logistic regression are similar to those of OLS regression, but the language and symbols differ slightly. Logistic coefficients replace b (beta) coefficients, standardized logit coefficients correspond with beta weights, and a pseudo-R^2 statistic is available to summarize the strength of the relationship (although the interpretation is not directly comparable to R^2 in OLS).

Practically speaking, logistic regression and least squares regression are almost identical. Both methods produce prediction equations, both have y-intercepts and coefficients (although raw logistic coefficients are much more difficult to interpret with some translation), and both sets of coefficients measure the predictive capability of independent variables on the outcome of interest.

To recap, OLS regression equations take the following form:

$$Y = a + b_1 x_{1i} + b_2 x_{2i} + \dots + b_n x_{ni} + e_i$$

Where:

- Y = the dependent variable
- a = the Y intercept
- b_1 = the partial slope of X_1 on Y
- b_2 = the partial slope of X_2 on Y
- b_n = the partial slope of X_n on Y
- x_{1i} = the first independent variable for individual i
- x_{2i} = the second independent variable for individual i
- x_{ni} = the nth independent variable for individual i
- e_i = error for individual i

---

[1] At least in theory. Using OLS for dichotomous outcomes is becoming increasingly popular in certain circumstances, particularly when outcome probabilities range between 0.3 and 0.7.

[2] A detailed explanation of what this means is also beyond this text, but in short: independent variables do not need to have equal variances or standard deviation for each value of the dependent variable.

The key differences between logistic regression and OLS are the assumptions about the dependent variable, and the relationship between independent variables and the dependent variable. Instead of predicting the score of Y, an observed variable, logistic regression predicts the *probability* of an occurrence (well, actually, the log odds).

Imagine that beneath the surface of every dichotomous outcome variable is a latent, or underlying, propensity score. This score is unobserved, which means that it is not measured, and that we cannot see it. A score of one on this unobserved propensity variable means that the event will certainly occur (a person will get a mortgage), and zero means that it certainly will not (a person's mortgage application will be rejected). So far the unobserved dependent variable corresponds with the observed dependent variable. Unlike the observed variable, which has only two values (zero and one), the unobserved variable has a range of values that are bounded by zero and one. Most individuals lie between zero and one—there's almost always a slight chance that a person will or will not get a mortgage—and the underlying propensity score is a useful way to understand differences between people.

Logistic regression does not directly predict the probability that our outcome Y is equal to one. Instead, it predicts the *log odds* that an observation will have an indicator equal to one, where the odds of an event is the ratio of the probability that an event occurs to the probability that it will not; often called an **odds ratio**. Stated as an equation:

$$Odds(Y = 1) = \left(\frac{\Pr(Y = 1)}{\Pr(Y \neq 1)}\right)$$

This can be read as 'the odds of Y being equal to one are equal to the probability of a positive occurrence over the probability of a negative occurrence.' Remember that instead of modelling the odds, we model the natural logarithm of the odds. The following equation articulates that:

$$LogOdds(Y = 1) = \ln\left(\frac{\Pr(Y = 1)}{\Pr(Y \neq 1)}\right)$$

You may also see the next equation to represent the log odds, but since exhausted probabilities are always equal to one it is actually identical to the last one:

$$LogOdds(Y = 1) = \ln\left(\frac{\Pr(Y = 1)}{1 - \Pr(Y = 1)}\right)$$

The dependent variable is also referred to as the logit. Unlike OLS coefficients, which measure the effect of a one-increment change in the independent variable on the dependent variable, logistic coefficients reflect the effect of a one-increment change in the dependent variable on the *log odds* of the dependent variable.

Why use the odds instead of the probabilities? Sociologist Paul Allison (2000) describes odds as a more sensible scale for multiplicative comparisons. He illustrates using voting as an example; if person one has a probability of 0.30 of voting, and person two has a probability of 0.60, it's reasonable to claim that the probability of person two voting is twice as high as it is for person one. But a probability that is twice as high as 0.60 is impossible, due to the ceiling of one (the event definitely will occur) for the probability of an event.

Allison notes that this is not a problem on the odds scale, since a probability of 0.60 is equivalent to the odds of 1.5:

$$odds = \frac{\Pr(y = 1)}{1 - \Pr(y = 1)}$$
$$= \frac{0.60}{1 - 0.60}$$
$$= 1.5$$

So we could say that one person is 1.5 times more likely to vote than the other person.

You are probably familiar with odds, especially if you've gambled or bought lottery tickets. In one well-known Canadian lottery example, six numbers must be matched in order for a ticket to win the jackpot. The odds of this occurring depend on the 13,983,816 possible combinations that exist between the six numbers. The odds of winning are 1 in 13,983,816, or 0.0000000715 to 1 (most people will use the first expression since they prefer integers, but however you express it, winning is unlikely). To convert the number to a probability, use the following equation; the inverse of the equation for converting probabilities to odds is:

$$probability = \frac{Odds(y = 1)}{1 + Odds(y = 1)}$$
$$= \frac{0.0000000715}{1 + 0.0000000715}$$
$$= 0.000000143$$

Hopefully you can see that using the odds instead of probabilities makes it easier to grasp how unlikely your prospects of winning are.

Converting the probability to the odds removes the upper bound of the dependent variable (it is no longer constrained by the value of one). Now only the lower value is constrained at zero, which can be addressed by using the log odds instead of the odds.

To illustrate, compare the three values in table 17.1.

Several points on the table are noteworthy. First, notice how a probability of 0.5 (where an event is just as likely to occur as it is to not occur) corresponds with an odds ratio of one. Odds lie between zero and +∞, with one as a neutral value at which both outcomes are equally likely (which is why it corresponds with a probability of 0.5). Second, when the roles of the two outcomes are switched with odds, each value in the range zero to one is transformed by taking its inverse (one/value) to a value in the range one to +∞. For example, if the odds of getting some form of cancer

for males are one in nine, the odds of not getting cancer are nine to one.

On the other hand, log odds are completely symmetrical, and lie in the range of -∞ to +∞. The value where both outcomes are equally likely is zero, (this might be considered the 'neutral value'). When the roles of the two outcomes are switched, the log odds are multiplied by –1, but the number remains the same. So if the log odds of getting some form of cancer for males are 2.20, the odds of not getting it are –0.220.

To illustrate how the log odds remove the upper and lower bounds, look at probability values of 0.01 and 0.99, the two extreme values. Although they are close to their theoretical limits of zero and one, it is possible to get much, much closer. We could have values of, say, 0.000000001 and 0.999999999, which would yield a log odds ratio of ±20.72. Although the increases would get smaller, it is possible to approach zero and one even more closely, so we give the log odds a range of -∞ to +∞.

As a further illustration, consider the bar charts of the distribution of a variable with propensity scores ranging between zero and one on 1,000 observations, found in figures 17.1–17.3. Figure 17.1 contains the probability scores.

As you can see, variables are scattered almost evenly across the range, and the chart does not resemble a normal distribution. Instead, it is heavily bounded by zero and one, and given that OLS models with an assumption of ± ∞, you can

Table 17.1 Probabilities Compared to Odds and Log Odds

Probability	Odds	Log odds
0.01	0.01	-4.60
0.05	0.05	-2.94
0.10	0.11	-2.20
0.15	0.18	-1.73
0.20	0.25	-1.39
0.30	0.43	-0.85
0.40	0.67	-0.41
0.50	1.00	0.00
0.60	1.50	0.41
0.70	2.33	0.85
0.80	4.00	1.39
0.85	5.67	1.73
0.90	9.00	2.20
0.95	19.00	2.94
0.99	99.00	4.60

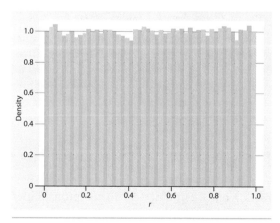

Figure 17.1 Plot of Hypothetical Variable *r*, Stated as a Probability

see that there will be estimation error. Let's compare this with a plot of the odds in figure 17.2.

Figure 17.2 is better in a way, because the constraint of an upper bound has been removed. The problem is that it still does not look like a normal distribution, so significant estimation error is still likely. Finally, compare this to the log odds in figure 17.3.

Figure 17.3 is almost a perfectly normally distributed variable. By now you should agree that the log odds ratio of a dichotomous variable is the best option for a dependent variable.

Modelling Logistic Regression

Thanks to log odds, the theoretical upper and lower bounds have been removed, and the similarities to OLS are now more obvious. Modelling the log odds of Y, instead of Y, produces a fairly familiar-looking equation:

$$LogOdds(Y = 1) = a + b_1x_{1i} + b_2x_{2i} + ... + b_nx_{ni} + e_i$$

Where:

- $LogOdds (Y = 1)$ is the natural logarithm of the odds of the dependent variable being one.
- a = the Y intercept
- b_1 = the partial slope of X_1 on Y
- b_2 = the partial slope of X_2 on Y
- b_n = the partial slope of X_n on Y
- x_{1i} = the first independent variable for individual i
- x_{2i} = the second independent variable for individual i
- x_{ni} = the nth independent variable for individual i
- e_i = error for individual i

To further illustrate logistic regression, let's look at an example. Suppose that we use the Ethnic Diversity Survey to fit a logistic regression equation that identifies the degree to which a person feels a strong sense of belonging in Canada, where Y = 1 if a person experiences a strong sense of belonging and 0 if they don't. We use sex of respondent ('female', where 1 = female, 0 = male) and place of birth ('Canada', where 1 = Canada, 0 = other country) as our two independent variables, producing the following predictive equation:

$$\text{log odds } (Y = 1) = \alpha + \text{female} + \text{Canada}$$

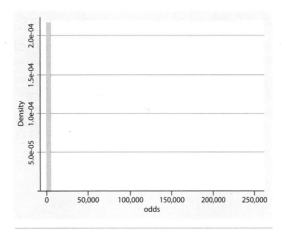

Figure 17.2 Plot of Hypothetical Variable r, Stated as Odds Ratios

or

$$\text{log [Pr(belong)/Pr(not belong)]} = \alpha + \text{female} + \text{Canada}$$

Estimating the equation in Stata gives us the results found in table 17.2.

The interpretation of log coefficients is different from those of OLS regression. We can determine the direction of the relationship by looking at the sign of the coefficients. Since the coefficient for both female and Canada is positive, the log odds (and, therefore, the probability) of belonging is higher for females and those born in Canada (but notice that the second result is not statistically significant).

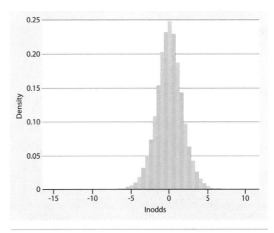

Figure 17.3 Plot of Hypothetical Variable r, Stated as Log Odds Ratios

Table 17.2   Gender and Place of Birth as Predictors of Belonging, Stated as Raw Coefficients

```
. logit belong female canada

Iteration 0:   log likelihood = -28161.371
Iteration 1:   log likelihood = -28128.081
Iteration 2:   log likelihood = -28128.079

Logistic regression                          Number of obs   =      41695
                                             LR chi2(2)      =      66.58
                                             Prob > chi2     =     0.0000
Log likelihood = -28128.079                  Pseudo R2       =     0.0012

------------------------------------------------------------------------------
      belong |     Coef.   Std. Err.      z    P>|z|     [95% Conf. Interval]
-------------+----------------------------------------------------------------
      female |   .1600882   .0199796    8.01   0.000     .120929    .1992474
      canada |   .0337001   .0225676    1.49   0.135    -.0105316   .0779318
       _cons |   .2711552   .0219193   12.37   0.000     .2281941   .3141163
------------------------------------------------------------------------------
```

Interpreting the Coefficients of a Logistic Regression Equation

To get a better sense of the magnitude of difference, and to make interpretation of the coefficients easier, we can exponentiate the results. Remember from chapter 2 that exponentiation is the inverse function of the logarithm, so the log odds will be changed into the odds. This can be done using e, which is the inverse of the natural logarithm. The equation from the last example:

$$\log [Pr(belong)/Pr(not\ belong)] = \alpha + female + Canada$$

becomes

$$Pr(belong)/Pr(not\ belong) = \exp(\alpha + female + Canada)$$

Or, once the coefficients from the output are inserted:

$$\log [Pr(belong)/Pr(not\ belong)] = \alpha + 0.160 * female + 0.034 * Canada$$

becomes

$$[Pr(belong)/Pr(not\ belong)] = \exp(\alpha + 0.160 * female + 0.034 * Canada)$$

Alternatively, it could also be listed as:

$$Pr(belong = 1) = \exp(\alpha + 0.160 * female + 0.034 * Canada) / [1 + \exp(\alpha + 0.160 * female + 0.034 * Canada)]$$

This final example is just a more cumbersome form of the same equation.

Exponentiating the coefficients will give the odds ratio, which corresponds with a one-unit change in each independent variable. For example, we could convert the coefficient of 0.160 for female as:

$$Odds\ ratio_{female} = e^{0.160}$$
$$= 1.174$$

For 'Canada', we'd have:

$$Odds\ ratio_{Canada} = e^{0.034}$$
$$= 1.035$$

Thus, the odds of a female feeling a sense of belonging is 1.174 times that of a male. Stated differently, a female is about 17 per cent more likely to feel a sense of belonging to Canada than a male.

For the variable 'Canada', those born in the country are 1.035 times, or 3.5 per cent, more likely than those born elsewhere to feel a sense of belonging. Notice that we cannot be 95 per cent confident that this result exists in the Canadian population, given the low z-score of 1.49, and the corresponding significance (denoted in the output by the column P>|z|) of 0.135.

With odds ratios, we don't usually convert the intercept, because there isn't really a comparable reference group. For females the odds ratio of 1.174 is the likelihood of females to feel a sense of belonging relative to males, and for Canada, 1.035 compares people born in Canada to those born outside of Canada. The intercept simply denotes the point where the regression line crosses the y-axis, and there isn't any reason to state that as an odds ratio.

To convince you of the accuracy of our calculation of the odds ratios, let's compare them with the same odds calculated using Stata (see table 17.3).

In most software packages there is an option to report the odds instead of the log odds (also referred to as the raw coefficients). Our calculations are identical to those produced in Stata. Also notice that the intercept is not reported.

As with OLS, logistic regression is far more intricate and complicated than the cursory overview provided here. The primary purpose of this chapter was to enhance your awareness, and to provide some very basic information on a frequently used technique.

A Note on Estimating Logistic Regressions

In OLS regression, a regression line is calculated with the explicit goal of minimizing the average distance between an observed value and a predicted value. This is done through a series of calculations, which we covered in chapter 12. Unlike OLS, the coefficient estimates of a logistic regression are obtained through an iterative and complicated process called 'maximum likelihood'. For many social scientists, the intricacies of maximum likelihood are treated like a 'black box', which means that we don't know or question how the results are obtained. Maximum likelihood is a very complicated procedure (and there are no truly gentle introductions to the topic that I'm aware of), so we will limit our discussion of it.

The goal of most statistical analysis is to produce a model that predicts our outcome of interest as often and/or accurately as possible. For our sense of belonging example above, we want

Table 17.3   Gender and Place of Birth as Predictors of Belonging, Stated as Odds Ratios

```
logit belong female canada, or

Iteration 0:    log likelihood = -28161.371
Iteration 1:    log likelihood = -28128.081
Iteration 2:    log likelihood = -28128.079

Logistic regression                           Number of obs    =      41695
                                              LR chi2(2)       =      66.58
                                              Prob > chi2      =     0.0000
Log likelihood = -28128.079                   Pseudo R2        =     0.0012

-------------------------------------------------------------------------
     belong | Odds Ratio   Std. Err.      z    P>|z|    [95% Conf. Interval]
------------+------------------------------------------------------------
     female |   1.173614   .0234483     8.01   0.000    1.128545    1.220484
     canada |   1.034274   .0233411     1.49   0.135    .9895236    1.081049
-------------------------------------------------------------------------
```

intercept 'female' and 'Canada' coefficient values that predict whether a person feels belonging as accurately as possible (that is, where there are as few misses as possible).

Maximum likelihood works by fitting a 'trial equation' to the data (often an OLS equation), and comparing the fitted equation to the observed values. 'Fitting' an equation means deriving coefficient estimates. The first equation probably won't maximize the likelihood that we could replicate the results observed in our data set, since the OLS coefficients are likely inaccurate, so the coefficient estimates are tweaked over and over in order to improve the fit. Iterations stop when the improvement from one step to the next is suitably small, suggesting that the likelihood of replicating the results observed in our data set has been maximized.

Maximum likelihood is widely used in statistical analysis, and is not limited to logistic regression alone. In fact, maximum likelihood is so flexible that it is possible to estimate an OLS regression using maximum likelihood techniques. However, most of the software packages recommend against that since standard OLS techniques allow for greater flexibility.

PRACTICE QUESTIONS

1. Convert the following logistic regression coefficients to odds ratios.

   a. –1.113   b. 0.223   c. 2.78   d. 0   e. –2.33   f. –7.8

   Answers to the practice questions for chapter 17 can be found on page 195.

PART FOUR

Advanced Topics

Regression Diagnostics

Learning Objectives

Although regression (both OLS and logistic) is a fairly straightforward technique (especially with a computer), numerous hard-to-detect problems can arise in the data. This chapter will cover a few simple diagnostic techniques for regression, focusing in particular on the techniques for ordinary least squares (OLS) regression. We'll discuss:

- influential and outlying cases
- leverage
- non-normality in the error term
- collinearity/multicollinearity

Introduction

Suppose you ran an OLS regression to estimate the factors that determine a person's blood pressure, using the variables of body mass index, calories consumed per day, and whether a person drinks or smokes (both of these are dummy variables). You might get sensible coefficient estimates for the slope and the intercept, calculations for Pearson's r, standard errors, and just about everything else, but there could still be a problem with your model. How can that be?

The problem might be with how your summary measures—essentially, what the various components of a regression are—represent the data. The model you've estimated may be a bad summarization of the relationship between a series of independent variables and your dependent variable.

This chapter will cover how this happens and, more importantly, what can be done about it.

When Ordinary Least Squares Regression Goes Wrong

In a 1973 article, Francis Anscombe demonstrated how it was possible to have similar coefficients, correlations, standard errors—just about everything between regressions—with very different data points.[1] To illustrate how that's possible, consider his original example in table 18.1.

In an article in *The American Statistician*, Anscombe demonstrated how it is possible to get identical univariate statistics (means, standard deviations) between *x* variables (*x*, *x*4) and *y*-variables (*y*1, *y*2, *y*3, *y*4), as well as bivariate correlations (R^2), mean squared errors, sums of squares, etc. For our purposes the most important revelation is that regression intercepts and coefficients are the same, even though each set of data points looks radically different when they are graphed on a scatterplot.

To illustrate this better, we'll continue with Anscombe's original example using four regressions and scatterplots for the data in table 18.1 (these four plots are sometimes referred to as the 'Anscombe Quartet'). In each figure, the regression output appears first, followed by the scatterplot. (See figures 18.1 to 18.4)

In each example, the regression results are identical. This means that the line of best fit is the same in each case, even though the observations

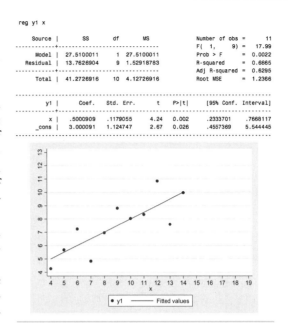

Figure 18.1 Anscombe's Original Demonstration of the Need for Regression Diagnostics, Data Example #1

have different values. In figure 18.1 the relationship between the independent variables appears straightforward and relatively linear, with what appears to be randomly distributed errors. How-

Table 18.1 Anscombe's Original 1973 Data for Illustrating Regression Diagnostics

x	y1	y2	y3	x4	y4
10.00	8.04	9.14	7.46	8.00	6.58
8.00	6.95	8.14	6.77	8.00	5.76
13.00	7.58	8.74	12.74	8.00	7.71
9.00	8.81	8.77	7.11	8.00	8.84
11.00	8.33	9.26	7.81	8.00	8.47
14.00	9.96	8.10	8.84	8.00	7.04
6.00	7.24	6.13	6.08	8.00	5.25
4.00	4.26	3.10	5.39	19.00	12.50
12.00	10.84	9.13	8.15	8.00	5.56
7.00	4.82	7.26	6.42	8.00	7.91
5.00	5.68	4.74	5.73	8.00	6.89

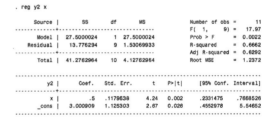

---

[1] In 1973 Anscombe was arguing for the importance of graphing raw data alongside regression analysis. As it happens, his example also beautifully illustrates the need for diagnostics.

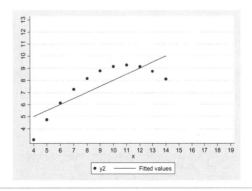

Figure 18.2 Anscombe's Original Demonstration of the Need for Regression Diagnostics, Data Example #2

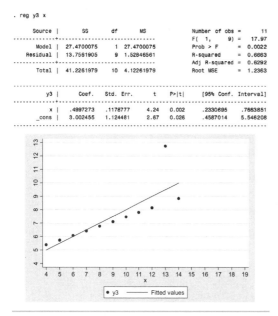

```
. reg y3 x

      Source |       SS       df       MS              Number of obs =      11
-------------+------------------------------           F(  1,     9) =   17.97
       Model |  27.4700075       1  27.4700075         Prob > F      =  0.0022
    Residual |  13.7561905       9  1.52846561         R-squared     =  0.6663
-------------+------------------------------           Adj R-squared =  0.6292
       Total |  41.2261979      10  4.12261979         Root MSE      =  1.2363

-------------------------------------------------------------------------------
         y3 |      Coef.   Std. Err.      t    P>|t|     [95% Conf. Interval]
-------------+-----------------------------------------------------------------
          x |   .4997273   .1178777     4.24   0.002     .2330695    .7663851
      _cons |   3.002455   1.124481     2.67   0.026     .4587014    5.546208
-------------------------------------------------------------------------------
```

Figure 18.3   Anscombe's Original Demonstration of the Need for Regression Diagnostics, Data Example #3

ever, figures 18.2–18.4 have very different relationships between the *x* and *y* variables.

As a statistical issue, the similarity between regressions is problematic because it glosses over the obvious differences in the data. With-

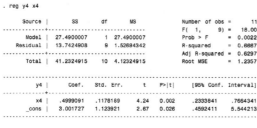

```
. reg y4 x4

      Source |       SS       df       MS              Number of obs =      11
-------------+------------------------------           F(  1,     9) =   18.00
       Model |  27.4900007       1  27.4900007         Prob > F      =  0.0022
    Residual |  13.7424908       9  1.52694342         R-squared     =  0.6667
-------------+------------------------------           Adj R-squared =  0.6297
       Total |  41.2324915      10  4.12324915         Root MSE      =  1.2357

-------------------------------------------------------------------------------
         y4 |      Coef.   Std. Err.      t    P>|t|     [95% Conf. Interval]
-------------+-----------------------------------------------------------------
         x4 |   .4999091   .1178169     4.24   0.002     .2333641    .7664341
      _cons |   3.001727   1.123921     2.67   0.026     .4592411    5.544213
-------------------------------------------------------------------------------
```

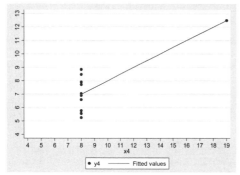

Figure 18.4   Anscombe's Original Demonstration of the Need for Regression Diagnostics, Data Example #4

out looking at the plots, we might conclude that each example does an equally good job of summarizing the nature of the relationship.

The scatterplots reveal something else. Ideally, we'd draw scatterplots whenever possible, but large samples make visualizing relationships increasingly difficult. Consider the plot of age of respondent and age of their spouse found in the 1666 census in figure 18.5.

With large samples, identify differences in relationships just by looking at visual data is difficult. We need to develop a set of tools to identify situations like the one in figure 18.5. In the following sections we'll cover some of the more common sources of error in regression specification. This usually involves examining the estimation error (also called a residual) to understand how well a regression approximates the observed relationship.

Influential Cases

By now you probably know that there are several factors that affect how well a line of best fit describes the relationship between a dependent variable and its independent variables. One factor is the assumption that there are no observations eliciting an inordinate impact on the calculation of regression coefficients. For example, the observation with an *x*-value of 19 and a *y*-value of 13.5 in figure 18.4 appears to have a greater effect on the calculation of the line of best fit than the other observations do. If that observation wasn't there the line would probably have a different slope and intercept.

These observations are called influential cases. Although 'influential case' has no firm defini-

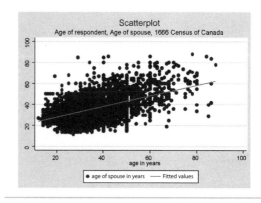

Figure 18.5   Age of Respondent, Age of Spouse, 1666 Census of Canada

tion, it is any case that exerts an extraordinary amount of influence on the slope and intercept. There are two types of influential cases: outliers and leveraged observations. An outlier refers to the distance an observation is from its estimated y-value (the distance between Y_i and $\hat{Y}$), leverage measures the distance between an x-value and the mean for that variable (the gap between X_i and $\hat{X}$). Both can have a big impact on the representativeness of the regression coefficients.

To detect an influential case (either an outlier or a leveraged case), find the point where an observation begins to influence the regression results to an 'unusual' degree. This can be guided by the nature of the study (for example, if we're studying housing and income, and we believe that the 15-year-old who earns $100,000 a year and owns a home is exceptional), or they can be identified statistically. There are many different ways to do this, but we're going to use Cook's Distance.

Cook's Distance
Introduced in the late 1970s by Dennis Cook, Cook's Distance, or Cook's D, determines the extent to which coefficient estimates (both slopes and intercepts) will change if a particular observation is removed from the analysis. To demonstrate, we'll work through one of Anscombe's original examples, relying on Lorenz's 1987 discussion of Cook's D (Lorenz, 1987).

First, obtain the predicted and residual values for each observation you're interested in determining the influence for. To help with that, figure 18.3 is reproduced as figure 18.6.

A good example of an influential observation would be the one with the highest y-value ($Y =$

12.74, $X = 13$). To get a sense of how much this observation influences the coefficients, calculate the predicted Y-value for observation i as:

$$\hat{Y}_i = ax_i + b$$
$$= 0.5(13) + 3$$
$$= 6.5 + 3$$
$$= 9.5$$

The error is calculated as:

$$e_i = Y_i - \hat{Y}_i$$
$$= 12.74 - 9.5$$
$$= 3.24$$

Next, determine the amount of influence an observation could have on the results by determining the distance of an average observation from the line of best fit. When X_i is far away from $\overline{X}$ (it is either a really high or a really low value), we say that it has a lot of leverage. To calculate leverage, use the formula:

$$h_{ii} = \left[\frac{1}{n} + \frac{(X_i - \overline{X})^2}{\Sigma(X_i - \overline{X})^2} \right]$$
$$= \left[\frac{1}{11} + \frac{(13 - 9)^2}{110} \right]$$
$$= 0.236$$

In both the numerator and the denominator the differences are squared so that the sum of values does not equal zero.

Finally, we calculate Cook's Distance as:

$$D_i = \frac{e_i^2}{p(MSE)} \left[\frac{h_{ii}}{(1 - h_{ii})^2} \right]$$
$$= \frac{3.24^2}{2(1.53)} \left[\frac{0.236}{(1 - 0.236)^2} \right]$$
$$= \frac{10.498}{3.06} \left[\frac{0.236}{0.584} \right]$$
$$= 4.431 * 0.404$$
$$= 1.386$$

Where:
- e_i = estimation error (calculated above)
- h_{ii} = The leverage of data point X_i. This refers to the ability of a particular data point to affect slope and intercept coefficients. High leverage denotes a strong capacity; low leverage denotes the opposite.
- MSE = Mean Squared Error

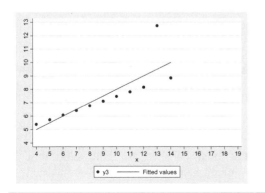

Figure 18.6 Anscombe's Original Demonstration of the Need for Regression Diagnostics, Data Example #3

- P = the number of parameters (coefficients) being estimated. For us, it is two because there is a single slope coefficient and an intercept

Cook's distance values are meaningless by themselves, but any value below one is regarded as being tolerable for influence. Any observation that has a value exceeding one (such as the calculation for figure 18.6) should be examined closely, and possibly deleted. The farther from one a Cook's D value is, the stronger the case for deleting a particular observation.

Homoscedasticity

Homoscedasticity is the distribution of estimation errors across x-values. A regression is considered homoscedastic if the standard deviation of the estimation error for each value of x is roughly similar. If that condition is not met (we want it to be), the model is heteroscedastic. Suppose you had an independent variable with 10 response categories; having a similar error variance across each response category would be important.

A real-life example is the relationship between total income and disposable income. If you wanted to determine whether people with large incomes have more or less disposable income, you could run an OLS regression, treating total income as the dependent variable, and disposable income as the independent variable. Most programs will estimate this model easily, even though the error variances are likely to be heteroscedastic. To demonstrate, think of how much more disposable income a person earning $100,000 could have compared to someone who earns $1,000. There is greater potential for us to 'miss' with our estimate for the $100,000 earner than there is for the $1,000 earner, suggesting that the error variance will not be consistent across all values of x.

When the condition of homoscedasticity is not met for a particular variable, the accuracy of that coefficient can be questioned. Heteroscedasticity is complicated, and often requires the use of different statistical models (such as weighted least-squares or heteroscedastic standard error) or for variables to be transformed using a power transformation (particularly a logarithmic transformation). These can quickly become complicated so we'll only focus on identifying heteroscedasticity.

The easiest way to detect heteroscedasticity is probably to look at a residual versus fitted value plot. To do that, use your statistical software to predict values for each observation, and plot the disparity across values of the independent variable. Figure 18.7 is an example conducted in Stata.

 BOX 18.1 THE STEPS: COOK'S DISTANCE

1. Obtain the predicted and residual y-values for each observation, using $\hat{Y}_i = ax_i + b$ to find $\hat{Y}_i$ and $e_i = Y_i - \hat{Y}_i$ to find the estimation error.

2. Calculate the leverage of each observation using the following formula:

$$h_{ii} = \left[\frac{1}{n} + \frac{(X_i - \overline{X})^2}{\Sigma(X_i - \overline{X})^2} \right]$$

3. Calculate Cook's Distance as

$$D_i = \frac{e_i^2}{p(MSE)} \left[\frac{h_{ii}}{(1 - h_{ii})^2} \right]$$

4. Treat Cook's D values that exceed one with caution; seriously consider dropping values that greatly exceed one.

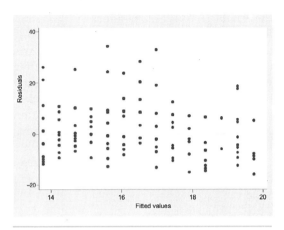

Figure 18.7 Heteroscedastic Data in the Canadian Community Health Survey

The plot shows the residuals from a model using the age of an individual to estimate the number of cigarettes that individual smokes per day. We can expect there to be wide variation at younger ages because, although there is likely to be some heavy smokers across all ranges, there is likely to be more casual smokers among young people, leading to the expectation of heteroscedasticity.

Although the full model includes all Canadians, to reduce the number of data points only women living in Prince Edward Island are plotted in figure 18.7. Notice how the dispersion of residual values (the *y*-axis) is not consistent across the fitted values (the *x*-axis). This suggests that there is greater variance at certain values of the independent variable than others. The variance gets smaller as age increases, which suggests that there is less variation in the number of cigarettes a person smokes as they age.

There are numerous statistical tests for heteroscedasticity (White's test, Bartlett's test, etc.); most are available in major statistical packages, but they go beyond what is appropriate for an introductory statistics course.

Collinearity (a.k.a. Multicollinearity)

To illustrate collinearity, let's continue with the example from the introduction; identifying the factors that affect a person's blood pressure. Suppose we suspect that there is a correlation between body mass index and calories consumed per day, two of our independent variables. If there

was a perfect bivariate correlation between those two variables, how might that affect our regression coefficient estimates? First, including both variables as predictors is unnecessary because the information in one variable (calories consumed per day) can be used to perfectly predict a score on the other variable (BMI), and vice versa. The variables are essentially duplicates of one another.

Remember that for an ordinary least-squares regression, coefficients represent the independent impact on the dependent variable of a one-unit increase in the independent variable of interest. Collinearity is important because the coefficients are calculated when all other independent variables are held to zero. When collinearity is strong, identifying the independent impact of BMI will be difficult, because whenever variable *A* is increased by one increment, so is the number of calories consumed. Finding the independent impact of either variable is virtually impossible because they are so intertwined.

Most of the time there is not perfect collinearity between two variables. What happens instead is a more moderate correlation, for example a Pearson's *r* value of 0.9. This can still be problematic since collinearity doesn't need to be between just two variables to be a problem. Correlation between one variable and several others also poses a problem in the regression because collinearity is calculated across all independent variables.

Identifying and Dealing with Multicollinearity

The easiest way to identify multicollinearity is probably to look at the variance inflation factor (VIF) for each variable. The VIF is a standardized version of Pearson's multiple correlation coefficient R^2. The equation for VIF is:

$$VIF_{X1} = \frac{1}{1 - R_{X1}^2}$$

Where R_{X1}^2 is equal to the multiple correlation coefficient from a regression of variable $X1$ on all other independent variables in a model. This suggests that each variable will have its own VIF value, because it will be the 'dependent variable' in a model, with all other independent variables used as predictors. With a little thought, using a version of R^2 makes sense. Multicollinearity is expected, since it refers to how a particular variable is correlated with all other variables in a model—precisely what R^2 allows us to measure. The lowest value of VIF will be one (this would correspond to an R^2 value of zero), and the highest value is positive infinity $(+\infty)$.

Although there is no clear consensus on what value of VIF points to multicollinearity, typically a conservative value of five or higher is deemed too high. However, a value of ten is more commonly used. Variables with values that exceed four are generally worthy of further investigation.

However you define multicollinearity, once you determine that your variables are too closely correlated, you have several options. The first one, dropping the problem variable, is the easiest, and will immediately solve multicollinearity. The second option is more difficult; combining the two offending variables to form one composite measure. However, this method might not make sense in every situation, so you will want to consider transforming one or both of the variables. You could conduct a power transformation (such as exponentiating, or taking the logarithm of one of the variables), or you could means-centre your variable by resetting your variable so that the mean is set to zero, and observations are measured by how they deviate from the new mean. Whichever transformation you choose, always use the transformed variable (rather than the old collinear one), and try to anticipate how the transformation may have changed the interpretation of your coefficients.

Conclusion

This chapter covered some of the diagnostic tools for identifying whether regression results are plausible and valid. As noted in the introduction, this is only a preliminary overview. There are entire courses dedicated to regression diagnostics. The aim of this chapter was to enhance your appreciation of the complexity of ordinary least-squares regression.

PRACTICE QUESTIONS

1. Here are Anscombe's fabricated data:

x	$y1$	$y2$	$y3$	$x4$	$y4$
10.00	8.04	9.14	7.46	8.00	6.58
8.00	6.95	8.14	6.77	8.00	5.76
13.00	7.58	8.74	12.74	8.00	7.71
9.00	8.81	8.77	7.11	8.00	8.84
11.00	8.33	9.26	7.81	8.00	8.47
14.00	9.96	8.10	8.84	8.00	7.04
6.00	7.24	6.13	6.08	8.00	5.25
4.00	4.26	3.10	5.39	19.00	12.50
12.00	10.84	9.13	8.15	8.00	5.56
7.00	4.82	7.26	6.42	8.00	7.91
5.00	5.68	4.74	5.73	8.00	6.89

Calculate the means and standard deviation for all of the variables. When calculating the standard deviation, treat the observations as sample data (use $N - 1$ instead of N in your calculations).

2. The data point located at x-value = 1,000 and y-value = 500 could be considered an outlier. If this point didn't exist, what would happen to the slope (would it be higher or lower) and intercept (would it cross the y-axis at a higher or lower point)?

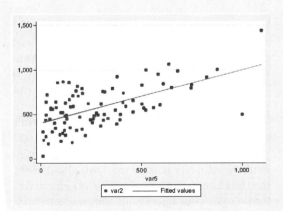

3. Consider the following data that were slightly modified from Anscombe's original:

x	$y1$
10.00	8.04
8.00	6.95
13.00	7.58
9.00	8.81
11.00	8.33
14.00	9.96
6.00	7.24
4.00	4.26
12.00	10.84
7.00	4.82
25.00	5.68

Here is some additional information:

- the means for x and $y1$ are 10.82 and 7.5, respectively
- the mean squared error (MSE) is 4.464
- the slope value is 0.0593 and the intercept value is 6.860

Calculate Cook's Distance for the 11th observation.

Answers to the practice questions for chapter 18 can be found on page 195.

Strategies for Dealing with Missing Data

Learning Objectives

Researchers often have to deal with **missing data**, or observations that do not have information on all variables. Chapter 19 examines some of the strategies for dealing with incomplete data, including:

- non-response and its impact on validity
- four kinds of missing data
- single imputation of missing data
- multiple imputation of missing data

Introduction

Paul Allison begins his monograph on missing data by stating '[s]ooner or later (usually sooner), anyone who does statistical analysis runs into problems with missing data' (2000, 1). Allison goes on to tell us that when practitioners are faced with these problems they must make several decisions that inevitably impact the conclusions that are made from the data.

There are three types of missing data in social surveys: household non-response, person non-response, and item non-response. Household non-response occurs when an entire household does not complete a questionnaire. This happens for various reasons, such as people not being at home, or being unwilling or unable to participate in the survey. Household non-response is difficult to deal with since there is no information whatsoever available.

Person non-response occurs when an interview is obtained from at least one household member, but not from one or more others in that household. Like household non-response, person non-response is the result of a person being unwilling, unable, or unavailable to answer survey questions. Person non-response is dealt with through editing and imputation of values.

Item non-response occurs when a respondent completes only part of a questionnaire, leaving blanks for some information. Item non-response can occur for many reasons, including:

1. A respondent refuses, or is unable, to provide requested information.
2. A respondent does not identify with any of the response categories and chooses to leave the question blank.
3. An interviewer fails to ask a question or an answer.
4. An interviewer makes an error when recording, or keying in, the response.

Since household and person non-response are usually handled by methodologists (which means that by the time you see a data set the data will have been cleaned up), in this chapter we'll look at item non-response, first by looking at the effects of non-response, and then we'll look at the four major types of missing data. Finally, we'll discuss common methods of dealing with these types of missing data.

What Effect Does Non-response Bias Have?

Non-response can have serious statistical consequences. In cases where an explanatory variable contains bias, consider the simple regression equation:

$$Y_i = \alpha + \beta_1 X_i + e_i \qquad (1)$$

Where

- Y_i = some dependent variable
- α = constant term
- β_1 = coefficient for X_i
- e_i = error term
- X_i = explanatory variable with coefficient β

If instead of X_i we observe $X^*_i + u_i$ (implying that $X_i = X^*_i + u_i$), where u_i = measurement error due to non-random non-response, our new equation above would need to be modified accordingly:

$$Y_i = \alpha + \beta_1(X_i + u_i) + e_i \qquad (2)$$

Notice that there are now two error terms, e_i and u_i, which can be simplified to form the compound error term z_i. One of the postulates of OLS regression—that error terms are uncorrelated with explanatory variables—has been violated with the introduction of non-response.

As a further illustration, consider a simple cross-sectional OLS equation with only one predictor variable, X, the average income of an individual, and one outcome, Y, the amount of money invested on the stock market per year (see figure 19.1). Line one demonstrates the linear relationship between those two variables. However, there are problems with missing data: although the sample was randomly drawn, people with lower income levels were less likely to report their income. Therefore, lower income earners are underrepresented, pulling line one upward at lower income amounts (see the curved line in the diagram). If we were to redraw the line of best fit, line two would replace line one as the best fitting line.

Clearly, validity—or the extent to which a variable is measuring what it is supposed to measure—has been compromised. The X variable, which allegedly measures respondent income, is no longer valid since it is doesn't measure what it purports to, which can be seen in the new line of best fit.

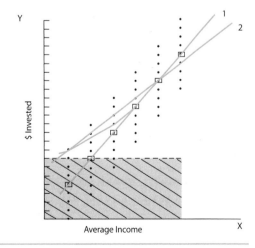

Figure 19.1 How Non-random Missing Data Affects Regression Estimates

Source: Berk, 1983

The Four Forms of Missing Data[1]

To motivate the discussion, suppose that we have a very simple regression equation, denoted as:

$$Y_i = \alpha + \beta_1 X1_i + \beta_2 X2_i + e_i \qquad (3)$$

Where Y = school average grade of a child in the last school year, $X1$ = mother tongue of the Person Most Knowledgeable (PMK) of the respondent, and $X2$ = income of PMK for the previous year. $X1$ and $X2$ are somewhat (though not completely) correlated with one another, and e is an error term. $X2$, the income of PMK for the previous year, is a problematic variable where some of the values are missing for reasons unknown. We could assume at least four possible reasons for the missing values (Little and Rubin, 1987):

1. $X2$ is Missing Completely at Random (MCAR), meaning the non-response on this question is entirely independent of patterns in either Y or $X1$ (we say that the reason for 'missingness' is contained in the error term e).
2. $X2$ is Missing at Random (MAR) but dependent on explanatory variable $X1$, so with certain values of $X1$ (such as mother tongue is neither French nor English), $X2$ is more likely to be missing.
3. $X2$ is Missing at Random but dependent on the focal outcome, and certain values of Y (e.g., if average grade is below 65 per cent) increase the probability that $X2$ will be missing.
4. Non-ignorable Missing value (NIM): $X2$ is often missing when it is a certain value (e.g., income < \$10,000).

Each of these four types of missing data is a non-response with different underlying causes, and all will have a different effect on coefficient estimates if left unaddressed. MCAR (#1) is unlikely to have any effect at all, MAR is likely to result in underestimated estimates of parameter $X1 + X2$ (for #2) or $X1 + Y$ (for #3), and NIM (#4) is likely to result in a biased estimated relationship between income and average grades—low income

parents with high aspirations for their children would be underrepresented in the analysis.

The next section deals with various missing data imputation methods. Due to space considerations, weighting is omitted. **Weights** are usually invoked to correct for household or person non-response, but not item non-response.

What to Do about Missing Data?

Missing data can be dealt with in several ways. Some are very simple, and others require a solid grasp of statistical theory and practice.

1. Do Nothing: List-Wise and Pair-Wise Deletion

List-wise deletion: delete all observations with missing data. In the previous example, anyone who didn't report their income was removed from the study.

Pair-wise deletion (or available case analysis): pair-wise deletions involve using all available data to compute these means. For example, when creating a covariance matrix for two variables, only valid values are used. In a regression equation, observations with missing values will still contribute to coefficient estimates, so the observations with missing $X1$ or $X2$ values will still be included in some calculations. For example, observations with missing $X1$ values would be included when calculating the coefficient for $X2$. The impact of missing data is slightly lower with pair-wise deletion than with list-wise deletion. However, the two techniques tend to produce similar results in practice. List-wise deletion is probably the most popular method of dealing with missing data. In a survey of recent research articles in political science by King et al., list-wise deletion was found to be the method of choice in 94 per cent of all papers (2001: 49)[2].

---

[1]Usually the four forms are reduced to three, since the two Missing at Random variants (#2 & #3) are usually handled similarly (Schafer, 1997).

[2]Since political scientists, for example, often use countries as their unit of analysis, they are constantly dealing with small sample sizes, making list-wise deletion very 'expensive' in terms of sample size. This suggests that list-wise deletion is even more common among sociologists.

List-wise deletion is problematic for several reasons. First, sample size is greatly reduced if problematic observations are deleted. Although sample size is not usually an issue with today's large data sets, it still places unnecessary constraints on the types of questions that can be asked.

The second, more serious, problem with list-wise and pair-wise deletion is that both hinge on the assumption that data are Missing Completely at Random (MCAR). Missingness often stems from the nature of the question, or survey, itself. To continue with the example, assuming that a random sample of people chose not to report their income is very presumptuous. In a recent study using the NLSCY, Worswick (2001) found that parents whose native language was neither English nor French were less likely to participate in surveys. There are several possible reasons for this, one being that people have difficulty answering surveys that are not administered in their native tongue. Unless the missing data stems from research design—the missing data was planned or a question was not asked—there is almost always an underlying pattern to missing data, and the MCAR assumption is rarely justified.

2. Do Something: Single Imputation Strategies[3]

Best Guess Imputation: Missing values are viewed in a quasi-subjective manner by the researcher, based on knowledge obtained from other variables. An example of a very successful Best Guess Imputation is what Steven Ruggles and Matthew Sobek did with the 1880 US census. Ruggles and Sobek were able to determine the relationship of all census respondents to the household head in the 1880 IPUMS data with remarkable accuracy (~ 99 per cent), through a series of best guess imputations using age, sex, and order on the census schedule, among other things. Although Ruggles and Sobek were successful, other data sources do not lend themselves so easily to best guessing techniques. When compared with subsequent censuses of Canada, the Best Guess Estimates of the visible minority indicator variable of the 1981 and 1986 censuses are not as accurate (1996 Census Codebook Online). One of the strengths of Best Guess is that it requires no assumptions about the nature of missingness or its distribution (King, 2002). Data can be MCAR, MAR, or NIM and values can be imputed without affecting sample size.

Zero Imputation: Missing values are replaced by a score of zero (or some other arbitrary numeric indicator) and a dummy variable is added to control for the imputed value. This is not a true imputation method, because no plausible value is provided for the missing data, but researchers can use this method to retain problematic cases. Another use of zero imputation is as a predictor in a regression model, to determine whether or not the missing data are missing at random in relation to the dependent variable. If the effect of the dummy variable is not significant, a persuasive argument can be made for the appropriateness of list-wise deletion, since no significant effect is elicited on the dependent variable (this only addresses one type of MAR data; missingness could still depend on values of other independent variables).

Mean Substitution: Replaces missing values with either the arithmetic average (for continuous data), or the most frequent value (for categorical data) of the variable, based on values from valid observations. This approach is simple; the mean value can be quickly calculated and analysis can proceed. The disadvantages include an underestimation of the standard error (through a reduction in the variance), and attenuation of correlations with other variables, producing overly optimistic fit statistics and significance levels (especially when values are not MAR or MCAR).

Hot Deck: A value from another observation is used as a 'donor' to replace the missing value. There are many methods for selecting suitable replacements: random selection of an observed value, or more complicated methods such as the Nearest Neighbour Imputation (NNI) methodology. For NNI (used for the 2000 Brazilian and US

---

[3]Space permits discussion of only a very limited number of imputation techniques. A complete list would include: Best Guess Imputation; Zero Imputation; Mean Substitution; Hot, Warm, and Cold Deck methods; and regression imputation methods, though many of the criticism outlined here also pertain to these methods.

censuses, as well as the 2001 Canadian, Ukrainian, Swiss, and Italian censuses) the donor is not drawn at random, but selected according to data values on variables that the statistician hypothesizes to be the most salient predictors of the missing value. The assumption is that the data are missing at random, and that there is a risk of using the same donor many times in small samples. This is a common method, but it's generally used before data are delivered to the end user.

Cold Deck: A missing value is derived using anything other than the same variable of that survey. It is the opposite of Hot Deck, in which non-respondent values are derived from respondent's values for the same variable. Values from a covariate, or a previous survey, are often used to impute the missing value. Cold Deck relies entirely on the MAR assumption to arrive at estimates, since other correlates form the basis for selection of a missing value.

$\hat{Y}$ Regression Imputation: A preliminary regression is run on all observations with the problematic variable as the focal outcome. A model for predicting the values of the missing data is derived from the regression. Missing values are filled by predicted regression values. The MAR assumption is heavily relied upon, and there is a significant underestimation of the standard error (predicted values are perfectly linear when y is unobserved, but scattered when it is observed (King, 2001)).

$\hat{Y}$ Regression Imputation with Random Error Term: Similar to regression imputation, except that error term is attached to the imputed value, allowing for an element of uncertainty in the estimate.

3. Do Multiple Things: Multiple Imputation

Multiple Imputation: This is the most mathematically abstract and complex method of imputation, but also the most accurate and consistent. The basic idea is simple, although in practice it's less straightforward:

1. Determine the model of interest that incorporates random explanatory variables (missing and non-missing).
2. Make random draws for the missing values from the valid cases that have similar scores on the given focal variables, using one of the other imputation techniques.
3. Do this M times (usually between three and five), creating M complete data sets. Observed values remain the same in all data, but missing values are different in each data set.
4. Perform analysis on M data sets, as though data are not missing.
5. Combine estimates by taking the average of coefficients to produce a single estimate.
6. Calculate standard errors by averaging the squared standard error of M estimates. Calculate the variance of M parameter estimates across samples by taking the square root of the sampling variance mean, plus a coefficient variance multiplied by a 'correction factor' of $1 + 1/M$ (to reward for increases in M).

Multiple Imputation: Advantages over Single Imputation

All other single imputation methods (except for the $\hat{Y}$ regression imputation with uncertainty element method) are essentially naïve edits. The type-one errors are too high, confidence intervals are too narrow, and there is no compensation for the uncertainty about the right to impute. Once imputation has occurred, unknown values are indistinguishable from known values, and analysis proceeds as though the values were never missing.

Multiple imputation 'builds in' a level of uncertainty (although there is no way of telling whether that level is the appropriate one), preserving, to some degree, the integrity and accuracy of the standard errors and model fit statistics. By running identical analyses on M data sets with slightly differing values for missing data, the non-observed values are less precise than observed values, and when coefficient estimates are combined, model uncertainty is retained.

Multiple Imputation: Disadvantages

Multiple Imputation has gained popularity with good reason; it is 'the only general purpose statistical technique that can validly handle missing data problems' (Rubin, 1987). Unlike single imputation methods and deletion methods, estimates retain uncertainty elements to maintain the imprecision of the model resulting from working with data that are incomplete.

Unfortunately, multiple imputation is complicated to use and computer intensive. King, Honaker, Joseph, and Scheve (2001) found some time ago that on a data set with 1,000 observations and 100 variables, which is not uncommonly large, multiple imputation takes anywhere from 4 minutes (imputing values for 5 variables with about 5 per cent missing data) to 3.5 days (with 40 variables with 5 per cent missing data). Although computers today are no doubt faster, computation time can still be substantial. The other problem with multiple imputation is that each time it is used different estimates are produced. Since quasi-random draws are taken from each variable, different values for each of the M data sets are selected each time, producing different results when combined.

Despite the advantages, multiple imputation might be too complex for the average user.

Since version 11, SPSS has had a module entitled MVA, which allows users to perform many of the single imputation methods with easy-to-use and intuitive diagnostics to compare means and variance structures before and after imputation, and assess change in model fit when imputed values are included.

What Difference Does It Make?

In the past, missing data was not thought to have a very big impact on results, but since the early 1990s social scientists have begun to realize that missing data can have a significant effect on the accuracy of results. As interest in correcting for missing data increases, software companies might begin to include more functions for multiple imputation. Whether multiple imputation will become the standard method for handling missing data in public-use data sets remains to be seen.

APPENDICES

Area under the Normal Curve

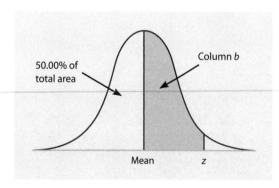

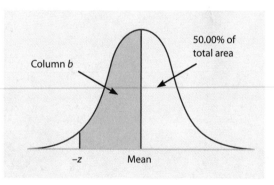

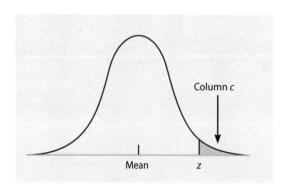

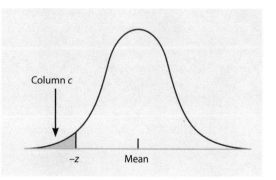

A z	B Area between mean and z	C Area beyond z	A z	B Area between mean and z	C Area beyond z
0.00	0.0000	0.5000			
0.01	0.0040	0.4960	0.51	0.1950	0.3050
0.02	0.0080	0.4920	0.52	0.1985	0.3015
0.03	0.0120	0.4880	0.53	0.2019	0.2981
0.04	0.0160	0.4840	0.54	0.2054	0.2946
0.05	0.0199	0.4801	0.55	0.2088	0.2912
0.06	0.0239	0.4761	0.56	0.2123	0.2877
0.07	0.0279	0.4721	0.57	0.2157	0.2843
0.08	0.0319	0.4681	0.58	0.2190	0.2810
0.09	0.0359	0.4641	0.59	0.2224	0.2776
0.10	0.0398	0.4602	0.60	0.2257	0.2743
0.11	0.0438	0.4562	0.61	0.2291	0.2709
0.12	0.0478	0.4522	0.62	0.2324	0.2676
0.13	0.0517	0.4483	0.63	0.2357	0.2643
0.14	0.0557	0.4443	0.64	0.2389	0.2611
0.15	0.0596	0.4404	0.65	0.2422	0.2578
0.16	0.0636	0.4364	0.66	0.2454	0.2546
0.17	0.0675	0.4325	0.67	0.2486	0.2514
0.18	0.0714	0.4286	0.68	0.2517	0.2483
0.19	0.0753	0.4247	0.69	0.2549	0.2451
0.20	0.0793	0.4207	0.70	0.2580	0.2420
0.21	0.0832	0.4168	0.71	0.2611	0.2389
0.22	0.0871	0.4129	0.72	0.2642	0.2358
0.23	0.0910	0.4090	0.73	0.2673	0.2327
0.24	0.0948	0.4052	0.74	0.2704	0.2297
0.25	0.0987	0.4013	0.75	0.2734	0.2266
0.26	0.1026	0.3974	0.76	0.2764	0.2236
0.27	0.1064	0.3936	0.77	0.2794	0.2207
0.28	0.1103	0.3897	0.78	0.2823	0.2177
0.29	0.1141	0.3859	0.79	0.2852	0.2148
0.30	0.1179	0.3821	0.80	0.2881	0.2119
0.31	0.1217	0.3783	0.81	0.2910	0.2090
0.32	0.1255	0.3745	0.82	0.2939	0.2061
0.33	0.1293	0.3707	0.83	0.2967	0.2033
0.34	0.1331	0.3669	0.84	0.2995	0.2005
0.35	0.1368	0.3632	0.85	0.3023	0.1977
0.36	0.1406	0.3594	0.86	0.3051	0.1949
0.37	0.1443	0.3557	0.87	0.3078	0.1922
0.38	0.1480	0.3520	0.88	0.3106	0.1894
0.39	0.1517	0.3483	0.89	0.3133	0.1867
0.40	0.1554	0.3446	0.90	0.3159	0.1841
0.41	0.1591	0.3409	0.91	0.3186	0.1814
0.42	0.1628	0.3372	0.92	0.3212	0.1788
0.43	0.1664	0.3336	0.93	0.3238	0.1762
0.44	0.1700	0.3300	0.94	0.3264	0.1736
0.45	0.1736	0.3264	0.95	0.3289	0.1711
0.46	0.1772	0.3228	0.96	0.3315	0.1685
0.47	0.1808	0.3192	0.97	0.3340	0.1660
0.48	0.1844	0.3156	0.98	0.3365	0.1635
0.49	0.1879	0.3121	0.99	0.3389	0.1611
0.50	0.1915	0.3085	1.00	0.3413	0.1587

A	B Area between	C Area beyond	A	B Area between	C Area beyond
z	mean and z	z	z	mean and z	z
1.01	0.3438	0.1562	1.51	0.4345	0.0655
1.02	0.3461	0.1539	1.52	0.4357	0.0643
1.03	0.3485	0.1515	1.53	0.4370	0.0630
1.04	0.3508	0.1492	1.54	0.4382	0.0618
1.05	0.3531	0.1469	1.55	0.4394	0.0606
1.06	0.3554	0.1446	1.56	0.4406	0.0594
1.07	0.3577	0.1423	1.57	0.4418	0.0582
1.08	0.3599	0.1401	1.58	0.4429	0.0571
1.09	0.3621	0.1379	1.59	0.4441	0.0559
1.10	0.3643	0.1357	1.60	0.4452	0.0548
1.11	0.3665	0.1335	1.61	0.4463	0.0537
1.12	0.3686	0.1314	1.62	0.4474	0.0526
1.13	0.3708	0.1292	1.63	0.4484	0.0516
1.14	0.3729	0.1271	1.64	0.4495	0.0505
1.15	0.3749	0.1251	1.65	0.4505	0.0495
1.16	0.3770	0.1230	1.66	0.4515	0.0485
1.17	0.3790	0.1210	1.67	0.4525	0.0475
1.18	0.3810	0.1190	1.68	0.4535	0.0465
1.19	0.3830	0.1170	1.69	0.4545	0.0455
− 1.20	0.3849	0.1151	− 1.70	0.4554	0.0446
1.21	0.3869	0.1131	1.71	0.4564	0.0436
1.22	0.3888	0.1112	1.72	0.4573	0.0427
1.23	0.3907	0.1093	1.73	0.4582	0.0418
1.24	0.3925	0.1075	1.74	0.4591	0.0409
− 1.25	0.3944	0.1056	1.75	0.4599	0.0401
1.26	0.3962	0.1038	1.76	0.4608	0.0392
1.27	0.3980	0.1020	1.77	0.4616	0.0384
1.28	0.3997	0.1003	1.78	0.4625	0.0375
1.29	0.4015	0.0985	1.79	0.4633	0.0367
1.30	0.4032	0.0968	1.80	0.4641	0.0359
1.31	0.4049	0.0951	1.81	0.4649	0.0351
1.32	0.4066	0.0934	1.82	0.4656	0.0344
1.33	0.4082	0.0918	1.83	0.4664	0.0336
1.34	0.4099	0.0901	1.84	0.4671	0.0329
1.35	0.4115	0.0885	1.85	0.4678	0.0322
1.36	0.4131	0.0869	1.86	0.4686	0.0314
1.37	0.4147	0.0853	1.87	0.4693	0.0307
1.38	0.4162	0.0838	1.88	0.4699	0.0301
1.39	0.4177	0.0823	1.89	0.4706	0.0294
1.40	0.4192	0.0808	1.90	0.4713	0.0287
1.41	0.4207	0.0793	1.91	0.4719	0.0281
1.42	0.4222	0.0778	1.92	0.4726	0.0274
1.43	0.4236	0.0764	1.93	0.4732	0.0268
1.44	0.4251	0.0749	1.94	0.4738	0.0262
1.45	0.4265	0.0735	1.95	0.4744	0.0256
− 1.46	0.4279	0.0721	1.96	0.4750	0.0250
1.47	0.4292	0.0708	1.97	0.4756	0.0244
1.48	0.4306	0.0694	1.98	0.4761	0.0239
1.49	0.4319	0.0681	1.99	0.4767	0.0233
1.50	0.4332	0.0668	2.00	0.4772	0.0228

A	B Area between	C Area beyond	A	B Area between	C Area beyond
z	mean and z	z	z	mean and z	z
2.01	0.4778	0.0222	2.51	0.4940	0.0060
2.02	0.4783	0.0217	2.52	0.4941	0.0059
2.03	0.4788	0.0212	2.53	0.4943	0.0057
2.04	0.4793	0.0207	2.54	0.4945	0.0055
2.05	0.4798	0.0202	2.55	0.4946	0.0054
2.06	0.4803	0.0197	2.56	0.4948	0.0052
2.07	0.4808	0.0192	2.57	0.4949	0.0051
2.08	0.4812	0.0188	2.58	0.4951	0.0049
2.09	0.4817	0.0183	2.59	0.4952	0.0048
2.10	0.4821	0.0179	2.60	0.4953	0.0047
2.11	0.4826	0.0174	2.61	0.4955	0.0045
2.12	0.4830	0.0170	2.62	0.4956	0.0044
2.13	0.4834	0.0166	2.63	0.4957	0.0043
2.14	0.4838	0.0162	2.64	0.4959	0.0041
2.15	0.4842	0.0158	2.65	0.4960	0.0040
2.16	0.4846	0.0154	2.66	0.4961	0.0039
2.17	0.4850	0.0150	2.67	0.4962	0.0038
2.18	0.4854	0.0146	2.68	0.4963	0.0037
2.19	0.4857	0.0143	2.69	0.4964	0.0036
2.20	0.4861	0.0139	2.70	0.4965	0.0035
2.21	0.4864	0.0136	2.71	0.4966	0.0034
2.22	0.4868	0.0132	2.72	0.4967	0.0033
2.23	0.4871	0.0129	2.73	0.4968	0.0032
2.24	0.4875	0.0125	2.74	0.4969	0.0031
2.25	0.4878	0.0122	2.75	0.4970	0.0030
2.26	0.4881	0.0119	2.76	0.4971	0.0029
2.27	0.4884	0.0116	2.77	0.4972	0.0028
2.28	0.4887	0.0113	2.78	0.4973	0.0027
2.29	0.4890	0.0110	2.79	0.4974	0.0026
2.30	0.4893	0.0107	2.80	0.4974	0.0026
2.31	0.4896	0.0104	2.81	0.4975	0.0025
2.32	0.4898	0.0102	2.82	0.4976	0.0024
2.33	0.4901	0.0099	2.83	0.4977	0.0023
2.34	0.4904	0.0096	2.84	0.4977	0.0023
2.35	0.4906	0.0094	2.85	0.4978	0.0022
2.36	0.4909	0.0091	2.86	0.4979	0.0021
2.37	0.4911	0.0089	2.87	0.4979	0.0021
2.38	0.4913	0.0087	2.88	0.4980	0.0020
2.39	0.4916	0.0084	2.89	0.4981	0.0019
2.40	0.4918	0.0082	2.90	0.4981	0.0019
2.41	0.4920	0.0080	2.91	0.4982	0.0018
2.42	0.4922	0.0078	2.92	0.4982	0.0018
2.43	0.4925	0.0075	2.93	0.4983	0.0017
2.44	0.4927	0.0073	2.94	0.4984	0.0016
2.45	0.4929	0.0071	2.95	0.4984	0.0016
2.46	0.4931	0.0069	2.96	0.4985	0.0015
2.47	0.4932	0.0068	2.97	0.4985	0.0015
2.48	0.4934	0.0066	2.98	0.4986	0.0014
2.49	0.4936	0.0064	2.99	0.4986	0.0014
2.50	0.4938	0.0062	3.00	0.4987	0.0013

A	B Area between mean and z	C Area beyond z	A	B Area between mean and z	C Area beyond z
z			z		
3.01	0.4987	0.0013	3.51	0.4998	0.0002
3.02	0.4987	0.0013	3.52	0.4998	0.0002
3.03	0.4988	0.0012	3.53	0.4998	0.0002
3.04	0.4988	0.0012	3.54	0.4998	0.0002
3.05	0.4989	0.0011	3.55	0.4998	0.0002
3.06	0.4989	0.0011	3.56	0.4998	0.0002
3.07	0.4989	0.0011	3.57	0.4998	0.0002
3.08	0.4990	0.0010	3.58	0.4998	0.0002
3.09	0.4990	0.0010	3.59	0.4998	0.0002
3.10	0.4990	0.0010	3.60	0.4998	0.0002
3.11	0.4991	0.0009	3.61	0.4998	0.0002
3.12	0.4991	0.0009	3.62	0.4999	0.0001
3.13	0.4991	0.0009	3.63	0.4999	0.0001
3.14	0.4992	0.0008	3.64	0.4999	0.0001
3.15	0.4992	0.0008	3.65	0.4999	0.0001
3.16	0.4992	0.0008	3.66	0.4999	0.0001
3.17	0.4992	0.0008	3.67	0.4999	0.0001
3.18	0.4993	0.0007	3.68	0.4999	0.0001
3.19	0.4993	0.0007	3.69	0.4999	0.0001
3.20	0.4993	0.0007	3.70	0.4999	0.0001
3.21	0.4993	0.0007	3.71	0.4999	0.0001
3.22	0.4994	0.0006	3.72	0.4999	0.0001
3.23	0.4994	0.0006	3.73	0.4999	0.0001
3.24	0.4994	0.0006	3.74	0.4999	0.0001
3.25	0.4994	0.0006	3.75	0.4999	0.0001
3.26	0.4994	0.0006	3.76	0.4999	0.0001
3.27	0.4995	0.0005	3.77	0.4999	0.0001
3.28	0.4995	0.0005	3.78	0.4999	0.0001
3.29	0.4995	0.0005	3.79	0.4999	0.0001
3.30	0.4995	0.0005	3.80	0.4999	0.0001
3.31	0.4995	0.0005	3.81	0.4999	0.0001
3.32	0.4995	0.0005	3.82	0.4999	0.0001
3.33	0.4996	0.0004	3.83	0.4999	0.0001
3.34	0.4996	0.0004	3.84	0.4999	0.0001
3.35	0.4996	0.0004	3.85	0.4999	0.0001
3.36	0.4996	0.0004	3.86	0.4999	0.0001
3.37	0.4996	0.0004	3.87	0.4999	0.0001
3.38	0.4996	0.0004	3.88	0.4999	0.0001
3.39	0.4997	0.0003	3.89	0.4999	0.0001
3.40	0.4997	0.0003	3.90	0.5000	0.0000
3.41	0.4997	0.0003	3.91	0.5000	0.0000
3.42	0.4997	0.0003	3.92	0.5000	0.0000
3.43	0.4997	0.0003	3.93	0.5000	0.0000
3.44	0.4997	0.0003	3.94	0.5000	0.0000
3.45	0.4997	0.0003	3.95	0.5000	0.0000
3.46	0.4997	0.0003	3.96	0.5000	0.0000
3.47	0.4997	0.0003	3.97	0.5000	0.0000
3.48	0.4997	0.0003	3.98	0.5000	0.0000
3.49	0.4998	0.0002	3.99	0.5000	0.0000
3.50	0.4998	0.0002	4.00	0.5000	0.0000

The Student's *t*-Table

For a One-Tailed Test:

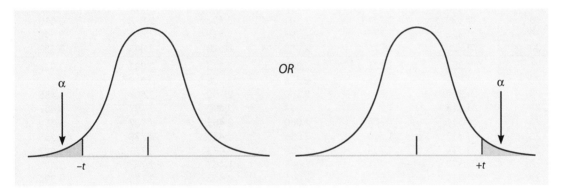

For a Two-Tailed Test:

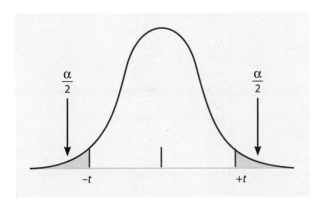

	Level of significance for one-tailed test					
	0.1	0.05	0.025	0.01	0.005	0.001
	Level of significance for two-tailed test					
df	0.2	0.1	0.05	0.02	0.01	0.002
1	3.078	6.314	12.706	31.821	63.657	318.313
2	1.886	2.920	4.303	6.965	9.925	22.327
3	1.638	2.353	3.182	4.541	5.841	10.215
4	1.533	2.132	2.776	3.747	4.604	7.173
5	1.476	2.015	2.571	3.365	4.032	5.893
6	1.440	1.943	2.447	3.143	3.707	5.208
7	1.415	1.895	2.365	2.998	3.499	4.782
8	1.397	1.860	2.306	2.896	3.355	4.499
9	1.383	1.833	2.262	2.821	3.250	4.296
10	1.372	1.812	2.228	2.764	3.169	4.143
11	1.363	1.796	2.201	2.718	3.106	4.024
12	1.356	1.782	2.179	2.681	3.055	3.929
13	1.350	1.771	2.160	2.650	3.012	3.852
14	1.345	1.761	2.145	2.624	2.977	3.787
15	1.341	1.753	2.131	2.602	2.947	3.733
16	1.337	1.746	2.120	2.583	2.921	3.686
17	1.333	1.740	2.110	2.567	2.898	3.646
18	1.330	1.734	2.101	2.552	2.878	3.610
19	1.328	1.729	2.093	2.539	2.861	3.579
20	1.325	1.725	2.086	2.528	2.845	3.552
21	1.323	1.721	2.080	2.518	2.831	3.527
22	1.321	1.717	2.074	2.508	2.819	3.505
23	1.319	1.714	2.069	2.500	2.807	3.485
24	1.318	1.711	2.064	2.492	2.797	3.467
25	1.316	1.708	2.060	2.485	2.787	3.450
26	1.315	1.706	2.056	2.479	2.779	3.435
27	1.314	1.703	2.052	2.473	2.771	3.421
28	1.313	1.701	2.048	2.467	2.763	3.408
29	1.311	1.699	2.045	2.462	2.756	3.396
30	1.310	1.697	2.042	2.457	2.750	3.385
31	1.309	1.696	2.040	2.453	2.744	3.375
32	1.309	1.694	2.037	2.449	2.738	3.365
33	1.308	1.692	2.035	2.445	2.733	3.356
34	1.307	1.691	2.032	2.441	2.728	3.348
35	1.306	1.690	2.030	2.438	2.724	3.340
36	1.306	1.688	2.028	2.434	2.719	3.333
37	1.305	1.687	2.026	2.431	2.715	3.326
38	1.304	1.686	2.024	2.429	2.712	3.319
39	1.304	1.685	2.023	2.426	2.708	3.313
40	1.303	1.684	2.021	2.423	2.704	3.307
41	1.303	1.683	2.020	2.421	2.701	3.301
42	1.302	1.682	2.018	2.418	2.698	3.296
43	1.302	1.681	2.017	2.416	2.695	3.291
44	1.301	1.680	2.015	2.414	2.692	3.286
45	1.301	1.679	2.014	2.412	2.690	3.281
46	1.300	1.679	2.013	2.410	2.687	3.277
47	1.300	1.678	2.012	2.408	2.685	3.273
48	1.299	1.677	2.011	2.407	2.682	3.269
49	1.299	1.677	2.010	2.405	2.680	3.265
50	1.299	1.676	2.009	2.403	2.678	3.261

	Level of significance for one-tailed test					
	0.1	0.05	0.025	0.01	0.005	0.001
	Level of significance for two-tailed test					
df	0.2	0.1	0.05	0.02	0.01	0.002
51	1.298	1.675	2.008	2.402	2.676	3.258
52	1.298	1.675	2.007	2.400	2.674	3.255
53	1.298	1.674	2.006	2.399	2.672	3.251
54	1.297	1.674	2.005	2.397	2.670	3.248
55	1.297	1.673	2.004	2.396	2.668	3.245
56	1.297	1.673	2.003	2.395	2.667	3.242
57	1.297	1.672	2.002	2.394	2.665	3.239
58	1.296	1.672	2.002	2.392	2.663	3.237
59	1.296	1.671	2.001	2.391	2.662	3.234
60	1.296	1.671	2.000	2.390	2.660	3.232
61	1.296	1.670	2.000	2.389	2.659	3.229
62	1.295	1.670	1.999	2.388	2.657	3.227
63	1.295	1.669	1.998	2.387	2.656	3.225
64	1.295	1.669	1.998	2.386	2.655	3.223
65	1.295	1.669	1.997	2.385	2.654	3.220
66	1.295	1.668	1.997	2.384	2.652	3.218
67	1.294	1.668	1.996	2.383	2.651	3.216
68	1.294	1.668	1.995	2.382	2.650	3.214
69	1.294	1.667	1.995	2.382	2.649	3.213
70	1.294	1.667	1.994	2.381	2.648	3.211
71	1.294	1.667	1.994	2.380	2.647	3.209
72	1.293	1.666	1.993	2.379	2.646	3.207
73	1.293	1.666	1.993	2.379	2.645	3.206
74	1.293	1.666	1.993	2.378	2.644	3.204
75	1.293	1.665	1.992	2.377	2.643	3.202
76	1.293	1.665	1.992	2.376	2.642	3.201
77	1.293	1.665	1.991	2.376	2.641	3.199
78	1.292	1.665	1.991	2.375	2.640	3.198
79	1.292	1.664	1.990	2.374	2.640	3.197
80	1.292	1.664	1.990	2.374	2.639	3.195
81	1.292	1.664	1.990	2.373	2.638	3.194
82	1.292	1.664	1.989	2.373	2.637	3.193
83	1.292	1.663	1.989	2.372	2.636	3.191
84	1.292	1.663	1.989	2.372	2.636	3.190
85	1.292	1.663	1.988	2.371	2.635	3.189
86	1.291	1.663	1.988	2.370	2.634	3.188
87	1.291	1.663	1.988	2.370	2.634	3.187
88	1.291	1.662	1.987	2.369	2.633	3.185
89	1.291	1.662	1.987	2.369	2.632	3.184
90	1.291	1.662	1.987	2.368	2.632	3.183
91	1.291	1.662	1.986	2.368	2.631	3.182
92	1.291	1.662	1.986	2.368	2.630	3.181
93	1.291	1.661	1.986	2.367	2.630	3.180
94	1.291	1.661	1.986	2.367	2.629	3.179
95	1.291	1.661	1.985	2.366	2.629	3.178
96	1.290	1.661	1.985	2.366	2.628	3.177
97	1.290	1.661	1.985	2.365	2.627	3.176
98	1.290	1.661	1.984	2.365	2.627	3.175
99	1.290	1.660	1.984	2.365	2.626	3.175
100	1.290	1.660	1.984	2.364	2.626	3.174
120	1.289	1.658	1.980	2.358	2.617	3.373
∞	1.282	1.645	1.960	2.326	2.576	3.090

Chi-Square

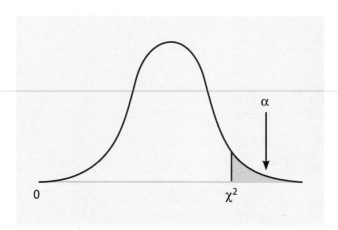

df	Critical values of chi-square Level of significance for two-tailed test				
	0.1	0.05	0.025	0.01	0.001
1	2.706	3.841	5.024	6.635	10.828
2	4.605	5.991	7.378	9.210	13.816
3	6.251	7.815	9.348	11.345	16.266
4	7.779	9.488	11.143	13.277	18.467
5	9.236	11.070	12.833	15.086	20.515
6	10.645	12.592	14.449	16.812	22.458
7	12.017	14.067	16.013	18.475	24.322
8	13.362	15.507	17.535	20.090	26.125
9	14.684	16.919	19.023	21.666	27.877
10	15.987	18.307	20.483	23.209	29.588
11	17.275	19.675	21.920	24.725	31.264
12	18.549	21.026	23.337	26.217	32.910
13	19.812	22.362	24.736	27.688	34.528
14	21.064	23.685	26.119	29.141	36.123
15	22.307	24.996	27.488	30.578	37.697
16	23.542	26.296	28.845	32.000	39.252
17	24.769	27.587	30.191	33.409	40.790
18	25.989	28.869	31.526	34.805	42.312
19	27.204	30.144	32.852	36.191	43.820
20	28.412	31.410	34.170	37.566	45.315
21	29.615	32.671	35.479	38.932	46.797
22	30.813	33.924	36.781	40.289	48.268
23	32.007	35.172	38.076	41.638	49.728
24	33.196	36.415	39.364	42.980	51.179
25	34.382	37.652	40.646	44.314	52.620
26	35.563	38.885	41.923	45.642	54.052
27	36.741	40.113	43.195	46.963	55.476
28	37.916	41.337	44.461	48.278	56.892
29	39.087	42.557	45.722	49.588	58.301
30	40.256	43.773	46.979	50.892	59.703
31	41.422	44.985	48.232	52.191	61.098
32	42.585	46.194	49.480	53.486	62.487
33	43.745	47.400	50.725	54.776	63.870
34	44.903	48.602	51.966	56.061	65.247
35	46.059	49.802	53.203	57.342	66.619
36	47.212	50.998	54.437	58.619	67.985
37	48.363	52.192	55.668	59.893	69.347
38	49.513	53.384	56.896	61.162	70.703
39	50.660	54.572	58.120	62.428	72.055
40	51.805	55.758	59.342	63.691	73.402
41	52.949	56.942	60.561	64.950	74.745
42	54.090	58.124	61.777	66.206	76.084
43	55.230	59.304	62.990	67.459	77.419
44	56.369	60.481	64.201	68.710	78.750
45	57.505	61.656	65.410	69.957	80.077
46	58.641	62.830	66.617	71.201	81.400
47	59.774	64.001	67.821	72.443	82.720
48	60.907	65.171	69.023	73.683	84.037
49	62.038	66.339	70.222	74.919	85.351
50	63.167	67.505	71.420	76.154	86.661

df	Critical values of chi-square Level of significance for two-tailed test				
	0.1	0.05	0.025	0.01	0.001
51	64.295	68.669	72.616	77.386	87.968
52	65.422	69.832	73.810	78.616	89.272
53	66.548	70.993	75.002	79.843	90.573
54	67.673	72.153	76.192	81.069	91.872
55	68.796	73.311	77.380	82.292	93.168
56	69.919	74.468	78.567	83.513	94.461
57	71.040	75.624	79.752	84.733	95.751
58	72.160	76.778	80.936	85.950	97.039
59	73.279	77.931	82.117	87.166	98.324
60	74.397	79.082	83.298	88.379	99.607
61	75.514	80.232	84.476	89.591	100.888
62	76.630	81.381	85.654	90.802	102.166
63	77.745	82.529	86.830	92.010	103.442
64	78.860	83.675	88.004	93.217	104.716
65	79.973	84.821	89.177	94.422	105.988
66	81.085	85.965	90.349	95.626	107.258
67	82.197	87.108	91.519	96.828	108.526
68	83.308	88.250	92.689	98.028	109.791
69	84.418	89.391	93.856	99.228	111.055
70	85.527	90.531	95.023	100.425	112.317
71	86.635	91.670	96.189	101.621	113.577
72	87.743	92.808	97.353	102.816	114.835
73	88.850	93.945	98.516	104.010	116.092
74	89.956	95.081	99.678	105.202	117.346
75	91.061	96.217	100.839	106.393	118.599
76	92.166	97.351	101.999	107.583	119.850
77	93.270	98.484	103.158	108.771	121.100
78	94.374	99.617	104.316	109.958	122.348
79	95.476	100.749	105.473	111.144	123.594
80	96.578	101.879	106.629	112.329	124.839
81	97.680	103.010	107.783	113.512	126.083
82	98.780	104.139	108.937	114.695	127.324
83	99.880	105.267	110.090	115.876	128.565
84	100.980	106.395	111.242	117.057	129.804
85	102.079	107.522	112.393	118.236	131.041
86	103.177	108.648	113.544	119.414	132.277
87	104.275	109.773	114.693	120.591	133.512
88	105.372	110.898	115.841	121.767	134.746
89	106.469	112.022	116.989	122.942	135.978
90	107.565	113.145	118.136	124.116	137.208
91	108.661	114.268	119.282	125.289	138.438
92	109.756	115.390	120.427	126.462	139.666
93	110.850	116.511	121.571	127.633	140.893
94	111.944	117.632	122.715	128.803	142.119
95	113.038	118.752	123.858	129.973	143.344
96	114.131	119.871	125.000	131.141	144.567
97	115.223	120.990	126.141	132.309	145.789
98	116.315	122.108	127.282	133.476	147.010
99	117.407	123.225	128.422	134.642	148.230
100	118.498	124.342	129.561	135.807	149.449

The *F*-distribution

*df*between	2	3	4	5	6	7	8
dfwithin							
1	199.50	215.71	224.58	230.16	233.99	236.77	238.88
2	19.00	19.16	19.25	19.30	19.33	19.35	19.37
3	9.55	9.28	9.12	9.01	8.94	8.89	8.85
4	6.94	6.59	6.39	6.26	6.16	6.09	6.04
5	5.79	5.41	5.19	5.05	4.95	4.88	4.82
6	5.14	4.76	4.53	4.39	4.28	4.21	4.15
7	4.74	4.35	4.12	3.97	3.87	3.79	3.73
8	4.46	4.07	3.84	3.69	3.58	3.50	3.44
9	4.26	3.86	3.63	3.48	3.37	3.29	3.23
10	4.10	3.71	3.48	3.33	3.22	3.14	3.07
20	3.49	3.10	2.87	2.71	2.60	2.51	2.45
21	3.47	3.07	2.84	2.69	2.57	2.49	2.42
22	3.44	3.05	2.82	2.66	2.55	2.46	2.40
23	3.42	3.03	2.80	2.64	2.53	2.44	2.38
24	3.40	3.01	2.78	2.62	2.51	2.42	2.36
25	3.39	2.99	2.76	2.60	2.49	2.41	2.34
26	3.37	2.98	2.74	2.59	2.47	2.39	2.32
27	3.35	2.96	2.73	2.57	2.46	2.37	2.31
28	3.34	2.95	2.71	2.56	2.45	2.36	2.29
29	3.33	2.93	2.70	2.55	2.43	2.35	2.28
30	3.32	2.92	2.69	2.53	2.42	2.33	2.27
40	3.23	2.84	2.61	2.45	2.34	2.25	2.18
50	3.18	2.79	2.56	2.40	2.29	2.20	2.13
60	3.15	2.76	2.53	2.37	2.25	2.17	2.10
70	3.13	2.74	2.50	2.35	2.23	2.14	2.07
80	3.11	2.72	2.49	2.33	2.21	2.13	2.06
90	3.10	2.71	2.47	2.32	2.20	2.11	2.04
100	3.09	2.70	2.46	2.31	2.19	2.10	2.03
120	3.07	2.68	2.45	2.29	2.18	2.09	2.02
∞	3.00	2.61	2.37	2.22	2.10	2.01	1.94

Area under the Normal Curve : A Condensed Version

A	B	C	A	B	C
z	Area between mean and z	Area beyond z	z	Area between mean and z	Area beyond z
0.0	0.0000	0.5000	2.0	0.4772	0.0228
0.1	0.0398	0.4602	2.1	0.4821	0.0179
0.2	0.0793	0.4207	2.2	0.4861	0.0139
0.3	0.1179	0.3821	2.3	0.4893	0.0107
0.4	0.1554	0.3446	2.4	0.4918	0.0082
0.5	0.1915	0.3085	2.5	0.4938	0.0062
0.6	0.2257	0.2743	2.6	0.4953	0.0047
0.7	0.2580	0.2420	2.7	0.4965	0.0035
0.8	0.2881	0.2119	2.8	0.4974	0.0026
0.9	0.3159	0.1841	2.9	0.4981	0.0019
1.0	0.3413	0.1587	3.0	0.4987	0.0013
1.1	0.3643	0.1357	3.1	0.4990	0.0010
1.2	0.3849	0.1151	3.2	0.4993	0.0007
1.3	0.4032	0.0968	3.3	0.4995	0.0005
1.4	0.4192	0.0808	3.4	0.4997	0.0003
1.5	0.4332	0.0668	3.5	0.4998	0.0002
1.6	0.4452	0.0548			
1.7	0.4554	0.0446			
1.8	0.4641	0.0359			
1.9	0.4713	0.0287			

Random Numbers between 1 and 1,000

388	250	87	729	502	962
185	60	160	117	714	496
524	19	360	95	784	800
494	6	951	606	40	530
603	504	919	973	620	320
203	167	195	920	447	756
690	647	821	594	111	918
10	899	275	191	22	988
930	816	335	717	413	470
65	993	620	201	66	949
332	273	128	656	220	326
717	477	37	580	905	421
832	51	422	106	204	42
16	194	916	364	507	405
390	34	243	464	912	453
868	609	556	252	554	487
164	347	163	588	898	889
958	537	166	119	826	880
996	365	168	214	106	644
876	774	271	625	74	821
738	929	550	471	762	994
31	793	556	1	752	300
198	595	960	200	288	362
302	997	409	337	253	310
694	994	8	41	24	456
511	204	686	941	546	70
500	622	64	467	752	448
153	339	447	609	339	938
698	662	134	248	285	532
4	511	701	892	178	943
197	635	960	22	672	440
492	959	399	654	111	174
937	986	741	947	730	734
979	538	226	541	809	445
541	911	105	613	974	961
359	728	913	159	281	951
938	20	224	702	166	998
581	341	124	55	592	881
709	660	216	59	29	162
15	411	172	825	192	174
191	959	230	161	873	915
788	928	56	915	785	881
586	951	839	161	155	239
485	415	627	971	840	824
595	329	648	985	251	18
856	523	860	788	172	525
359	681	246	157	928	997
419	94	519	199	200	593
699	256	903	339	303	140
93	418	735	486	801	21

Equation Summary

The arithmetic mean: $\overline{X} = \dfrac{\sum X_N}{N}$

The range: $Range = H - L$

Mean deviation: $MeanDeviation = \dfrac{\sum |X - \overline{X}|}{N}$

Variance: $\sigma^2 = \dfrac{\sum (X - \mu)^2}{N}$ or $s^2 = \dfrac{\sum (X - \overline{X})^2}{n-1}$

Standard deviation:

$\sigma = \sqrt{\dfrac{\sum (X - \mu)^2}{N}}$ or $s = \sqrt{\dfrac{\sum (X - \overline{X})^2}{n-1}}$

Standard deviation of the difference between sample proportions:

$s_{\overline{X}_1 - \overline{X}_2} = \sqrt{P_u(1 - P_u)} \sqrt{\dfrac{n_1 + n_2}{n_1 n_2}}$

The standard score: $z = \dfrac{X - \mu}{\sigma}$ or $z = \dfrac{X - \overline{X}}{s}$

Standard error of the mean:

$\sigma_{\overline{X}} = \dfrac{\sigma_X}{\sqrt{n}}$ or $s_{\overline{X}} = \dfrac{s_X}{\sqrt{n}}$ or $s_p = \sqrt{\dfrac{P(1 - P)}{n}}$

Observed *t*-score:

$t_{observed} = \dfrac{\overline{X} - \mu}{\sigma_X / \sqrt{n}}$ or $t_{observed} = \dfrac{\overline{X} - \mu}{\sigma_{\overline{X}}}$

or $t_{observed} = \dfrac{\overline{X} - \mu}{s_{\overline{X}}}$ or $t_{observed} = \dfrac{\overline{X} - \mu}{s_X / \sqrt{n-1}}$

- To assess *r*: $t_{observed} = r\sqrt{\dfrac{N-2}{1-r^2}}$

Observed *z*-score:

- In a sample: $z = \dfrac{X - \overline{X}}{s}$

- Between two sample means: $z = \dfrac{(\overline{X}_1 - \overline{X}_2)}{s_{\overline{X}_1 - \overline{X}_2}}$

- With proportions

$z_{obtained} = \dfrac{P_{sample} - P_{population}}{\sqrt{P_{population}(1 - P_{population})/n}}$

Degrees of freedom:

- for a *t*-test: $df = n - 1$

- for chi-square test of independence: $df = (r-1)(c-1)$

- **When calculating the significance of difference between two means:**
  $df = (n_1 + n_2 - 2)$

- **Within groups in ANOVA:**
  $df_{within} = N_{total} - k$

- **Between groups in ANOVA:**
  $df_{between} = k - 1$

Confidence interval:

- **Confidence interval when z is known:**

  Confidence Interval $= \overline{X} \pm z_{critical} * \sigma_{\overline{X}}$

  or

  Confidence Interval $= \overline{X} \pm z_{critical} * \dfrac{\sigma_{\overline{X}}}{\sqrt{n}}$

- **Confidence interval when t is known:**

  Confidence Interval $= \overline{X} \pm t_{critical} * s_{\overline{X}}$

  or

  Confidence Interval $= \overline{X} \pm t_{critical} * \dfrac{s_{\overline{X}}}{\sqrt{n-1}}$

Chi-square: $\chi^2 = \sum \dfrac{(f_o - f_e)^2}{f_e}$

- **Expected cell frequencies:**

  $f_e = \dfrac{\sum_{column} * \sum_{row}}{N}$

Phi: $\phi = \sqrt{\dfrac{\chi^2}{n}}$

Cramer's V: $V = \sqrt{\dfrac{\chi^2}{(n)(\min(r-1) \mid (c-1))}}$

Lambda: $\lambda = \dfrac{E_1 - E_2}{E_1}$

Association between dummy and interval/ratio variables, same group measured twice:

- **Differences between observations:**

  $\overline{X}_d = \dfrac{\sum d_i}{n}$

- **Standard deviation of differences:**

  $s_d = \sqrt{\dfrac{\sum (d - \overline{X}_d)^2}{n-1}}$ or $s_d = \sqrt{\dfrac{\sum d^2}{n-1} - (\overline{X}_1 - \overline{X}_2)^2}$

- **Standard error of the difference between means (when the same group is measured twice):**

  $s_{\overline{d}} = \dfrac{s_d}{\sqrt{n-1}}$

- **t-observed for significance of differences:**

  $t = \dfrac{\overline{X}_1 - \overline{X}_2}{s_{\overline{d}}}$

Standard error of the difference between means:

- **When using z:** $s_{\overline{X}_1 - \overline{X}_2} = \sqrt{\dfrac{s_1^2}{n_1 - 1} + \dfrac{s_2^2}{n_2 - 1}}$

- **When using t:**

  $s_{\overline{X}_1 - \overline{X}_2} = \sqrt{\left(\dfrac{n_1 s_1^2 + n_2 s_2^2}{n_1 + n_2 - 2}\right)\left(\dfrac{n_1 + n_2}{n_1 n_2}\right)}$

Kruskal's gamma: $G = \dfrac{N_{same} - N_{different}}{N_{same} + N_{different}}$

Spearman's rho: $r_s = 1 - \dfrac{6 * \sum D^2}{N(N^2 - 1)}$

Somer's d: $d = \dfrac{N_{same} - N_{different}}{N_{same} + N_{different} + Ties_y}$

Pearson's r:

$r = \dfrac{N \sum XY - (\sum X)(\sum Y)}{\sqrt{[N \sum X^2 - (\sum X)^2][N \sum Y^2 - (\sum Y)^2]}}$

Total sum of squares (ANOVA):

$SS_{total} = \sum X^2_{total} - N_{total} \overline{X}^2_{total}$

Within-group sum of squares (ANOVA):

$SS_{within} = \sum X^2_{total} - \sum N_{group} \overline{X}^2_{group}$

Between-group sum of squares (ANOVA):

$$SS_{between} = \sum N_{group}\overline{X}^2_{group} - N_{total}\overline{X}^2_{total}$$

Mean squares within groups: $MS_{within} = \dfrac{SS_{within}}{df_{within}}$

Mean squares between groups:

$$MS_{between} = \dfrac{SS_{between}}{df_{between}}$$

$F_{observed}$: $F_{observed} = \dfrac{MS_{between}}{MS_{within}}$

Ordinary least-squares regression (observed):

$Y = a + b_1x_{1i} + b_2x_{2i} + \dots + b_nx_{ni} + e_i$

Ordinary least-squares regression (expected):

$\hat{Y} = a + b_1x_{1i} + b_2x_{2i} + \dots + b_nx_{ni}$

- **Partial slope coefficient:**

$$b = \dfrac{\sum (X - \overline{X})(Y - \overline{Y})}{\sum (X - \overline{X})^2}$$

- **y-intercept:** $a = \overline{Y} - b\overline{X}$

- **Error term:** $e = Y - \hat{Y}$

- **Correlation between X and Y:**

$$r_{xy} = \dfrac{N\sum XY - (\sum X)(\sum Y)}{\sqrt{[N\sum X^2 - (\sum X)^2][N\sum Y^2 - (\sum Y)^2]}}$$

- **Per cent explained variance in Y:**

$R^2 = r^2_{yx1} + r^2_{yx1.x2}(1 - r^2_{yx1})$ **or**

$$R^2 = \dfrac{\sum (\hat{Y} - \overline{Y})^2}{\sum (Y - \overline{Y})^2}$$

- **Where:** $r^2_{y\,x1.x2} = \dfrac{r_{yx2} - (r_{yx1})(r_{x1x2})}{\sqrt{1 - r^2_{y\,x1}}\sqrt{1 - r^2_{x\,1x2}}}$

- **Standardized partial slopes:**

$$b_1^* = b_1\left(\dfrac{s_1}{s_y}\right)$$

Logistic regression (observed):

$Logodds(Y = 1) = a + b_1x_{1i} + b_2x_{2i} + \dots + b_nx_{ni} + e_i$

Logistic regression (expected):

$Logodds(\hat{Y} = 1) = a + b_1x_{1i} + b_2x_{2i} + \dots + b_nx_{ni}$

- $Odds(Y = 1) = \left(\dfrac{\Pr(Y = 1)}{\Pr(Y \neq 1)}\right)$ **or**

$LogOdds(Y = 1) = \ln\left(\dfrac{\Pr(Y = 1)}{\Pr(Y \neq 1)}\right)$ **or**

$LogOdds(Y = 1) = \ln\left(\dfrac{\Pr(Y = 1)}{1 - \Pr(Y = 1)}\right)$

- $Odds\ ratio_b = e^b$

Some Statistical Terms to Remember[1]

Absolute value: The value of a number disregarding its positive or negative sign. It is denoted by a pair of '|' symbols: thus the absolute value, or modulus, of –2.5 is | –2.5 | = 2.5.

ANOVA: A measure of the total variability in a set of data is given by the sum of squared differences of the observations from their overall mean. This is the *total sum of squares* (TSS). It is often possible to subdivide this quantity into components that are identified with different causes of variation (referred to as the within-group sum of squares and the between-group sum of squares). The mean square corresponding to RSS is often used as the yardstick for assessing the importance of the specified sources of variation. One method involves comparing ratios of mean squares with the critical values of an *F*-distribution.

Arithmetic average: See **Mean**.

Associations: Two variables are associated if they are not independent (i.e., if the value of one variable affects the value, or the distribution of the values, of the other). Thus, for a human population, height and weight are associated, and so are actual skin-colour and ethnicity.

Asymptotic normality: The distribution of a statistic is said to be asymptotically normal if the distribution of the statistic approaches a normal distribution as the sample size increases.

Axis scales: The values that appear along the *x*- and *y*-axis of any plot.

Axis titles: The titles used to describe the data on the *x*- and *y*-axis of any plot.

BEDMAS: A mnemonic device for remembering the order of operations. It stands for: Brackets Exponents Division Multiplication Addition Subtraction.

Bell curve: A term used to describe the bell-like resemblance of a normal distribution.

Between-group sum of squares: See ANOVA.

Bimodal: Having two modes or modal classes.

Binary variables: Any variable that has only two response categories.

Bivariate analysis: Any analytical technique that requires two variables.

Bivariate relationships: See **Associations**.

Bivariate statistics: A suite of statistical procedures used to describe the relationship between two variables.

Categorical variables: A variable whose values are not numerical. Examples include gender (male, female), paint colour (red, white, blue), and type of bird (duck, goose, owl).

---

[1]Many of these definitions are used with permission from Graham Upton and Ian Cook. 2006. *Oxford Dictionary of Statistics*. Oxford: Oxford University Press.

Central limit theorem: Proposed by Laplace, explaining the importance of the normal distribution for a large random sample of observations from a distribution with mean [*mu*] and variance. The distribution of the sample mean is approximately normal with mean [*mu*] and variance $\frac{1}{n}\sigma^2$, and the distribution of the sample total is approximately normal with mean n[*mu*] and variance $n\sigma^2$. The phrase 'central limit theorem' appears in a 1919 article by von Mises.

Chi-square: A statistical test to determine the similarity of the number of occurrences being investigated to the expected occurrences. The symbol for chi-square is χ^2.

Concordant and discordant pairs: Concordant pairs (in bivariate association) refers to a situation in which a positive (or negative) score on one variable corresponds with a positive (or negative) score on another variable. Discordant pairs describes the opposite situation, where a positive score on one variable corresponds with a negative score on another. Often used with ordinal data.

Confidence interval: A confidence interval for an unknown population parameter is an interval calculated from sample values by a procedure such that if a large number of independent samples is taken, a certain percentage of the intervals obtained will contain the unknown population parameter. The term 'confidence interval' was introduced in 1934 by Neyman.

Confidence limits: The end points of a confidence interval.

Confidentiality: The concern that an individual in a study can be identified by the information they provide.

Contingency tables: A table displaying the frequencies for each combination of two or more variables. The variables are either categorical variables or numerical variables for which the possible outcomes have been arranged in groups. The term was first used by Karl Pearson in 1904. Each location in a table is called a *cell*, and the corresponding frequency is the *cell frequency*. Also called cross-classification, or cross-tabulation, tables.

Continuous variable: A variable whose set of possible values is a continuous interval of real numbers x, such that $a < x < b$, in which a can be -∞ and b can be +∞.

Control: A variable that has an effect that is of no direct interest. The analysis of the variable of interest is made more accurate by controlling for variation in the covariate.

Convenience sample: A cheap method of obtaining a sample. An example would be interviewing supermarket customers. This would be a reasonable procedure provided that the purpose of the sampling was unrelated to the convenience of the sample (thus it would be appropriate to ask the customers about car colour preferences, but not about food preferences).

Correlation matrix: A square symmetric matrix in which the element in row j and column k is equal to the correlation coefficient between random variables X_j and X_k. The diagonal elements are always equal to one because the diagonal denotes a correlation between a variable and itself, and a variable is always perfectly correlated with itself.

Covariance: The covariance of two random variables is the difference between the expected value of their product and the product of their separate expected values. For random variables X and Y,

$$\text{Cov}(X, Y) = \text{E}(XY) - \text{E}(X) \times \text{E}(Y).$$

Cramer's V: In 1946 Cramer suggested that a measure of association could be based on the value of X^2. This is *Cramer's* V; it reduces to Phi in a 2 by 2 table.

Critical value of z or z(*critical*) or $z_{critical}$: An end point of a critical region. In a hypothesis test, comparison of the value of a test statistic with the appropriate critical value determines the result of the test. For example, 1.96 is the critical value for a two-tailed test in the case of a normal distribution and a 5 per cent significance level: thus if the test statistic z is such that $|z| > 1.96$, then the alternative hypothesis is accepted in preference to the null hypothesis.

Degrees of freedom: A parameter that appears in some probability distributions used in statistical inference, particularly the *t*-distribution, the chi-squared distribution, and the *F*-distribution. The phrase 'degrees of freedom' was introduced by Sir Ronald Fisher in 1922.

Dependent variable: The outcome of interest in a bivariate or multivariate analysis.

Dichotomization: The process of transforming a categorical variable into a series of dummy variables.

Dichotomous or dummy variables: A variable, taking only the values zero and one, derived from a polytomous categorical variable. If the categorical variable has k categories, then $(k - 1)$ dummy variables are required. For example, with four categories the three dummy variables (x_1, x_2, x_3) could be assigned the values (1, 0, 0) for category one, (0, 1, 0) for category two, (0, 0, 1) for category three, and (0, 0, 0) for category four. Dummy variables enable the inclusion of categorical information in regression models.

Direction: Used to describe association; it can be either positive or negative.

Discrete (outcome) variables: A dichotomous dependent variable.

Dispersion: See **Distribution**.

Distribution: The set of values of a set of data, possibly grouped into classes, together with their frequencies or relative frequencies. In the case of random variables the distribution is the set of possible values together with their probabilities in the discrete case and the probability density function in the case of a continuous variable.

Dummy variable: See **Dichotomous variables**.

Experiment: Any design that investigates the effects of a single explanatory variable in highly controlled conditions. Rarely used in social science research.

Explained variation: The amount of variation in a dependent variable explained by one or more independent variables.

Face validity: A test is said to have face validity if a reading of the items appears to reflect the areas that the test purports to measure.

F-distribution: A theoretical relative frequency distribution of the ratio of two independent sample variances.

Frequency: The number of times that a particular data value is obtained in a sample. For example, the frequency of 5 in the sample 4, 6, 5, 7, 4, 5, 2, 5 is 3. The sum of the frequencies is the sample size. The term is also used in connection with a set of values. For example, the number of people aged between 20 and 30, or the number of people with blue or green eyes.

Grand mean: When the data comes from different groups (e.g., 'males' and 'females'), the grand mean is the mean of all the values, irrespective of their group.

Hypothesizing relationships: A formal statement about the possibility of an association between two or more variables.

Independent variable: Any variable that is believed to affect or explain the values of an outcome of interest in a bivariate or multivariate analysis.

Inferential statistical tests: Involve generalizing from samples to populations, performing hypothesis testing, determining relationships among variables, and making predictions.

Interval — level of measurement: A scale of measurement that can be used to measure the difference, or distance, between two general states or points. For example, use of a ruler to measure length, use of a stop-watch to measure a time interval, or measurement of a musical interval (octave, fifth, etc.).

Inverse function: If A is a function of B for variable f, then the inverse function for f is in the opposite direction, from B to A.

Kendall's tau-b: A measure of association often used with but not limited to 2 by 2 tables. It is computed as the excess of concordant over discordant pairs. It is often used in 2 by 2 tables.

Kruskal and Goodman's gamma: Kruskal and Goodman's gamma is a symmetric measure that varies from +1 to –1, based on the difference between concordant pairs (P) and discordant pairs (Q). Essentially, gamma is calculated as $(P - Q) / (P + Q)$.

Kruskal and Goodman's lambda: For two categorical variables (A and B having, respectively, J and K categories) a measure with a probabilistic interpretation is *Kruskal and Goodman's lambda*, suggested by Goodman and Kruskal in 1954. Suppose that we are asked to guess the category of B for the next observation. An intelligent guess would be the category that was the commonest so far.

Latent or unobserved concept: An unobserved variable that may account for variation in the data and/or for apparent relations between observed variables.

Law of large numbers: The law of large numbers states that an empirical probability will increasingly resemble its theoretical probability as the number of trials increases.

Least squares regression line: Typically used with OLS regression. It is a line that best approximates the relationship between dependent variables and one or more independent variables.

Legends: A box that describes the contents of a graph or chart.

Levels of measurement: A term used to describe the relationship between response categories in any variable. See **nominal**, **ordinal**, **interval**, and **ratio** levels of measurement.

Line of best fit: See **Least squares regression line**.

Logarithms: An alternative notation for expressing an exponent; the inverse of exponentiation. It is often used with logistic regression.

Longitudinal surveys: Any survey that observes the same respondent at more than one point in time.

Marginals: If the cell frequencies of a (multidimensional) contingency table are totalled over one or more of the categorizing variables, the result is a set of marginal totals. For a two-dimensional table, the marginal totals are the row and column totals.

Maximum likelihood: A commonly used method for obtaining an estimate of an unknown parameter of an assumed population distribution. The likelihood of a data set depends upon the parameter(s) of the distribution or probability density function from which the observations have been taken.

Mean: The mean of a set of n items of data $x_1, x_2, ..., x_n$ is $\overline{X} = \dfrac{\sum X_N}{N}$, which is the arithmetic mean of the numbers $x_1, x_2, ..., x_n$. The mean is usually denoted by placing a bar over the symbol for the variable being measured.

Mean square: Used in ANOVA, it can be conceived as a standardized sum of squares that can be assessed against known distribution F.

Measure of central tendency: Any measure of the tendency of quantitative data to cluster around some central value. The central value is commonly estimated by the mean, median, or mode, whereas the closeness with which the values surround the central value is commonly quantified using standard deviation or variance. The phrase 'central tendency' was first used in the late 1920s.

Median: The middle value in any vector of numbers.

Missing data: Data that have not been collected by the respondent for a variety of reasons (refusal, uncertainty, etc.).

Mode: The most common value in any vector of numbers.

Multimodal: Any variable with more than one mode. Usually refers to variables with more than two modes.

Multiple correlation coefficient: A measure of the linear dependence of more than one numerical random variable on another.

Multivariate statistics: Any technique that involves more than one variables. Usually refers to analysis with more than two variables.

Nominal — level of measurement: V whose values are not numerical. Examples include gender (male, female), paint colour (red, white, blue), and type of bird (duck, goose, owl). A variable with just two categories is said to be *dichotomous*, whereas one with more than two categories is described as *polytomous*. The corresponding nouns are *dichotomy* and *polytomy*.

Non-integer: Any number that is not whole.

Non-parametric test: Any test that makes no distributional assumptions about the sample or population under investigation.

Non-probability/non-random sampling strategies: Any sampling technique where individuals in a population do not have an equal probability of selection.

Normal, Gaussian, or **Bell curve**: Any curve that resembles the axial cross-section of a bell.

Normality: The property of a random variable or population having a normal distribution.

Null hypothesis: Any hypothesis that states that there is no difference between two samples on a variable of interest. For example, positing that there is no difference in income between men and women.

Odds ratio: The ratio of the odds on something occurring in one situation to the odds of the same event occurring in a second situation. An odds ratio of one implies that the odds of an event occurring (and hence the probability of its occurrence) are unaffected by the change in situation: they are independent of the situation.

One-tailed assessments: See **One-tailed test**.

One-tailed test: A one-sided test is a statistical hypothesis test in which the values for which we can reject the null hypothesis are located entirely in one tail of the probability distribution.

Operationalize: The practice of deciding how to measure a concept.

Order of operations: A protocol for the order in which equations are solved. See BEDMAS.

Ordinal — level of measurement: A categorical variable in which the categories have an obvious order (e.g., strongly disagree, disagree, neutral, agree, strongly agree), but the distances between categories cannot be accurately measured.

Ordinary least squares (OLS) regression: The simplest and most used of all statistical regression models. The model states that the random variable Y is related to the variable x by $Y = \alpha + \beta_x + \varepsilon$, where the parameters α and β correspond to the intercept and the slope of the line, respectively, and ε denotes a random error.

Outliers: An observation that is very different to other observations in a set of data.

Paired samples *t*-test or **repeated measures *t*-test** or ***t*-test for dependent samples**: Any *t*-test with samples that are not completely idependent from one another. An example of this would be people that are measured at different points in time.

Partial slope coefficients: The slope coefficient between two variables (usually an independent variable and a dependent variable) after allowing for the effect of other variables.

Pearson's *r*: A measure of the degree to which n pairs of values of random variables X and Y are related. When the correlation between two variables is positive, the values of one variable rise as the values of the other variable rise. The correlation is negative if the values of one variable rise as the values of the other fall.

Percentile: A 1/100 slice of a sample or population that's been ranked and divided according to scores on one variable.

Phi: See **Cramer's V**.

Pilot testing: A preliminary test or study of a program or questionnaire used to try out procedures and make any needed changes or adjustments. A pilot test should always be conducted on people that are not part of the final sample.

Population: The complete set of all people in a country, or a town, or any region (or just the number of such people). By extension the term is used for the complete set of objects of interest.

Post-hoc tests: Any test that occurs after analysis has occurred.

Predicted values: The values predicted by a model fitted to a set of data.

Probability: The probability of an event is a number lying in the interval $0 <= p <= 1$, with zero corresponding to an event that never occurs and one to an event that is certain to occur.

Probability samples: Any sampling technique where individuals in a population have an equal (or roughly equal) probability of selection.

Proportional reduction of error: Any measure that indicates the degree to which an estimate is superior to a complete guess. It may also be interpreted as the per cent of explained variation in a dependent variable.

Qualitative outcome variables: A dichotomous outcome variable.

Quota sample: Any sample where the numbers of people in particular groups is used as criteria for selection.

Random process: Any process in which results may not be certain.

Rates: A rate is a special kind of ratio, of two measurements with different units, but usually with an intuitive denominator (such as kilometres per hour, cents per kilogram).

Ratio — level of measurement: A scale of measurement where the difference, or distance, is measured between a state or point of interest and a standard state or point. For example, height above sea-level, distance from London, frequency of a musical note (in cycles per second), temperature in °Kelvin (above absolute zero), clock-time (13:05 on 5 November 2001 AD). Confusingly, comparison of ratio scale measurements gives an interval scale, and in music an interval is measured by the ratio of the frequencies.

Ratios: A stated relationship between two quantities. Rates are a special type of ratio.

Reference group, with dummy variables: An omitted group for whom values can be derived from other variables in a model.

Regression equation: An equation that represents a formal statement about a hypothesized relationship between a series of independent variables and one or more dependent variables.

Relationships: See **Associations**.

Sample: A portion of a population, often chosen for the purpose of statistical analysis.

Sample distribution of means: A distribution that describes the variation in the values of the mean over a series of samples. Tends to asymptotically resemble the normal distribution.

Sampling error: The degree to which a sample 'misses' its population on quantities of interest.

Sampling frame: A list of members of the population of interest.

Simple random sample: The most basic form of probability sample, where members are chosen with reliance on randomly generated numbers.

Skewness: If the distribution of a variable is not symmetrical about the median or the mean, it is said to be skewed. The distribution has *positive* skewness if, in some sense, the tail of high values is longer than the tail of low values, and *negative skewness* if the reverse is true.

Snowball sample: A non-probability sampling method, where each person interviewed may be asked to suggest additional people for interviewing.

Somer's *d*: A non-proportional reduction in error measure of association for ordinal data.

Sparsity: The inverse of density, or the property of being scanty or scattered. In statistics, it typically refers to an area in a distribution where there are too few observations to confidently generalize from a sample to a population.

Spearman's rho: A rank correlation coefficient that may be used as an alternative to Kendall's tau-*b*. Individuals are arranged in order according to two different criteria (or by two different people). The null hypothesis is that the two orderings are independent of one another. It is based on the differences in the ranks given in two orderings.

Standard deviation: The square root of the variance. Karl Pearson introduced the term in 1893, using the symbol σ in the following year.

Standard error of the mean: The square root of the variance of a statistic, used to detect the accuracy with which a variable is measured in a particular analysis.

Standardized: A variable is said to be standardized when it has the same unit of measurement as other variables, and is therefore appropriate for comparison. Converting all currencies to the US dollar, for example, allows you to compare currencies with a common metric. Standard deviations, rates, and ratios are also examples of standardization.

Standard score, normal score, or *z*-score: The normal score corresponding to the *k*th largest of *n* observations is the expected value of the *k*th largest of *n* independent observations from a standard normal distribution.

Statistical significance: The probability that an event or difference observed in a sample occurred by chance alone.

Stratified/hierarchical random sample: The process of separating a sample into several groups, then randomly assigning subjects to those groups.

Student's *t*-distribution: The form of the distribution was published in 1908 by Gosset, writing under the pen-name 'Student', in the context of a random sample of size *n* from a population having a normal distribution. Often used with smaller samples because it is asymptotically equal to the normal distribution.

Sum of squares: A measure of the variability in a set of data is given by the sum of squared differences of the observations from their overall mean. This variability can either be explained by a grouping variable (within-group sum of squares), or unexplained by a grouping variable (between-group sum of squares). The sum of these two is the total sum of squares.

Symmetrical: Having similarity in size, shape, and relative position. Usually used to describe distributions on either side of a mean.

Systematic random sample: A type of probability sample that starts at a random position on a list and selects every *n*th unit of a sampling frame until the desired sample size is reached.

Tau-*c*: Like *Kendall's Tau*-b, except that adjustments are made for table size.

Theoretical probability: Any probability generated from an infinite number of trials. Said differently, it is what the probability of an occurrence should be. For example, the theoretical probability of a coin landing heads is 0.5.

Total sum of squares: See **Sum of squares**.

Total variation: The amount of variation in a dependent variable that is available to be explained by an independent variable.

***t*-test**: A test to assess whether there is an equality of means between two variables having normal distributions and equal variances. Also called student's *t*-test.

Two-tailed assessment, two-tailed test: A two-sided test is a statistical hypothesis test in which the values for which we can reject the null hypothesis are located in two tails of the probability distribution.

Type one error: The chance of accepting the research hypothesis when the null hypothesis is actually true. Often called a false positive.

Type two error: The chance of rejecting the research hypothesis when it is actually true.

Unexplained variation: The amount of variation in a dependent variable that is not explained by one or more independent variables.

Unimodal: Any variable with only one mode.

Univariate: Pertaining to one variable.

Variable: The characteristic measured or observed when an experiment is carried out or an observation is made. Variables may be non-numerical (see categorical variable) or numerical.

Variance: A measure of the variability in the values of a random variable. It is defined as the expectation of the squared difference between the random variable and its expectation (often the mean).

Weights: A derived value that denotes how many population observations are represented by a sample observation. For example, if an observation in a sample has a weight of five, then that person represents five people in the total population.

Within-group sum of squares: See **Sum of squares**.

***X*-axis**: The scale that runs horizontally across a chart.

***Y*-axis**: The scale that runs vertically across a chart.

Zero-order correlations: A correlation between two variables without any assumptions of temporal ordering or causality.

***Z*-score**: See **Standard score**.

Answer Key for Practice Questions

Answers to Chapter 2 Practice Questions

1. $10 + 15 = \mathbf{25}$

2. $10 + 15 - 5 = \mathbf{20}$

3. $10 - (-2) = \mathbf{12}$

4. $(10 + 15) - 5 = \mathbf{20}$

5. $(10 - 15) - 2 = \mathbf{-7}$

6. $10 * 15 = \mathbf{150}$

7. $10 * 15 - 5 = \mathbf{145}$

8. $10 * (15 - 5) = \mathbf{100}$

9. $10 * 15 - 15/5 = \mathbf{147}$

10. $10/5 * 15 - 5 = \mathbf{25}$

11. $(X * Y)^a + b = \mathbf{X^a * Y^a + b}$

12. $(X^a)(X^b) = \mathbf{X^{a+b}}$

13. $\sqrt{x} = \mathbf{x^{1/2}}$

14. if $e = 2.718, y = 5$, and $\ln 5 = 1.61$, then $e^{1.61} = \mathbf{5}$

Identify the levels of measurement (nominal, ordinal, interval, or ratio) for the following:

15. Percentage scores on a math exam: **Ratio**

16. Letter grades on a math exam: **Ordinal**

17. Flavours of ice cream: **Nominal**

18. Fitness training levels on an exercise machine classified as: Easy, Difficult, or Impossible: **Ordinal**

19. Ethnic origins: **Nominal**

20. Political parties: **Nominal**

21. Commuting times to school in kilometres: **Ratio**

22. Years between important historical events: **Ratio**

23. Age (in years): **Ratio**

24. Amount of money in your savings accounts: **Ratio**

25. Temperature on the moon: **Interval**

Answers to Chapter 3 Practice Questions

A. 1. Jorge was correct 37 times and incorrect 3 times. This translates into a ratio of 37:3.

2. His score is calculated as 37/40, or 92.5%.

3. His percentile rank is calculated as 113/1,432, which equals 0.0789. Given this, we could say that he placed in the top 8th percentile.

B. 1. Ethel's contact rate would be calculated by first determining the percentage of people that she contacts, which is 432/541, or 79.9%. When stated as a rate (percentages are essentially a rate per 100), we'd need to multiply the numerator and the denominator by 10, which would yield 799 per 1,000 people.

2. Ethel's contact/non-contact rate is 432:109, which is roughly equivalent to 4:1.

3. The participation rate as a percentage is 112/432, or 25.9%.

C. The approval rate for Charles is calculated as 13/30, or 43.3%; as a ratio, it is 13:17.

Answers to Chapter 4 Practice Questions

1. c.

2. 40%

3. 1/36

4. 3/5

5. 26%

6. 8/16575

7. 0.000495

8. The probability that the one essay question Ryan hasn't studied for is on the exam is:

1/8 = 0.125.

Because one essay question has already been chosen for the exam, the probability that the second essay question Ryan has not studied for will appear on the exam is:

1/7 = 0.143.

The probability that both questions Ryan has not studied for will appear on the exam is:

0.125 * 0.143 = 0.02.

Answers to Chapter 5 Practice Questions

1. Dr Knifewell might like to know that the data will probably be skewed to the right, and that it will likely be unimodal.

2. The data are unimodal and skewed to the right.

3. The outlier is at the value 10,000. It appears to be flattening the normal curve, having a negative effect on the kurtosis value.

Answers to Chapter 6 Practice Questions

1. a. 7
   b. $248,000

2. Mean = 29.4, mean deviation = 30.9

3. Mean = 4.67, standard deviation = 1.84, variance = 3.39

4. The mean would be larger than the median and the histogram would be skewed with a long right tail.

5. The median remains the same, but the mean is increased.

6. Income is almost always positively skewed, which will pull the mean past the median. Very few Canadians earn negative income (except for some self-employed), suggesting that the distribution of income values hits a wall at $0. On the high side of the distribution there are many high earners, and these factors collectively produce a mean that exceeds the median.

7. All of the values will increase. The mean, median, and range will rise due to a broader set of age values, whereas the standard deviation will increase because of an increase in the average distance from the mean.

Answers to Chapter 7 Practice Questions

1. Answers can be found by looking at column B of Appendix A
   a. 0.3810
   b. 0.2995
   c. 0.4803
   d. 0.4131

2. Answers can be found in column C of Appendix A and, when z values are positive, subtracting the value from 1.

   a. Percentile rank = 0.9878 (1–0.012)

   b. Percentile rank = 0.0475

   c. Percentile rank = 0.9236 (1–0.0764)

   d. Percentile rank = 0.3300

3. Answers can be found in column C of Appendix A and, when z values are negative, subtracting the value from 1.

   a. 40.13% of all cases are above a z-value of 0.25

   b. 88.69% of all cases are above a z-value of –1.21 (1–0.1131)

   c. 11.31% of all cases are above a z-value of 1.21

   d. 97.78% of all cases are above a z-value of –2.01 (1–0.0222)

4. Answers can be found in column B of Appendix A.

   a. 59.64%

   b. 12.88%

   c. 83.53%

   d. 7.69%

5. Sigmund's percentile rank is 8.08. We get that number by calculating z as:

$$z = \frac{X - \mu}{\sigma}$$

$$= \frac{45 - 52}{5}$$

$$= -1.40$$

This value comes from column C of Appendix A. Clearly, Sigmund didn't do very well.

6. Lesley did a bit better, and her percentile rank is 0.6554, which comes from subtracting 0.3446 (the area beyond z, or everyone that beat her) from 1. Here's the calculation for z:

$$z = \frac{X - \mu}{\sigma}$$

$$= \frac{54 - 52}{5}$$

$$= 0.40$$

7. Your child is quite bright, beating 93.7% of all people who wrote the exam (this value comes from column C of Appendix A).

$$z = \frac{X - \mu}{\sigma}$$

$$= \frac{148 - 125}{15}$$

$$= 1.53$$

8. For Feng:

$$z = \frac{X - \mu}{\sigma}$$

$$= \frac{76 - 80}{8}$$

$$= -0.50$$

   For Lucy:

$$z = \frac{X - \mu}{\sigma}$$

$$= \frac{94 - 80}{8}$$

$$= 1.75$$

65.14% of all people are between these two scores (use column B to find this).

Answers to Chapter 8 Practice Questions

1. Since representativeness is the goal, a simple random sample would be preferred.

2. Given the focus on representativeness across faculties, a stratified random sample would be preferred.

3. Snowball samples are often used for vulnerable populations. A convenience sample might also be appropriate.

4. Since each instrument is needed in the sample, a stratified random sample would be preferred.

5. Given that the sample is random, selected cases will likely differ. Depending on how you choose to stratify, values here will also vary. There should only be six individuals in the sample.

Answers to Chapter 9 Practice Questions

1.

	Men	Women
a.		
Mean	44.50	28.10
Standard deviation	8.68	8.54
Variance	75.39	72.99
b.	2.75	2.70

   c. For men (28.35, 60.65)
   For women (12.22, 43.98)

2. First, calculate the mean, standard deviation and the standard error:

   Mean = 10.92
   Standard error = 1.14

   Then, find the appropriate t-value at $n - 1$ degrees of freedom:

   $t = 2.069$ for a 95% confidence interval at $df = 23$.

   Confidence interval at 95%: 8.33 < population mean < 13.05.

   We can be 95% confident that the actual population mean for the number of hours students worked on their assignment was between 8.33 hours and 13.05 hours.

3. First, calculate the proportion standard of error:

   $$s_p = \sqrt{\frac{P(1-P)}{n}}$$

   $$= \sqrt{\frac{0.34(1-0.34)}{50}}$$

   $$= 0.0670$$

   Confidence interval $= P \pm t_{critical}*s_p$

   $$= 0.34 \pm 2.680*0.0670$$

   $$= 0.160, 0.520$$

Answers to Chapter 10 Practice Questions

1. a.

   $$z_{obtained} = \frac{\overline{X} - \mu}{\sigma/\sqrt{n}}$$

   $$= \frac{73 - 75}{8/\sqrt{5}}$$

   $$= \frac{-2}{3.578}$$

   $$= -0.559$$

   b. The absolute value of 0.559 does not exceed the critical z-value of 1.96, suggesting that we cannot be 95% confident in the superiority of Amber's new route.

2.

   $$z_{obtained} = \frac{\overline{X} - \mu}{\sigma/\sqrt{n}}$$

   $$= \frac{31000 - 29000}{27000/\sqrt{16}}$$

   $$= \frac{2000}{6750}$$

   $$= 0.296$$

   Jasper's income was significantly higher than the Canadian average, because the $z_{obtained}$ value does not exceed the critical value of 1.96.

3. We can be 95% confident that the population proportion lies between 50.3% and 53.7%.

Answers to Chapter 11 Practice Questions

1. First, we need to calculate the mean and the sample standard deviation:

   For Leslie:
   Mean = 519
   Sample standard deviation = 110.6

   For Dayle:
   Mean = 492
   Sample standard deviation = 305.7

   With this information, we can calculate the standard error of the difference between means:

   $$s_{\overline{X}_1 - \overline{X}_2} = \sqrt{\left(\frac{n_1 s_1^2 + n_2 s_2^2}{n_1 + n_2 - 2}\right)\left(\frac{n_1 + n_2}{n_1 n_2}\right)}$$

   $$= \sqrt{\left(\frac{10*110.6^2 + 10*305.7^2}{10+10-2}\right)\left(\frac{10+10}{10*10}\right)}$$

   $$= \sqrt{\left(\frac{1056848.5}{18}\right)\left(\frac{20}{100}\right)}$$

   $$= \sqrt{58713.8*0.2}$$

   $$= 108.36$$

Next, we calculate t as:

$$t = \frac{\overline{X}_1 - \overline{X}_2}{s_{\overline{X}_1 - \overline{X}_2}}$$

$$= \frac{519 - 492}{108.36}$$

$$= 0.249$$

To find $t_{critical}$, calculate degrees of freedom as $df = (n_1 + n_2 - 2)$, which equals 18. At this level, $t_{critical} = 2.101$, which is much larger than $t_{observed}$, leading us to conclude that we cannot be 95% more confident that Leslie will beat Dayle.

2. Since we have fairly large samples (>120), we can use the z-distribution and, consequently, the simpler calculation for the standard error of the difference between means:

$$s_{\overline{X}_1 - \overline{X}_2} = \sqrt{\left(\frac{s_1^2}{n_1 - 1}\right)\left(\frac{s_2^2}{n_2 - 1}\right)}$$

$$= \sqrt{\left(\frac{7^2}{200 - 1}\right)\left(\frac{5^2}{200 - 1}\right)}$$

$$= \sqrt{\frac{49}{199} + \frac{25}{199}}$$

$$= 0.610$$

This we use to calculate $z_{observed}$:

$$z_{observed} = \frac{\overline{X}_1 - \overline{X}_2}{s_{\overline{X}_1 - \overline{X}_2}}$$

$$= \frac{48 - 45}{0.610}$$

$$= 4.918$$

Comparing $z_{observed}$ to $z_{critical}$ value of 1.96, we can conclude that there are significant differences in the life satisfaction levels of women and men.

3. First, we need to calculate P_u:

$$P_u = \frac{n_1 P_{s1} + n_2 P_{s2}}{n_1 + n_2}$$

$$= \frac{201*0.76 + 218*0.68}{201 + 218}$$

$$= \frac{301}{419}$$

$$= 0.718$$

Next, we use P_u to calculate the standard error of the difference between means:

$$s_{\overline{X}_1 - \overline{X}_2} = \sqrt{P_u(1 - P_u)}\sqrt{\frac{n_1 + n_2}{n_1 n_2}}$$

$$= \sqrt{0.718(1 - 0.718)}\sqrt{\frac{201 + 218}{201 * 218}}$$

$$= \sqrt{0.202}\sqrt{\frac{419}{43818}}$$

$$= 0.449 * 0.098$$

$$= 0.044$$

Finally, we can calculate $z_{obtained}$:

$$z_{obtained} = \frac{(P_{sample1} - P_{sample2})}{s_{\overline{X}_1 - \overline{X}_2}}$$

$$= \frac{0.76 - 0.68}{0.044}$$

$$= 1.36$$

Comparing $z_{obtained}$ to $z_{critical}$ of 1.96, we can conclude that the differences are not statistically significant.

Answers to Chapter 12 Practice Questions

1. They are nominal because the distance between response categories cannot be identified, nor can the categories be ranked.

2. Chi-square = 1133.1

3. 6

4. Phi = 0.656, Cramer's V = 0.464. It is preferable to use Cramer's V because the table is bigger than 2 x 2.

Answers to Chapter 13 Practice Questions

1. 0.270

2. 0.60

Answers to Chapter 14 Practice Questions

1. −0.2239

2. 0.281

Answers to Chapter 15 Practice Questions

1. a.

	Bicycling		Cleaning		Health club		Yoga		Tennis	
	X	X^2	X	X^2	X	X^2	X	X^2	X	X^2
	236	55,696	207	42,849	325	105,625	236	55,696	413	170,569
	321	103,041	249	62,001	401	160,801	312	97,344	599	358,801
	345	119,025	292	85,264	452	204,304	345	119,025	604	364,816
	292	85,264	302	91,204	474	224,676	281	78,961	434	188,356
	301	90,601	222	49,284	353	124,609	301	90,601	477	227,529
Sum	**1,495**	**453,627**	**1,272**	**330,602**	**2,005**	**820,015**	**1,475**	**441,627**	**2,527**	**1,310,071**
$\overline{X}$	**299**		**254.4**		**401**		**295**		**505.4**	

$N = 25$ grand mean = 350.96

b. SS_{total} $= \sum X^2_{total} - N_{total}\overline{X}^2_{total}$

$= (453627 + 330602 + 820015 + 441627 + 1310071) - 25(350.96)^2$

$= 3355942 - 25\,(123172.92)$

$= 276619$

SS_{within} $= \sum X^2_{total} - \sum N_{group}\overline{X}^2$

$= 3355942 - [5(299)^2 + 5(254.4)^2 + 5(401)^2 + 5(295)^2 + 5(505.4)^2]$

$= 3355942 - [447005 + 323596.8 + 804005 + 435125 + 1277145.8]$

$= 3355942 - 3286877.61$

$= 69064.39$

$SS_{between}$ $= \sum N_{group}\overline{X}^2_{group} - N_{total}\overline{X}^2_{total}$

$= 3286877.6 - 3079323.04$

$= 207554.56$

$SS_{between}$ $= SS_{total} - SS_{within}$

$= 276619 - 69064.39$

$= 207554.61$

c. df_{within} $= N_{total} - k$ $df_{between}$ $= k - 1$

$= 25 - 5$ $= 5 - 1$

$= 20$ $= 4$

d. MS_{within} $= SS_{within}/df_{within}$ $MS_{between}$ $= SS_{between}/df_{between}$

$= 69064.39/20$ $= 207554.56/4$

$= 3453.22$ $= 51888.64$

e. F $= MS_{between}/MS_{within}$

$= 51888.64/3453.22$

$= 15.03$

f. $F_{calculated}$ vs $F_{critical} = 15.03 > 2.87$

We can be 95% confident that at least two groups differ significantly in the number of calories burnt per hour.

2.   a.

Durability of Jeans								
	Levi's		People's Liberty		Silvers		Guess	
	X	X^2	X	X^2	X	X^2	X	X^2
1	182	33,124	209	43,681	1,040	1,081,600	260	67,600
2	130	16,900	225	50,625	780	608,400	624	389,376
3	91	8,281	156	24,336	520	270,400	416	173,056
4	200	40,000	260	67,600	340	115,600	222	49,284
5	154	23,716	101	10,201	416	173,056	85	7,225
Σ	757	122,021	951	196,443	3,096	2,249,056	1,607	686,541
$\overline{X}$	151.4		190.2		619.2		321.4	

$N = 20$ Grand mean = 320.55

$$SS_{total} = \Sigma X^2_{total} - N_{total}\overline{X}^2_{total}$$
$$= (122021 + 196443 + 2249056 + 686541) - 20(320.55)^2$$
$$= 3254061 - 20(102752.30)$$
$$= 1199015$$

$$SS_{within} = \Sigma X^2_{total} - \Sigma N_{group}\overline{X}^2_{group}$$
$$= (122021 + 196443 + 2249056 + 686541) - [5(151.4)^2 + 5(190.2)^2$$
$$+ 5(619.2)^2 + 5(321.4)^2]$$
$$= 3254061 - [114609.8 + 180880.2 + 1917043.2 + 516489.8]$$
$$= 3254061 - 2729023$$
$$= 525038$$

$$SS_{between} = \Sigma N_{group}\overline{X}^2_{group} - N_{total}\overline{X}^2_{total}$$
$$= [5(151.4)^2 + 5(190.2)^2 + 5(619.2)^2 + 5(321.4)^2] - 20(320.55)^2$$
$$= 2729023 - 2055046.05$$
$$= 673976.95$$

$$df_{within} = N_{total} - k \qquad df_{between} = k - 1$$
$$= 20 - 4 \qquad\qquad\qquad = 4 - 1$$
$$= 16 \qquad\qquad\qquad\quad = 3$$

$$MS_{within} = \frac{SS_{within}}{df_{within}} \qquad MS_{between} = \frac{SS_{between}}{df_{between}}$$
$$= 525038 / 16 \qquad\qquad = 673976.95 / 3$$
$$= 32814.88 \qquad\qquad\quad = 224658.98$$

b.

$$F_{observed} = \frac{MS_{between}}{MS_{within}}$$

$= 224658.98/32814.88$

$= 6.846$

$6.846 > 3.24$

Since the $F_{observed}$ value of 6.846 exceeds the $F_{critical}$ value of 3.24, we know with 95% certainty that at least two of our groups differ significantly in terms of durability.

Answers to Chapter 16 Practice Questions

1. a. $\overline{X} = 2.33$

   $\overline{Y} = 771.42$

   b. and c.

X	$(X - \overline{X})$	Y	$(Y - \overline{Y})$	$(X - \overline{X})(Y - \overline{Y})$	$(X - \overline{X})^2$	$(Y - \overline{Y})^2$
3	0.67	890	118.58	79.45	0.45	14,061.22
2	−0.33	568	−203.42	67.13	0.11	41,379.7
3	0.67	860	88.58	59.35	0.45	7,846.42
1	−1.33	625	−146.42	194.74	1.77	21,438.82
1	−1.33	775	3.58	−4.76	1.77	12.82
3	0.67	900	128.58	86.15	0.45	16,532.82
3	0.67	1,095	323.58	216.8	0.45	104,704.02
3	0.67	800	28.58	19.15	0.45	816.82
2	−0.33	765	−6.42	2.12	0.11	41.22
3	0.67	629	−142.42	−95.42	0.45	20,283.46
1	−1.33	600	−171.42	227.99	1.77	29,384.82
3	0.67	750	−21.42	−14.35	0.45	458.82
			Σ	838.35	8.68	256,960.96

$SP = 838.35$

$SS_x = 8.68$

$SS_y = 256960.96$

d.

$$b = \frac{SP}{SS_X}$$

$= 838.35/8.68$

$= 96.58$

e. $a = \overline{Y} - b\,\overline{X}$

   $= 771.42 - (96.58)(2.33)$

   $= 771.42 - 225.03$

   $= 546.39$

f.

$$r = \frac{SP}{\sqrt{SS_X SS_Y}}$$

$$= \frac{838.35}{\sqrt{(8.68)(256960.96)}}$$

$$= \frac{838.35}{\sqrt{2230421.13}}$$

$$= 838.35/1493.46$$

$$= 0.56$$

g. $r^2 = 0.56 * 0.56$

$$= 0.31$$

By knowing the number of rooms in a house the prediction of monthly rent increases by 31%.

2. a. $\overline{X} = 2.33$

$\overline{Y} = 139.56$

# of people (X)	$(X - \overline{X})$	Bills (Y)	$(Y - \overline{Y})$	$(X - \overline{X})(Y - \overline{Y})$	$(X - \overline{X})^2$	$(Y - \overline{Y})^2$
3	0.67	175	35.44	23.74	0.45	1,255.99
2	−0.33	130	−9.56	3.15	0.11	91.39
3	0.67	231	91.44	61.26	0.45	8,361.27
3	0.67	278	138.44	92.75	0.45	19,165.63
2	−0.33	40	−99.56	32.85	0.11	9,912.19
3	0.67	205.83	66.27	44.4	0.45	4,391.71
1	−1.33	0	−139.56	185.61	1.77	19,476.99
1	−1.33	38.41	−101.15	134.53	1.77	10,231.32
1	−1.33	41.23	−98.33	130.78	1.77	9,668.79
3	0.67	44.2	−95.36	−63.89	0.45	9,093.53
3	0.67	176	36.44	24.41	0.45	1,327.87
3	0.67	315	175.44	117.54	0.45	30,779.19
			Σ	787.13	8.68	123,755.87

$$b = \frac{SP}{SS_X}$$

$$= 787.13/8.68$$

$$= 90.68$$

$$a = \overline{Y} - b\overline{X}$$

$$= 139.56 - (90.68)(2.33)$$

$$= 139.56 - 211.28$$

$$= -71.72$$

$$r = \frac{SP}{\sqrt{SS_X SS_Y}}$$

$$= \frac{787.13}{\sqrt{(8.68)(123755.87)}}$$

$$= \frac{787.13}{\sqrt{1074200.95}}$$

$$= 787.13/1036.44$$

$$= 0.76$$

$$r^2 = 0.58$$

b. First, we need to calculate the standard deviation:

$$s_X = \sqrt{\frac{\sum (X - \overline{X})^2}{n - 1}}$$

$$= \sqrt{\frac{8.68}{11}}$$

$$= 0.89$$

$$s_Y = \sqrt{\frac{\sum (Y - \overline{Y})^2}{n - 1}}$$

$$= \sqrt{\frac{123756}{11}}$$

$$= 106.07$$

Next, we substitute the appropriate values into the equation for standardized partial slopes:

$$b_1^* = b_1 \left(\frac{s_1}{s_y} \right)$$

$$= 90.68 \left(\frac{0.89}{106.07} \right)$$

$$= 0.78$$

Answers to Chapter 17 Practice Questions

1. a. 0.3286
    b. 1.2498
    c. 16.119
    d. 1
    e. 0.0973
    f. 0.0004

Answers to Chapter 18 Practice Questions

1. The mean and standard deviation for the x-variables are 9.00 and 3.32, and for the y-variables they are 7.5 and 2.03, respectively.

2. The slope would be higher and the y-intercept would be lower.

3. Cook's Distance = 8.1.

Solution Key for Boxes

Box 7.1: It's Your Turn: Determining the Proportion of Observations at Various Standard Deviation Cut-Points

1. 2.5%

2. 99.5%

3. 50%

4. 16%

5. 97.5%

Box 7.3: It's Your Turn: Converting Standard Scores to Percentile Ranks

1. Range of values ±1 standard deviation from the mean.

   a. We know that z will equal ±1, therefore we solve the standard score equation for X.

   b. For the lower bound:

$$z = \frac{X - \overline{X}}{s}$$

$$-1 = \frac{X - 5.7}{5.1}$$

$$5.1 * -1 = X - 5.7$$

$$-5.1 + 5.7 = X$$

$$0.6 = X$$

   c. For the upper bound:

$$z = \frac{X - \overline{X}}{s}$$

$$1 = \frac{X - 5.7}{5.1}$$

$$5.1 * 1 = X - 5.7$$

$$5.1 + 5.7 = X$$

$$10.8 = X$$

Therefore 68% of Canadians between ages 18 and 29 go out to a restaurant, movie, or theatre approximately 1 (0.6) to 11 (10.8) evenings per month.

2. Value that the lowest 10% of all observations fall below.

   a. Because we are looking for a value that extends towards the tail (not from the value to the mean), we look in column C for 0.10 (or column B for 0.40). The z-score value is –1.28 (remember to change from an absolute value to the end of the distribution you are focused on).

$$z = \frac{X - \overline{X}}{s}$$

$$-1.28 = \frac{X - 5.7}{5.1}$$

$$5.1 * -1.28 = X - 5.7$$

$$-6.528 + 5.7 = X$$

$$-0.828 = X$$

b. Since a person cannot go out less than zero times a month, we can say that the 10% of people who go out least frequently go out about 0 times per month.

3. Value which the highest 40% of all observations are above.

   a. We are looking for a value that extends towards the tail (not from the value to the mean); we will look in column C for 0.40 (or column B for 0.10). The z-score value is 0.25

$$z = \frac{X - \overline{X}}{s}$$

$$0.25 = \frac{X - 5.7}{5.1}$$

$$5.1 * +0.25 = X - 5.7$$

$$1.275 + 5.7 = X$$

$$6.975 = X$$

   b. We can say we expect that the 40% of people who go out the most frequently go out at least 7 times per month.

4. The percentage of cases that fall between the values of 4 and 9.

   a. We will need to calculate the z-score for both the upper and lower limits that we have:

   b. Lower limit:

$$z = \frac{X - \overline{X}}{s}$$

$$= \frac{4 - 5.7}{5.1}$$

$$= \frac{-1.7}{5.1}$$

$$= -0.333$$

The z-score of −0.333 is equal to 0.129 or 12.9%. Thus 12.9% of people fall between the mean and going out 4 nights per month.

c. Upper limit:

$$z = \frac{X - \overline{X}}{s}$$

$$= \frac{9 - 5.7}{5.1}$$

$$= \frac{3.3}{5.1}$$

$$= 0.647$$

The z-score of 0.647 is equal to 0.242 or 24.2%. Thus 24.2% of people fall between the mean and going out 9 nights per month.

d. Adding the percentage between the mean and 4, and between the mean and 7 will give the total % of people in this range. 12.9 + 24.2 = 37.1% of people between the ages of 18 and 29 go out between about 4 and 9 nights per month to a restaurant, movie, or theatre.

5. Value which 75% of all observations fall below.

   a. This time we are looking at a value above 50%, or more than half of the distribution. Therefore our value must be above the mean. Since we know that 50% covers from the mean to the lowest value, we know that 25% will fall above the mean (75% − 50%). Therefore we are looking for the z-score at which 25% of cases are between it and the mean.

   b. We are looking for a value towards the mean (column B) for 0.25. The z-score value is 0.67.

$$z = \frac{X - \overline{X}}{s}$$

$$0.67 = \frac{X - 5.7}{5.1}$$

$$5.1 * +0.67 = X - 5.7$$

$$3.417 + 5.7 = X$$

$$9.12 = X$$

   c. We can expect that 75% of Canadians aged 18 to 29 go out 9 times or less per month.

Box 10.1: It's Your Turn: t-Test for the Same Sample Measured Twice

Individual	# of partners per year at age 18	# of partners per year at age 21	$d_i = x_{i1} - x_{i2}$	d^2
1	2	1	1	1
2	0	0	0	0
3	3	2	1	1
4	1	2	−1	1
5	8	1	7	49
6	1	1	0	0
7	2	1	1	1
8	0	2	−2	4
9	0	4	−4	16
10	3	1	2	4
	$\overline{X}_1$ 2.00	$\overline{X}_2$ 1.50	$\sum d_i$ 5	$\sum d^2$ 77

1. For each age (column), calculate the average ($\overline{X}_1$ and $\overline{X}_2$).

2. For each individual, calculate the difference between the number of partners at age 18 and 21 ($d_i = x_{i1} - x_{i2}$) and then sum this value ($\sum d_i$).

3. To simplify, use the formula $s_d = \sqrt{\dfrac{\sum d^2}{n-1} - (\overline{X}_1 - \overline{X}_2)^2}$ to calculate the standard deviation:

$$s_d = \sqrt{\frac{77}{9} - (2.0 - 1.5)^2}$$

$$= \sqrt{8.56 - 0.25}$$

$$= 2.88$$

If we calculate this with the two formulas, we get:

$$\overline{X}_d = \frac{\sum d_i}{n} = \frac{5}{10} = 0.50$$

$$s_d = \sqrt{\frac{\sum (d - \overline{X}_d)^2}{n-1}} = \sqrt{\frac{74.5}{9}} = 2.877$$

Finally, if we use the combined formula but divide 77 by 9 ($N - 1$), we get 2.882. The only difference between the two formulas is rounding.

4. $s_{\overline{d}} = \dfrac{s_d}{\sqrt{n-1}}$

$$= \frac{2.73}{\sqrt{9}}$$

$$= 0.91$$

5. $t = \dfrac{\overline{X}_1 - \overline{X}_2}{s_{\overline{d}}}$

$= \dfrac{2.0 - 1.5}{0.91}$

$= 0.54$

6. There is no significant difference between ages, because $t_{observed}$ does not exceed the $t_{critical}$ value of 2.262.

Box 11.1: It's Your Turn: The Two-Sample t-Test

1. There will be no difference in feelings of attachment between people who are second generation Canadians versus third generation Canadians.

2. Sophia has asked a question that requires a two-sample t-test (actually, a z-test is what's asked for, but given the large sample size, you could do either).

3. First, calculate the standard error of the difference between means:

$s_{\overline{X}_1 - \overline{X}_2} = \sqrt{\left(\dfrac{N_1 s_1^2 + N_2 s_2^2}{N_1 + N_2 - 2}\right)\left(\dfrac{N_1 + N_2}{N_1 N_2}\right)}$

$= \sqrt{\left(\dfrac{6799*0.776^2 + 23237*0.593}{6799 + 23237 - 2}\right)\left(\dfrac{6799 + 23237}{6799*23237}\right)}$

$= \sqrt{\left(\dfrac{12265.46}{30034}\right)\left(\dfrac{30036}{157988363}\right)}$

$= \sqrt{0.408*0.00019}$

$= 0.0088$

Then, calculate t: $t = \dfrac{\overline{X}_1 - \overline{X}_2}{s_{\overline{X}_1 - \overline{X}_2}}$

$= \dfrac{4.59 - 4.78}{0.0088}$

$= -21.59$

3. You would reject the null hypothesis.

Box 11.2: It's Your Turn: The Two-Sample Proportion

1. Calculate P_u, the estimate of the proportion of the population in the category of interest (the proportion of somewhat spiritual men and women who use prayer) using the equation:

$P_u = \dfrac{N_1 P_{S1} + N_2 P_{S2}}{N_1 + N_2} = \dfrac{114734*0.381 + 143013*0.516}{114734 + 143013} = \dfrac{43713.65 + 73794.71}{257747} = 0.456$

2. Use this value to calculate the standard deviation of the difference between sample proportions:

$$s_{\bar{X}_1 - \bar{X}_2} = \sqrt{P_u(1 - P_u)}\sqrt{\frac{N_1 + N_2}{N_1 N_2}}$$

$$= \sqrt{0.456(1 - 0.456)}\sqrt{\frac{114734 + 143013}{114734 * 143013}}$$

$$= \sqrt{0.248}\sqrt{\frac{257747}{16408453542}}$$

$$= 0.498 * 0.0040$$

$$= 0.0020$$

3. Calculate the value of $z_{obtained}$ using:

$$z_{obtained} = \frac{(P_{sample1} - P_{sample2})}{s_{\bar{X}_1 - \bar{X}_2}} = \frac{0.381 - 0.516}{0.002} = -67.5$$

4. Compare the value of $z_{obtained}$ to the critical value. (Hint: remember that my hypothesis had direction!)

As –67.5 is much larger than the one-tailed critical value of –1.65, we can be 95% confident that Aboriginal women who consider themselves very, somewhat, or not very spiritual are more likely to use prayer than Aboriginal men who consider themselves very, somewhat, or not very spiritual to maintain their religion or spirituality.

Box 12.3: It's Your Turn: Phi—Drinking and Daily Exercise

1.

	Regularly has more than 12 drinks a week		
Exercises daily	Yes	No	Total
Yes	4	2	6
No	5	9	14
Total	9	11	20

2. Upper left: $f_e = \dfrac{\Sigma_{column} * \Sigma_{row}}{N} = \dfrac{9*6}{20} = \dfrac{54}{20} = 2.7$

Upper right: $f_e = \dfrac{\Sigma_{column} * \Sigma_{row}}{N} = \dfrac{11*6}{20} = \dfrac{66}{20} = 3.3$

Lower left: $f_e = \dfrac{\Sigma_{column} * \Sigma_{row}}{N} = \dfrac{9*14}{20} = \dfrac{126}{20} = 6.3$

Lower right: $f_e = \dfrac{\Sigma_{column} * \Sigma_{row}}{N} = \dfrac{11*14}{20} = \dfrac{154}{20} = 7.7$

Exercises daily	Regularly has more than 12 drinks a week		Total
	Yes	No	
Yes	4 (2.7)	2 (3.3)	6
No	5 (6.3)	9 (7.7)	14
Total	9	11	20

3.

Group	f_o	f_e	$(f_o - f_e)^2$	$\dfrac{(f_o - f_e)^2}{f_e}$
YY	4	2.7	1.69	0.63
YN	2	3.3	1.69	0.51
NY	5	6.3	1.69	0.27
NN	9	7.7	1.69	0.22
Total				$\chi^2 = 1.63$

4.

$$\phi = \sqrt{\frac{\chi^2}{N}} = \sqrt{\frac{1.63}{20}} = 0.285$$

There is a moderate association between daily exercise and regularly drinking 12 or more drinks a week.

Box 12.5: It's Your Turn: Cramer's V

Work Status in 2000	Marital Status			Total
	Married	Divorced/separated	Single	
Worked mainly full-time weeks	3,485,748 (1,624,006)	604,011 (257,131.1)	1,193,175 (701,797.2)	5,282,934
Worked mainly part-time weeks	1,291,201 (1,455,333.0)	152,330 (230,424.9)	871,134 (628,907.1)	2,314,665
Total	4,776,949	756,341	2,064,309	7,597,599

1. Note: in this table we have used the non-squared term for $(f_o - f_e)$.

   You will still need to square the term.

Group	f_o	f_e	$(f_o - f_e)$	$\dfrac{(f_o - f_e)^2}{f_e}$
FM	3,485,748	3,321,615.99	164,132.01	8,110.30
FD	604,011	525,916.09	78,094.91	11,596.55
FS	1,193,175	1,435,401.92	−242,226.92	40,876.27
PM	1,291,201	1,455,333.00	−164,132.00	18,510.76
PD	152,330	230,424.90	−78,094.90	26,467.68
PS	871,134	628,907.10	242,226.90	93,294.97
Total	7,597,599	7,597,599.00		198,856.5451

2. Instead of computing phi, compute Cramer's V using:

$$V = \sqrt{\frac{\chi^2}{(N)(\min(r-1)\,|\,(c-1))}} = \sqrt{\frac{198856.5451}{(7597559)(2-1)}} = 0.162$$

Box 12.8: It's Your Turn: Lambda

Wears all protective equipment for in-line skating	Female	Male	Row total
Yes	9	2	11
No	42	47	89
Column total	51	49	100

1. Make the two extreme predictions for the dependent variable.

   Wears protective equipment: 100 – 11 = 89 misclassifications

   Does not wear protective equipment: 100 – 89 = 11 misclassifications

   Based on smaller value E_1 = 11

2. Calculate the extreme predictions using the independent variable; determine E_2.

   Predicting that a female wears protective equipment: 51 – 9 = 42

   Predicting that a female does not wear protective equipment: 51 – 42 = 9

   Predicting that a male wears protective equipment: 49 – 2 = 47

   Predicting that a male does not wear protective equipment: 49 – 47 = 2

   As lowest classification errors for each sex are for not wearing protective equipment we sum 9 (females) and 2 (males). Thus E_2 = 11.

3. Calculate lambda (or the percentage increase in predictive accuracy):

$$\lambda = \frac{E_1 - E_2}{E_1} = \frac{11 - 11}{11} = 0$$

Thus knowing if a person is male or female will not improve our ability to predict whether they will wear protective gear while in-line skating.

Box 13.2: It's Your Turn: Calculating Gamma

Walk alone * Quick justice					
Counts					
		Courts do good job of quick justice			
		Good	Average	Poor	Total
Walk alone at night	At least once a week	40	77	86	203
	Up to once a month	18	61	51	130
	Never	16	26	38	80
	Total	74	164	175	413

1. Compute N_S and N_D (use tables):

Cell	# of concordant cells	# of concordant observations	Contribution to N_S
A	4 (e, f, h, i)	$61 + 51 + 26 + 38 = 176$	$40 * 176 = 7040$
B	2 (f, i)	$51 + 38 = 89$	$77 * 89 = 6853$
C	0		
D	2 (h, i)	$26 + 38 = 64$	$18 * 64 = 1152$
E	1 (i)	38	$61 * 38 = 2318$
F	0		
G	0		
H	0		
I	0		
			$N_S = 17363$

Cell	# of discordant cells	# of discordant observations	Contribution to N_D
A	0		
B	2 (d, g)	$18 + 16 = 34$	$77 * 34 = 2618$
C	4 (d, e, g, h)	$18 + 61 + 16 + 26 = 121$	$86 * 121 = 10406$
D	0		
E	1 (g)	16	$61 * 16 = 976$
F	2 (g, h)	$16 + 26 = 42$	$51 * 42 = 2142$
G	0		
H	0		
I	0		
			$N_D = 16142$

2. Calculate gamma: $G = \dfrac{N_{same} - N_{different}}{N_{same} + N_{different}} = \dfrac{17363 - 16142}{17363 + 16142} = \dfrac{1221}{33505} = 0.036$

3. Is there a weak, moderate, or strong relationship between people's views on the efficiency of the courts and walking alone in neighbourhoods after dark?

   There is a weak relationship.

Box 13.4: It's Your Turn: Calculating Spearman's Rho

1. Complete table:

Case	Number of drinks a week	Drinks rank	Grade	Grade rank	D	D²
1	10	2	65	4	−2	4
2	2	5.5	75	2	3.5	12.25
3	2	5.5	52	7	−1.5	2.25
4	0	8	98	1	7	49
5	1	7	45	8	−1	1
6	5	3	55	6	−3	9
7	20	1	70	3	−2	4
8	3	4	60	5	−1	1
					0	8.25

2.
$$r_s = 1 - \frac{6 * \sum D^2}{N(N^2 - 1)}$$

$$= 1 - \frac{6 * 82.5}{8(64 - 1)}$$

$$= 1 - \frac{495}{504} = 0.018$$

3. Squared rho = 0.000324

4. By knowing the number of drinks a student has, one could reduce their errors of prediction by 0.03%. As this is incredibly low, it doesn't seem that the amount he drinks explains why Andy is doing better than Marianne. Maybe Andy is studying more than he admits?

Box 13.7: It's Your Turn: Calculating Somer's d

The relationship between educational status and hours spent on unpaid labour per week				
	Educational status			
Hours on unpaid household labour/week	Not studying	Part-time student	Full-time student	Total
Less than 5	52 (a)	1 (b)	20 (c)	73
5 to 14	59 (d)	2 (e)	5 (f)	66
15 or more	106 (g)	2 (h)	3 (i)	111
Total	217	5	28	250

Source: 2001 Individual Census

1. Compute N_S, N_D, and $Ties_y$.

$$
\begin{aligned}
N_S &= a(e + f + h + i) + b(f + i) + d(h + i) + e(i) \\
&= 52(2 + 5 + 2 + 3) + 1(5 + 3) + 59(2 + 3) + 2(3) \\
&= 624 + 8 + 295 + 6 \\
&= 933
\end{aligned}
$$

$$
\begin{aligned}
N_D &= b(d + g) + c(d + e + g + h) + e(g) + f(g + h) \\
&= 1(59 + 106) + 20(59 + 2 + 106 + 2) + 2(106) + 5(106 + 2) \\
&= 165 + 3380 + 212 + 540 \\
&= 4297
\end{aligned}
$$

$$
\begin{aligned}
Ties_y &= a(b + c) + b(c) + d(e + f) + e(f) + g(h + i) + h(i) \\
&= 52(1 + 20) + 1(20) + 59(2 + 5) + 2(5) + 106(2 + 3) + 2(3) \\
&= 1092 + 20 + 413 + 10 + 530 + 6 \\
&= 2071
\end{aligned}
$$

2. Calculate Somer's d.

$$
d = \frac{N_{same} - N_{different}}{N_{same} + N_{different} + Ties_y} = \frac{933 - 4297}{933 + 4297 + 2071} = \frac{-3364}{7301} = -0.461
$$

3. What can you say about the relationship between hours on unpaid housework and being a student, based on Somer's d?

The value indicates that there is a strong relationship between being a student and how many hours you spend on housework. That it is a negative value represents that as you increase on one (more of a student) you decrease on the other (less time on housework).

Box 13.9: It's Your Turn: Kendall's Tau-*b*

1. Compute the value for $Ties_x$.

$$
\begin{aligned}
Ties_x &= 52(59 + 106) + 59(106) + 1(2 + 2) + 2(2) + 20(5 + 3) + 5(3) \\
&= 8580 + 6254 + 4 + 4 + 160 + 15 \\
&= 15017
\end{aligned}
$$

2. Calculate Kendall's Tau-*b*:

$$
\begin{aligned}
tau\text{-}b &= \frac{N_{same} - N_{different}}{(N_{same} + N_{different} + Ties_y)(N_{same} + N_{different} + Ties_x)} \\[2mm]
&= \frac{933 - 4297}{\sqrt{(933 + 4297 + 2071)(933 + 4297 + 15017)}} \\[2mm]
&= \frac{-3367}{\sqrt{(7301)(20247)}} = \frac{-3367}{12158.3} = -0.277
\end{aligned}
$$

3. Does the inclusion of the ties on the independent ties change what Isa can say about the relationship between students and hours on housework?

By including $Ties_x$ we can see that the relationship is not as strong as it had appeared. There is certainly a moderate (and SPSS tells us significant) relationship, but its strength has decreased.

Box 14.2: It's Your Turn: Calculating Pearson's r

1. As always, the first step is to organize the provided information, as well as the sums and products, into a chart:

obs#	X	Y	X²	Y²	XY
1	38	2	1,444	4	76
2	40	2	1,600	4	80
3	60	2	3,600	4	120
4	50	2	2,500	4	100
5	60	2	3,600	4	120
6	50	4	2,500	16	200
7	35	1	1,225	1	35
8	50	2	2,500	4	100
9	36	2	1,296	4	72
10	30	3	900	9	90
11	65	1	4,225	1	65
12	45	1	2,025	1	45
13	48	3	2,304	9	144
14	40	2	1,600	4	80
15	55	3	3,025	9	165
Sum	702	32	34,344	78	1,492

Next, we have our equation for r:

$$r = \frac{N \sum XY - (\sum X)(\sum Y)}{\sqrt{[N \sum X^2 - (\sum X)^2][N \sum Y^2 - (\sum Y)^2]}}$$

When we combine the two, we get:

$$r = \frac{15*1492 - (702)(32)}{\sqrt{[15*34344 - (702)^2][15*78 - (32)^2]}}$$

$$= \frac{-84}{\sqrt{22356*146}}$$

$$= -0.0465$$

3. There is a weak negative correlation between hours of work per week and involvement in organizations.

4. There is now a slightly positive correlation in the weighted sample.

References

Allison, Paul D. 2000. *Logistic Regression Using the SAS System: Theory and Application*. Cary, NC: The SAS Institute.

Anscombe, F.J. 1973. 'Graphs in Statistical Analysis'. *American Statistician* 27:17–22.

Berk, Richard A. 1983. 'An Introduction to Sample Selection Bias in Sociological Data'. *American Sociological Review*, 48, 3: 386–398.

Campbell, Rachel. 2006. 'Teenage Girls and Cellular Phones: Discourses of Independence, Safety, and "Rebellion"'. *Journal of Youth Studies* 9:195–212.

Canadian Centre for Justice Statistics. 2003. 'Crime Statistics'. *The Daily*. Ottawa: Statistics Canada.

Desrosièrs, A. 1998. *The Politics of Large Numbers: A History of Statistical Reasoning*. C. Naish, trans. Cambridge, MA; London: Harvard University Press.

Galton, Francis. 1889. *Natural Inheritance*. London: MacMillan & Co.

Gigerenzer, G., Z. Swijtink, T. Porter, L. Daston, J. Beatty, and L. Krüger. 1991. *The Empire of Chance: How Probability Changed Science and Everyday Life*. Cambridge: Cambridge University Press.

Hacking, Ian. 1975. *The Emergence of Probability: A Philosophical Study of Early Ideas about Probability, Induction and Statistical Inference*. London: Cambridge University Press.

Hald, A. 1990. *A History of Probability and Statistics and Their Applications before 1750*. New York: Wiley.

Huff, Darrell. 1954. *How to Lie with Statistics*. New York: Norton.

King, Gary, James Honaker, Anne Joseph, and Kenneth Scheve. 2001. 'Analyzing Incomplete Political Science Data: An Alternative Algorithm for Multiple Imputation'. *American Political Science Review* 95, 1: 49–69.

Kranzler, Gerald, and Janet Moursund. 1999. *Statistics for the Terrified*. Upper Saddle River, N.J.: Prentice Hall.

Lorenz, Frederick O. 1987. 'Teaching about Influence in Simple Regression'. *Teaching Sociology* 15:173–177.

Maistrov, L. E. 1974. *Probability Theory: A Historical Sketch*. S. Kotz, trans. New York; London: Academic Press.

Pearson, Karl. 1894. 'Contributions to the Mathematical Theory of Evolution. - I. On the Dissection of Asymmetrical Frequency-curves'. *Philosophical Transactions* (see p.80) CLXXXV.

Porter, T. 1986. *The Rise of Statistical Thinking, 1820–1900*. Cambridge, MA: Princeton University Press.

Rowntree, Derek. 2000. *Statistics without Tears: An Introduction for Non-Mathematicians*. London: Penguin.

Rubin, D. B. 1987. *Multiple Imputation for Nonresponse in Surveys*. New York: John Wiley & Sons.

Statistics Canada. 2001. *Aboriginal Peoples Survey (APS), 2001: User's Guide to the Public Use Microdata File*. Catalogue no. 89M0020GPE.

Statistics Canada. 2002. *Ethnic Diversity Survey: User's Guide*. Catalogue no. 89M0019GPE.

Statistics Canada. 2006. 'Income of Individuals'. *The Daily*. Accessed from http://www.statcan.ca/Daily/English/060523/d060523c.htm on January 16, 2007. 23 May 2006.

Stigler, S. M. 1986. *The History of Statistics: The Measurement of Uncertainty Before 1900*. Cambridge, MA; London: Harvard University Press.

Worswick, C. 2001. *School Performance of the Children of Immigrants, 1994–1998* (No. 178). Ottawa: Statistics Canada.

An Introduction to Statistics for Canadian Social Scientists

A Companion Lab Manual for SPSS

Julie Beth Hudson and Michael Haan

LAB1

Introduction to SPSS

Learning Objectives

What is SPSS?

SPSS stands for Statistical Package for the Social Sciences. It allows you to analyze and describe data.

How Does It Work?

SPSS applies a series of commands to a set of data. Within SPSS, you can select commands from a menu or type them in dialogue boxes. SPSS then produces an output displaying the results. The commands will occur in the following order:

- Enter your data into SPSS.
- Tell SPSS to apply commands to the data (using menus and dialogue boxes).
- Wait for SPSS to produce the output.

How to Begin an SPSS Session

Once you have logged on to a computer, you will see the start icon at the bottom of your screen. Left click on **Start Menu > All Programs > SPSS for Windows > SPSS 15 for Windows**.

What Will I See First?

A window like the one below will pop up, asking you what you would like to do. You will have a variety of options, including **Run the tutorial** and **Run an existing query**. Select **Open an existing data source**, then double click on **More Files > My Computer**. Find your data in **My Computer** and double click on the file. For the examples in this manual, you will be using CCHS2-1.sav.

Once you have opened the CCHS2-1.sav data set, the SPSS data editor will open in a new screen.

The Various Windows within SPSS

The Data Editor

The data editor screen looks like a spreadsheet. If you had selected **Type in data** in the first pop-up window rather than **Open an existing data source**, you would be able to manually fill in your data here. The data editor window has two tabs, one for viewing your data (Data View) and the other for viewing information about the variables (Variable View). Within Data View, the rows list observational units (e.g., the subjects) and the columns list the variables for the observational units. The following screen is in Data View, and the columns contain the variables for the observed cases.

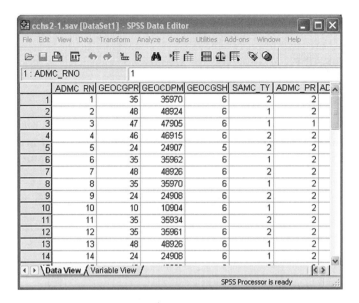

Along the top of the screen you will see the menu bar, which gives you access to all of the available commands. The menu bar has a number of headings, dividing the commands into categories with similar functions (**File**, **Edit**, **View**, **Data**, **Transform**, **Analyze**, **Graphs**, **Utilities**, **Window**, and **Help**). Browse through these pull-down menus to become familiar with their contents.

The Syntax File

The SPSS syntax file will help you organize your records and analyses. You can think of it as a text editor that reads SPSS programming. There are two approaches to working in SPSS—using a point-and-click approach or writing SPSS codes to program commands. In this course you will be primarily using the point-and-click technique; however, both techniques are presented in this lab manual to help familiarize you with the pros and cons of each. While not required for analysis, the syntax tool is useful for storing your analysis. Note that the menu bar that appeared above the data editor screen also appears in the syntax file.

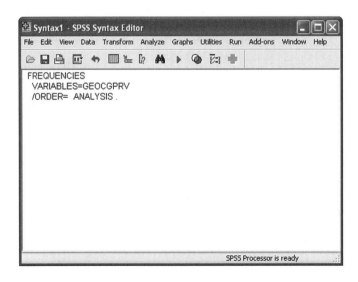

The Output Window

The output window displays the output from the analysis you perform in the data editor. Along the left side of the window is a running log of the commands you have executed during the current session. Like the data editor and syntax windows, there is a menu bar along the top of the screen. The commands you have executed are displayed within the window, a useful feature when you are analyzing large amounts of data and executing many commands. If you don't see the syntax, you can turn it on by selecting **Edit > Options > Viewer tab > Display commands in log**.

Objects within output files can be exported as text files, HTML files, or in the case of charts, as *.gif and *.jpg files. Within the output file you can edit tables by double clicking on them. Notice on the following screen shot that you can either edit the table or pivot it to change the way it appears. If you would like to save a series of outputs from your analysis, SPSS saves them with the extension *.spo.

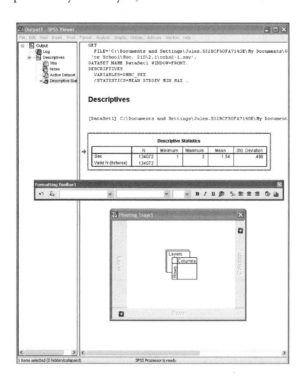

Editing Options in SPSS

There are some default options in SPSS that you may want to change. To adjust these options, select **Options** from the **Edit** menu. You will see a dialogue box that looks like this:

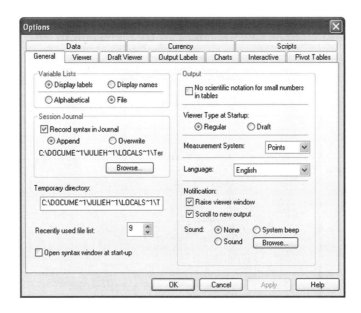

You may find it useful to adjust the default setting for displaying commands in the log, as mentioned above. To do this, click on **Display commands in the log** within the **Viewer** tab. Remember to click **Apply** or **OK** to save your changes in SPSS.

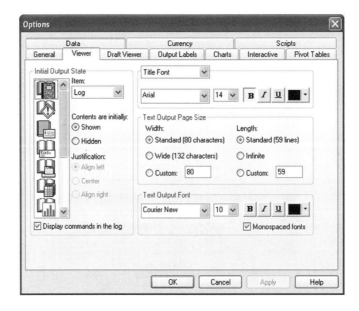

Entering SPSS Commands

You can enter commands into SPSS either by selecting the commands you wish to execute from the drop-down menus or by entering command programming into the syntax file. The first is known as the point-and-click technique. You can use this technique within the data editor window, the output window, or the syntax window.

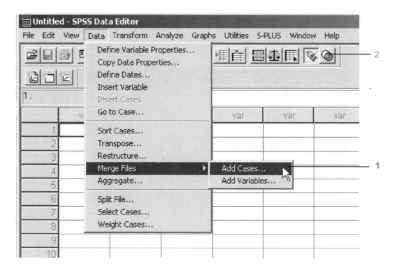

You can also enter SPSS commands by programming them into a syntax file. This method allows you to keep a record of your work. You can save your syntax file (*.sps) and rerun it later. If your analysis is lengthy and complex, saving your syntax file can be extremely helpful.

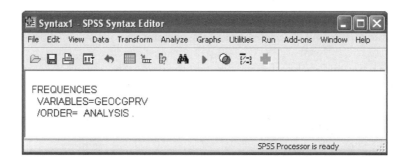

Saving Your SPSS Files

To save your spss file, click on the **File** menu and select **Save As**. Move to the directory in which you want to save the file and give your document a name. If you have previously saved your file and modified it, select **Save** from the **File** menu or click the menu bar icon that looks like a floppy disk.

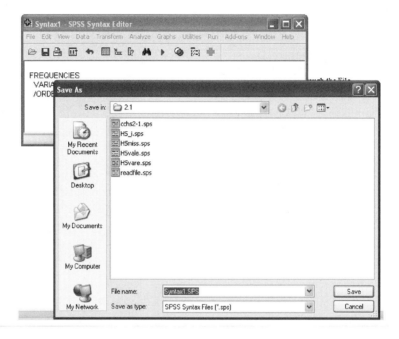

Generating Frequency Tables in SPSS

A frequency table shows the number of cases associated with each value of a given variable. Generating frequency tables in spss will illustrate some of the basic operations outlined in your introduction to the program.

We will use the point-and-click technique through the data editor screen.

1. In the menu bar, click on **Analyze > Descriptive Statistics > Frequencies**.

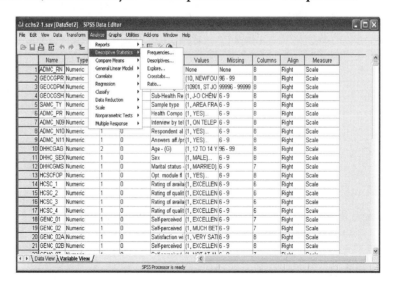

2. When the dialogue box opens, highlight the variable 'sex' in the left-hand box, click on the arrow to move the variable into the right-hand box, and click **OK**.

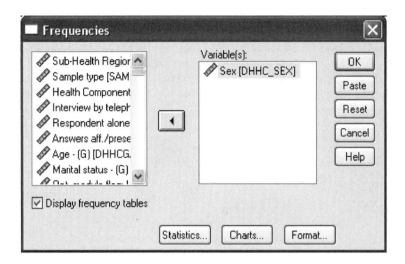

The output from the frequencies procedure will look like this:

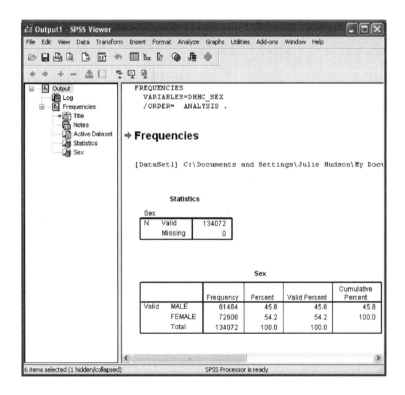

Note the following things about the output:

1. The commands are displayed in the output because we previously changed the default setting to display commands in the log.

2. Under the heading 'Statistics', we can see how many cases are valid and how many are missing.

3. In the table we can see the distribution of males versus females by raw frequencies and by percentages. The differences between per cent, valid per cent, and cumulative per cent will become clear as the course progresses.

The point-and-click technique is an easy way to see quick results, but there is one disadvantage. If you want to rerun this analysis at a later time, you will have to go back through the menus, trying to remember what you did last time. While this would not be difficult for simple analyses like the one above, it will become increasingly difficult for longer series of analyses. You may find it preferable to enter commands into the syntax.

Within the syntax file, you can create syntax codes in three ways:

1. Type them in yourself.

2. Paste the text commands from the pull-down menus into a syntax file.

2. Open a syntax file in which the commands are already written.

Let's look at each of the first two methods in turn.

Writing Syntax Codes

Using the previous example, let's see how you could execute the frequency procedure by writing the syntax code yourself. Type the word **FREQ**, followed by the name of the variable and a period.

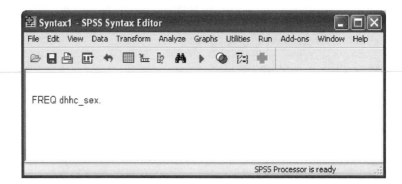

When writing your own SPSS programming, remember that all SPSS codes must end in a period. Notice that frequency is not spelled out in its entirety. In SPSS, you can often use the first four letters of a procedure as the syntax code. As the course develops, you will be exposed to a variety of codes that you may want to memorize.

Using Pull-Down Menus and Pasting Syntax Codes

Now we will execute the frequency procedure using the pull-down menus.

1. In the menu bar, click **Analyze** > **Descriptive Statistics** > **Frequencies**.

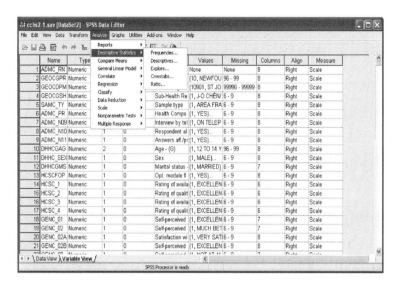

2. In the dialogue box, highlight the variable 'sex' in the left-hand box, click on the arrow to move the variable into the right-hand box, then click **Paste**. This will paste the SPSS program coding into your syntax file. Recall that recording commands in a syntax file, while not necessary to complete your analysis, is useful if you wish to save your commands and rerun them later.

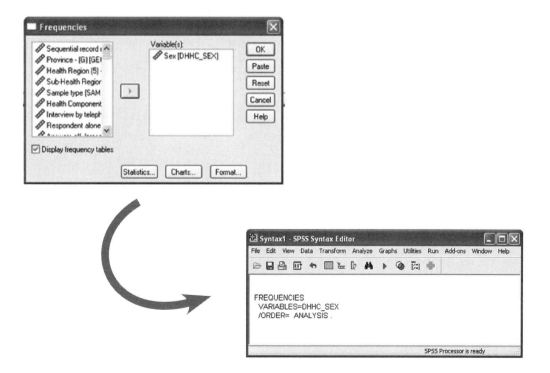

3. In the menu bar, click on the blue arrow that points to the right to execute the commands, or put your cursor on the command you want to execute and press **CTRL + R**. This will run the analysis and bring it up in an SPSS output window.

4. Save your syntax file.

Summary

In this section you were introduced to the basics of SPSS, including the anatomy of a data file and a variety of SPSS screens and menus. You were shown three ways to enter SPSS commands: writing the codes yourself, using existing codes from a syntax file, and employing the point-and-click technique. Finally, you were introduced to a basic and frequently employed SPSS procedure, generating frequency tables.

Syntax Commands Learned in This Section

Frequency Distributions:
```
FREQ <variable name>.
```

Assignment 1

Using SPSS and the CCHS2-1.sav data set, answer the following questions:

1. What is the total number of variables in the CCHS2-1 database? (Hint: look at the frequency output.)

2. How many males and females are there?

3. Obtain a frequency distribution, both by using the point-and-click technique and by writing the syntax code, for the following variables: 'marital status' (DHHCGMS), 'has food allergies' (CCCC_011), and 'ever smoked whole cigarette' (SMKC_01B).

4. Choose one of the above variables and interpret your results. Which category is the most common? Least common?

Presenting Data

Understanding how to present data is an important part of data analysis. This section will explore three methods of data presentation: pie charts, bar graphs, and frequency tables.

In the last section you learned how to obtain a frequency distribution by using the point-and-click technique and by entering commands into a syntax file. This lab will apply those skills to basic data-presentation techniques. In your textbook, you were introduced to levels of measurement in chapter 2 and to univariate statistics in chapter 3. Understanding levels of measurement, frequencies, and measures of central tendency will help you decide when to use each of the formats for data presentation that will be introduced in this section.

Pie Charts

A pie chart is an effective way to summarize categorical data. (Remember: a set of data is categorical when the values or observations belonging to it can be sorted into groups.) Each value is chosen from a set of mutually exclusive categories. For example, 'sex' is a categorical variable with two categories, 'male' and 'female', and in the data set people cannot belong to both categories. We can then say that 'male' and 'female' are mutually exclusive. A pie chart is a circle divided into segments, where each segment represents a particular category. The area of each segment is proportional to the number of cases in the category it represents.

The following is an example of a pie chart for the 'marital status' variable (DHHCGMS) found in the CCHS2-1 data set. Note that in this example we have included the missing values. In a formal report you would not typically include these cases, unless you had a strong theoretical or methodological reason for doing so.

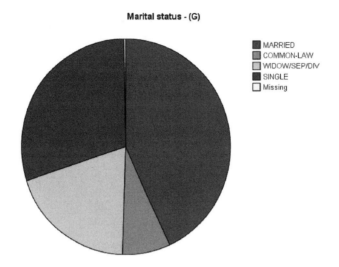

Here is how to create a pie chart using the point-and-click technique within SPSS:

1. Within the data editor window, click on **Analyze** > **Descriptive Statistics** > **Frequencies** on your menu bar.

2. In the window that opens, highlight the variable 'marital status' and click on the arrow to move the variable from the left-hand box to the right-hand box. Then click on **Charts**.

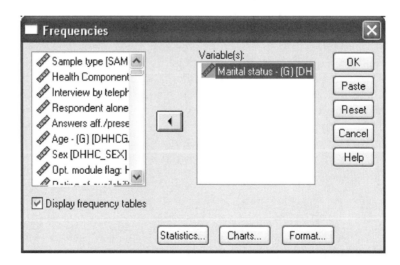

3. The window that opens will prompt you to select the chart type you would like to create. Select **Pie charts**, then click **Continue** to close the menu screen, and **Paste** to copy your command into the syntax record. The **Paste** command is optional, but highly recommended for record-keeping. If you decide not to keep a syntax record simply click **OK**. For the purposes of this lab manual we will paste all commands into a syntax file.

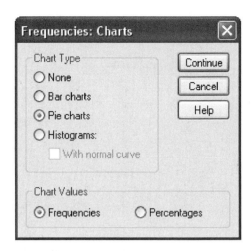

After running the commands, you should get an output file containing a pie chart that looks like this:

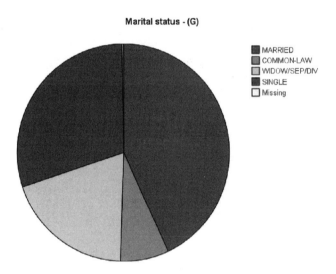

You can also use the graphs function to create a pie graph by selecting **Graphs > Pie**, although that method will not provide you with frequency tables.

Bar Graphs

A bar graph is another way to summarize categorical data. It displays the data using a number of bars, each representing a particular category. The length of each bar is proportional to the number of cases in the category it represents.

The following is an example of a bar graph for the 'province of residence' variable (GEOCGPRV) found in the CCHS2-1 data set.

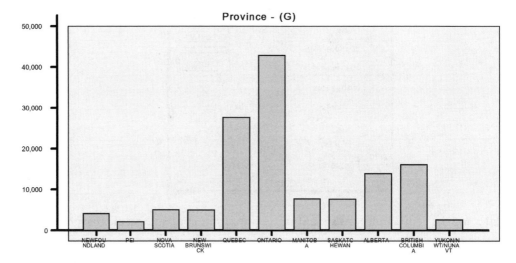

To create a bar graph, follow the same procedure as for pie charts, but select **Bar charts** instead of **Pie charts**.

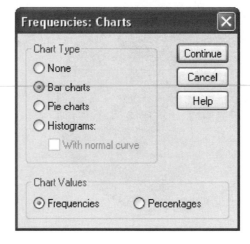

You can also create a bar chart by selecting **Graphs > Bar**, although once again that will not produce a frequency table.

Frequency Tables

A frequency table is a way of summarizing a set of data. It tells you how often each value (or set of values) for a variable occurs and what percentage of values falls into each category. A frequency table can be used to summarize categorical, nominal, and ordinal data, and may also be used to summarize continuous data, such as age, once the data set has been divided up into sensible groups, such as age by ten-year increments. A frequency table created from a data set with more than one variable is sometimes called a contingency table because the figures found in the rows are contingent (dependent) upon those found in the columns.

You can create a frequency table in much the same way you created pie charts and bar graphs. Since frequency tables are the default chart type in SPSS, you can skip the step where you select **Charts**—instead, just hit **Paste**. Here is a frequency table for the variable 'last time visited the dentist' (DENC_132), found in the CCHS2-1 data set.

| **Last time visited dentist** | | | | |
	Frequency	Percent	Valid percent	Cumulative percent
Valid < 1 YEAR	57230	42.7	62.7	62.7
1 TO <2 YEARS	10752	8.0	11.8	74.5
2 TO < 3 YEARS	5719	4.3	6.3	80.8
3 TO < 4 YEARS	2606	1.9	2.9	83.7
4 TO < 5 YEARS	2306	1.7	2.5	86.2
5 YEARS OR MORE	11917	8.9	13.1	99.2
NEVER	690	.5	.8	100.0
Total	91220	68.0	100.0	
Missing NOT APPLICABLE	40432	30.2		
DON'T KNOW	261	.2		
REFUSAL	68	.1		
NOT STATED	2091	1.6		
Total	42852	32.0		
Total	134072	100.0		

If you look at the valid per cent values (which are usually preferable because they exclude missing cases), you can see that 62.7 per cent of your respondents visited the dentist within the past year. Approximately 13 per cent have not visited the dentist in five years or more.

Which Mode of Presentation Is Best?

Some presentation formats might be better suited to your data than others. When deciding which format to use, take into account the level of measurement of your selected variable and the number of response categories. For example, if you have a categorical variable with a large number of categories, a pie chart might crowd your presentation, whereas a bar graph would not.

Here are some general suggestions you may want to consider:

- Use tables to display data details that would be lost in graphs or charts.
- Opt for a bar graph when comparing data.
- Use a pie chart to show how percentages relate to each other within a whole.
- Identify the main point you want your chart to make and choose the format that emphasizes this point.
- Consider your audience. Try to think of what they would find most useful.

Summary

In this section you were introduced to the basics of data presentation. You explored three methods of data presentation: pie charts, bar graphs, and frequency tables. In addition to learning how to create these in SPSS, you learned when and why you might prefer certain presentation types based on the level of measurement of your variables and the complexity of your data.

Assignment 2

Use the CCHS2-1 data set and SPSS to complete the following exercises:

1. Create a frequency table, a bar graph, and a pie chart for a variable of your choice.

2. Imagine you have been hired to write a newspaper article on the topic of the variable you selected. Write a couple of sentences summarizing your findings. Which method of data presentation is most appropriate for this variable? Justify your answer, considering both your audience and the level of measurement of your variable.

LAB 3

The Normal Curve

In this section, you will learn about **measures of central tendency** (mean, median, and mode), as well as the relationship between the **standard deviation** and the **normal curve**.

Measures of central tendency allow you to understand or describe a single variable with a single summary measure. In other words, they are **univariate** (one-variable) statistics. They are used to compare or generalize values across a population. For example, if you wanted a summary measure of the number of alcoholic drinks Canadians consume during any given month, you could use the mean, median, or mode, the three measures of central tendency. To recap what is covered in chapter 6 of the textbook, here's a reminder of what each term means:

The Mode

The mode is the most common or frequent score contained within a variable. The mode can be used with variables at all levels of measurement, but it is most often used with nominal-level variables.

The Mean

The mean is the arithmetic average, probably the most commonly reported measure of central tendency. It should only be used with interval- and ratio-level data.

The Median

The median is the middle score of any variable. If your sample is normally distributed, the mode, mean, and median will be the same. The median cannot be used with nominal-level variables, and it should be used with ordinal-level variables only when there is an odd number of scores, or when the two values on either side of the middle of a data set with an even number of values are the same. To find the median in interval- and ratio-level variables with an even number of observations, divide the difference between the two middle scores to create a mid-point between the two scores.

Understanding these concepts, especially the mean and median, will help you to understand the normal curve. The normal curve, or normal distribution, is a theoretical continuous probability distribution that represents all possible values and the probability of obtaining those values.

Calculating the Mode, Mean, and Median with SPSS

Open a new syntax file. To do so, open your SPSS data editor, then click on **File** > **Open** > **Syntax**.

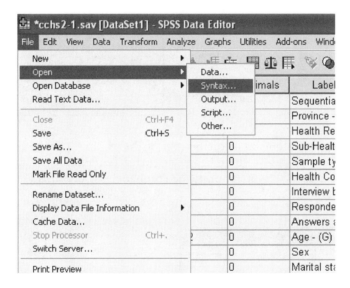

Once you have opened your syntax file, you're ready to calculate the mode.

1. Click on **Analyze > Descriptive Statistics > Frequencies.**

2. You will see a window with a list of the variables in the data set on the left side and an empty box on the right side. In this example, we are interested in knowing the most common marital status among Canadians. Select the variable 'marital status', then click on the arrow between the two boxes to move the variable to the empty box as seen below.

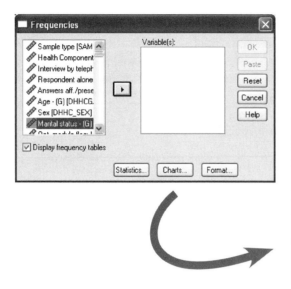
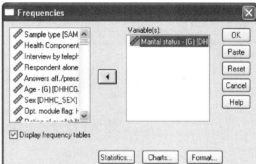

3. Click on the **Statistics** button at the bottom of the window. On the right side of the next window that opens, find the column heading **Central Tendency**. Underneath it, select **Mode,** then click **Continue**. When you return to the **Frequencies** window, as seen in the figure below, click on **Paste**.

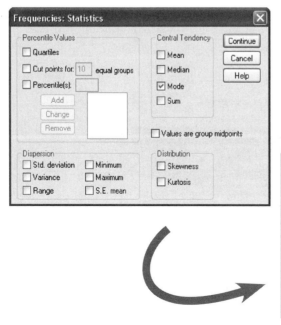
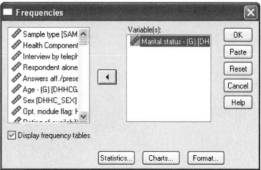

4. Notice that your syntax file now contains the appropriate codes for calculating the mode. Place your cursor within the syntax code and click on **Run** > **Current**. This will run only the command you have placed your cursor within. To run more than one command, highlight the commands you are interested in running and click on **Selection** instead of **Current**. To run all the commands in your syntax file, click on **All**.

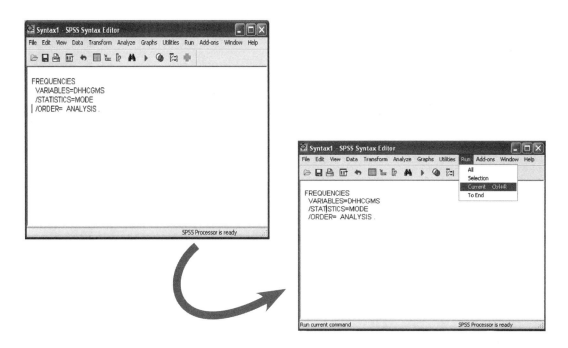

This will bring up an output file with your data analysis.

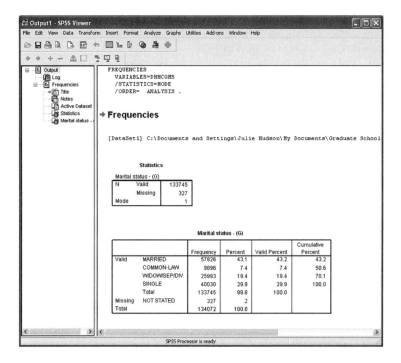

The output screen lists the number of valid cases (respondents who gave applicable responses to the marital status question) and the number of missing cases (respondents who did not state their marital status). The mode and measure of central tendency that we told the program to compute are also listed. Here we find that the most frequent marital status was response one, 'married'.

To calculate the mean and the median alongside the mode, go back to the window labelled **Frequencies: Statistics**. Check the mean, median, and mode boxes. Remember to calculate the mean and the median only when your level of measurement is sufficient to give you meaningful results. The mean is only useful for interval or ratio data; the median is always useful for interval and ratio data and sometimes for ordinal data.

Standard Deviation and Variance

Now that you know how to calculate the mean, median, and mode in SPSS, let's obtain the **standard deviation** and **variance**. Variance, as defined in your textbook, is the average of the squared deviations from the mean value. The equation is as follows:

$$s^2 = \frac{\sum (X - \overline{X})^2}{n - 1}$$

Where s^2 equals the variance (the standard deviation is the square root of the variance), X is any variable, $\overline{X}$ is the mean of that variable, and N is the number of observations. Understanding standard deviation allows you to visualize the proportion of your sample, or population, that falls within certain key values of the normal curve. For more information on this topic, see chapter 6 of your textbook. This is the equation for standard deviation:

$$s = \sqrt{\frac{\sum (X - \overline{X})^2}{n - 1}}$$

To calculate the variance and the standard deviation within SPSS, follow the same steps you did to calculate the mean, median, and mode. When you are looking at the window labelled **Frequency: Statistics**, check **Std. Deviation** and **Variance** under the heading **Dispersion**.

Summary

In this section you were introduced to the properties of the normal curve through an examination of measures of central tendency. Specifically, you learned how to obtain the mean, median, and mode, along with the variance and standard deviation, using the point-and-click technique within SPSS.

Assignment 3

How often do Canadians consume alcoholic beverages?

1. Use CCHS2-1 and SPSS to calculate the following for observations 15–21:
   a. The mean, median, and mode on variable ALCC_5A6, 'number of drinks on Fridays'.
   b. The standard deviation and the variance of the mean.
   c. Calculate the mean, median, mode, standard deviation, and variance by hand. Compare your calculations with those done by SPSS.

2. When considering which measure of central tendency you should report, think about:
   a. The level of measurement.
   b. The nature of the information you seek.
   c. The number of observations.
   d. The distribution of values.

Given these considerations, which measure of central tendency is most appropriate if you are reporting on Canadian drinking habits? Why?

Generalizing from Samples to Populations

This section will introduce you to sampling and sampling distribution. As you work through the section, keep two things in mind:

- The larger the sample, the more accurately the estimates will represent the population that they are drawn from.
- The means of repeated samples from a population will form a normal distribution.

Populations and Sampling

A **population** is a group of persons, institutions, events, or other subjects of study that a researcher wants to describe and generalize. Researchers often generalize about a population based on representative samples drawn from the original population of interest.

Since the data we study is usually not from a complete population, we must try to create a more accurate representation of the population. To do this, we apply weights to the data. Weights are multiplication factors that make the data more reflective of the population they are intended to represent. They adjust for differences in the number of population units and the number of cases within a variable. For example, suppose we want to generalize about elderly people's attitudes towards health care. We have a sample of one hundred 85-year-old women and one hundred 85-year-old men. We might want to give more weight to the elderly women's attitudes on health care since we know that, due to differences in women's and men's life expectancies, the population of 85-year-olds includes more women than men. The weights would normalize the sample so that it is more reflective of the entire population, correcting for any over- or under-sampling.

Sometimes weighting data can create other problems in statistical analysis—for example, it can inflate any standard errors. Consequently, we usually use normalized weights, or weights with an average value of one. Some programs automatically use normalized weights, but SPSS is not one of them.

In many data sets there is a predefined variable that will adjust for over- or under-sampling to make the data set more representative of the general population. For example, in the CCHS2-1 data set, the population weight variable is WTSC_M. Let's see how the weight variable works.

How to Weight Data in SPSS

Let's look at the frequency of males and females in the sample before applying the weight variable. To do this, we will run a frequency distribution on the 'sex' variable (DHHC_SEX).

1.   Click on **Analyze** > **Descriptive Statistics** > **Frequencies**.

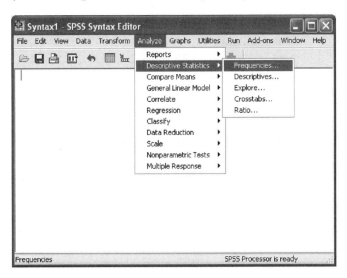

2. You should see a window with the variables listed in a box on the left and an empty box on the right. In this example, we want to know the distribution of males and females in our sample and in the Canadian population. Click on the 'sex' variable, then hit the arrow between the two boxes to move the variable to the empty box, as seen below. If you would like to paste this into your syntax editor (and you have it open), hit **Paste.**

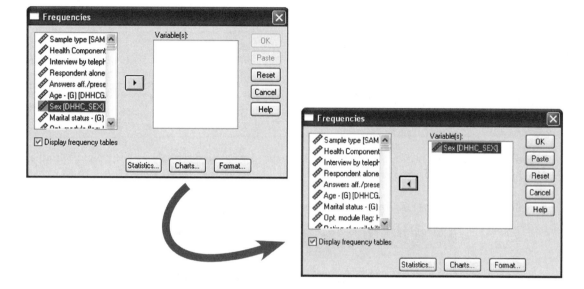

3. If you pasted your syntax, it should look like the figure below. Now, highlight the command and click on **Run > Selection**.

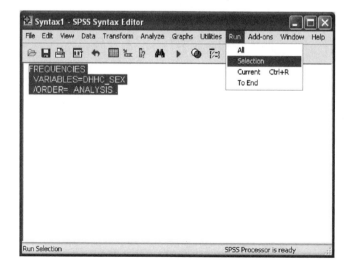

The analysis should appear in the output file. Note that there are 134,072 valid cases, of which 61,464 (45.8 per cent) are males and 72,608 (54.2 per cent) are females.

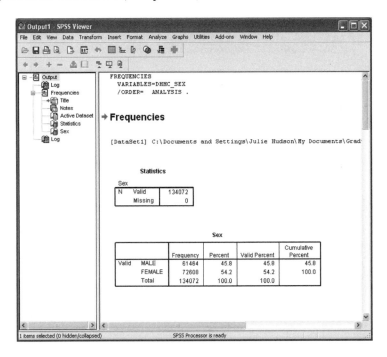

Let's apply the weights and rerun the analysis.

1. Go back into your syntax file. Click on **Data** > **Weight Cases**.

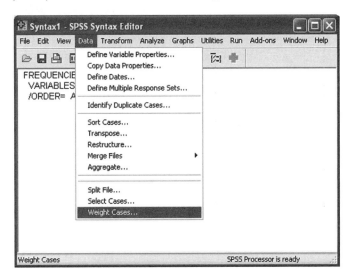

2. Click on **Weight cases by**, find the variable 'weights' (wtsc_m) in the list at left, and click the arrow button to bring it over into the **Frequency Variable** box. If you are using a syntax file, hit **Paste**.

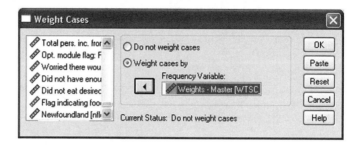

3. Your syntax file should now contain the weight command. Copy and paste the frequencies command below the weight command, as shown below. Run the weight and frequencies commands by highlighting both commands and clicking **Run > Selection**.

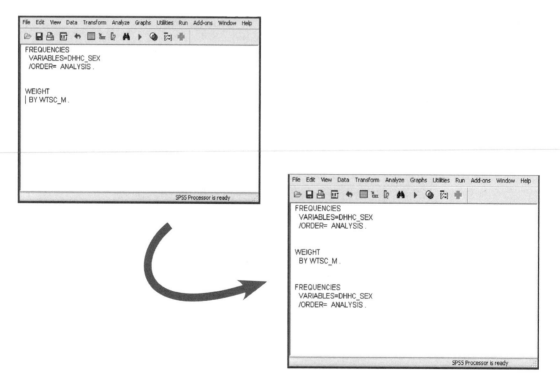

You should get the following output:

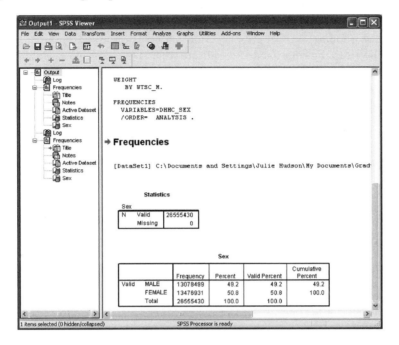

Consider some of the differences between the initial output, obtained before weighting, and the current output, obtained after weighting. What are the differences?

The output now shows 26,555,430 cases, compared to 134,072 before the weights were applied. Of these cases, 13,078,499 (49.2 per cent) are male, compared to 61,464 (45.8 per cent) before weighting, and 13,476,931 (50.8 per cent) are female, compared to 72,608 (54.2 per cent) before weighting. Each observation in the data set has been inflated to represent more than one case. Usually weight variables are determined by the survey taker (in this case, Statistics Canada) and are designed to make the sample resemble the population more closely. Here, since women were over-sampled, the weights decreased the proportion of women so that the sample would better represent the Canadian population.

Taking a Random Sample from a Population

When researchers cannot obtain information from every member of a population, they gather data from a **sample** of the population, or a selection of cases that represent the population. Researchers can then generalize the data from their sample to the larger population.

For a moment, pretend that our weighted data is a population and take a random sample from it. Random sampling means selecting a group, where each observation has an equal probability of being selected as part of that group. In this lab, you will learn how to take a random sample.

Follow the steps previously demonstrated to apply the weight variable to your data set. Then get a random sample by instructing SPSS to select a portion of your data set by clicking **Data > Select Cases > Random Sample of Cases**. A new window will open, prompting you to select your sample size. Type in '2', instructing SPSS to take a 2 per cent random sample of your data, and hit **OK**. At the bottom of the next window you must choose between filtering out unselected cases, copying them to a new data set, or deleting them. Select **Filter out unselected cases**, then hit **OK**, so that SPSS will retain the cases you're not using, but set them aside during the proceeding analysis. (You can reintegrate your unselected cases later on, if you wish, by clicking **Data > Select Cases > Reset**.) In the data editor screen, unselected cases will appear with a diagonal line drawn through their leftmost column.

To select a random sample using the syntax method, issue a temporary command so that you can retain unselected cases. Type the following syntax code:

Temporary.

The command that follows directly after the code will only be applied once.

Now execute the sampling command and indicate what size sample you would like to obtain. In this example ask for a 2 per cent sample. Use the following syntax code:

Sample .02.

If your syntax file looks like the following, highlight the commands and click **Run > Selection**.

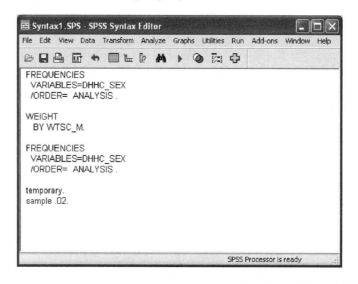

Now that you have selected a 2 per cent sampling frame, rerun your frequency distribution on gender. Compare your totals to the weighted totals. Notice that you now have 252,520 (49.0 per cent) males and 263,025 (51.0 per cent) females, compared to 13,078,499 (49.2 per cent) males and 13,476,931 (50.8 per cent) females in your weighted total. Whether or not a 2 per cent sample is sufficient depends on 1) the size of your population, 2) the diversity in your population, and 3) the type of analysis you plan to conduct.

Summary

In this lab you were introduced to the concept of sampling. You used the weight command to create a projected Canadian population, and from this population you drew a random sample. You compared the percentages of men and women in this sample to the percentages in the larger population to determine whether your sampling frame was high enough to be representative of the Canadian population.

Assignment 4

1. In spss, calculate the mean, median, mode, and standard deviation of the variable DHHCGAGE using the weighted Canadian population sample.

2. Obtain 10 repeated samples using a 5 per cent sampling frame. (Hint: run the same command ten times.) Record the mean, the standard error of the mean, and the standard deviation for each of the 10 samples.

3. Calculate the mean of the 10 means, the mean of the 10 standard errors of the mean, and the mean of the 10 standard deviations. On average, how close are your sample estimates to the population mean?

4. Now that you have the average mean and the average standard deviation, use the formula below to compute the coefficient of variation, a measure of relative dispersion.

$$\text{coefficient of variation} = (\text{standard deviation} / \text{mean}) \times 100$$

A higher coefficient of variation suggests wider dispersion. Given this, what can you conclude about your samples? Do they have the same relative dispersion? How do they compare to the weighted mean for the entire sample?

To get a sense of what these values mean, use the following conventions:

0% to 16.5%	Estimates can be considered accurate
16.6% to 33.3%	Estimates can be used with caution
Over 33.3%	Estimates should be used only with extreme caution

Bivariate Statistics: Categorical Data and Chi-Square

In this section you will learn how to answer simple research questions in SPSS by examining basic bivariate statistics through crosstabulations (often abbreviated as crosstabs).

Bivariate Statistics and Contingency Tables

Bivariate statistics, as introduced in Part II of your textbook, quantify the relationship between two variables, such as gender and university attendance, family size and religion, or political party affiliation and sexual orientation. Crosstabulations are usually presented within a **contingency table**, which looks similar to the frequency table you learned about in lab 2. However, while a frequency table presents the distribution of one variable, a contingency table presents the distribution of two or more variables simultaneously. Each cell within a contingency table shows the number of respondents who gave a specific combination of responses (e.g., how many respondents are female and attended university). In other words, each cell contains a single crosstabulation, and an entire contingency table is composed of many crosstabulations. (See chapter 12 of your textbook for a full discussion on bivariate statistics at the nominal level.)

Creating Contingency Tables with SPSS

Suppose you were interested in determining whether or not men and women significantly differ in their opinions about their own weights. To simplify the calculation of chi-square we will not be using weighted data in this lab. Usually the computer would calculate chi-square for us and we could use the weighted variables. However, here we'll stick to non-weighted data for the purpose of illustration.

1. Once you have opened the data set within the data editor, open a new syntax file. Click on **Analyze > Descriptive Statistics > Crosstabs**.

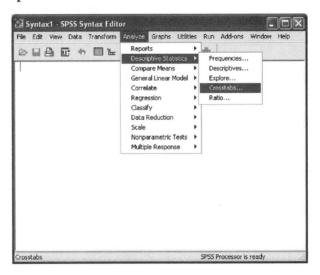

2. This will bring up the crosstabs window. Select the dependent variable, 'respondent's opinion of their weight', and click on the topmost arrow to move the variable into the box labelled **Row(s)**. Then select the independent variable, 'sex', and click on the middle arrow to move the variable into the box labelled **Column(s)**. Now click on the **Statistics** button.

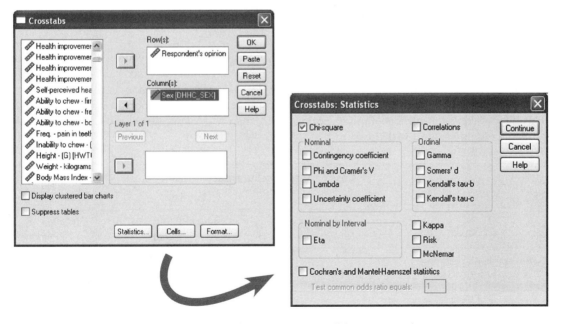

3. In the window that opens, select **Chi-square**. We will be using a chi-square test to measure the statistical significance of the relationship between gender and opinion of body weight. Hit **Continue**.

4. Return to the crosstabs window. Click on the **Cells** button. Within the new window that opens, select **Columns** under the heading **Percentages**. Select columns because you want to display percentages for both males and females in order to compare the differences across gender. Hit **Continue,** which returns you to the crosstabs window. Once there, click on **Paste** and run the commands from your syntax file.

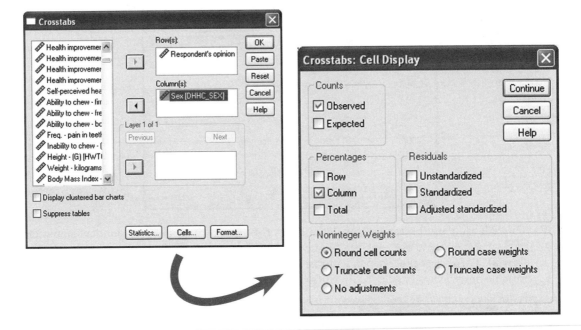

Take a look at your output file: first is the case processing summary. Here you will find the number of valid cases, 128,149, constituting 95.6 per cent of the total number of cases. Valid cases are those that are meaningful to your analysis. In this example, valid cases are respondents who indicated being male or female, excluding those who did not give an applicable response or did not answer. This is followed by the number of missing cases, 5,923, and the total number of cases, including both valid and missing cases, 134,072.

Case Processing Summary						
	\multicolumn{6}{c}{Cases}					
	Valid		Missing		Total	
	N	Percent	N	Percent	N	Percent
Respondent's opinion of own weight * Sex	128149	95.6%	5923	4.4%	134072	100.0%

After the case summary report is the contingency table, where you will see both raw frequencies and percentages. Let's interpret the results. There appear to be differences between men and women in their opinions about their weight. Women are more likely to report being overweight than men— 44.1 per cent of women report this compared to 35.6 per cent of men. But are these differences statistically significant? How do we know that the observed differences did not occur by chance? How do we know whether the differences seen in the sample also exist within the population?

Respondent's opinion of own weight * Sex Crosstabulation				
Sex				
Respondent's opinion of own weight		Male	Female	Total
OVERWEIGHT	Count	21055	30434	51489
	% within Sex	35.6%	44.1%	40.2%
UNDERWEIGHT	Count	3570	2277	5847
	% within Sex	6.0%	3.3%	4.6%
JUST ABOUT RIGHT	Count	34513	36300	70813
	% within Sex	58.4%	52.6%	55.3%
Total	Count	59138	69011	128149
	% within Sex	100.0%	100.0%	100.0%

Chi-Square Tests

One way to test the significance of differences across groups is to use a chi-square test. Since chi-square is nonparametric, you can use it for all levels of measurement without having to make any assumptions about the data's distribution (such as that the data is normally distributed). Chi-square tests the **null hypothesis** and measures the discrepancy between observed and expected events. The events are assumed to be independent and have the same distribution, and the outcomes of each event must be mutually exclusive. To calculate chi-square, find the difference between the observed and theoretical frequencies for each possible outcome, square the difference, divide it by the theoretical frequency, and take the sum of the results. Here is the equation:

$$\chi^2 = \Sigma \frac{(f_o - f_e)^2}{f_e}$$

f_o = the observed frequency
f_e = the expected (theoretical) frequency if no relationship exists, as asserted by the null hypothesis

   To evaluate whether we will reject, or fail to reject, the null hypothesis that no differences exist between males and females (see chapter 11 for a lengthier discussion of null hypotheses), we need to determine the degrees of freedom, found in the SPSS output. For our results, the degrees of freedom equals 2. Since chi-square has a known distribution, we know that the critical chi-square value for 2 degrees of freedom is 5.991 at the 0.05 level of statistical significance, and our chi-square value is 1286.453. Since our chi-square value exceeds the critical chi-square value, we can reject the null hypothesis and conclude that there are statistically significant differences between males and females with respect to their opinions about body weight.

Chi-Square Tests			
	Value	df	Asymp. Sig. (2-sided)
Pearson Chi-Square	1286.453(a)	2	.000
Likelihood Ratio	1290.021	2	.000
Linear-by-Linear Association	694.812	1	.000
N of Valid Cases	128149		

Summary

In this section you were introduced to the basics of bivariate analysis and crosstabulations in SPSS. You explored the relationship between two variables and answered simple research questions. Part of examining the relationship between two variables is establishing whether the relationship seen in the sample also exists in the population, that is, whether the relationship is statistically significant. In this lab you used chi-square to determine whether a statistically significant relationship existed between men's and women's opinions of their weight.

Assignment 5

Who smokes more cigarettes, men or women? Use the variables DHHC_SEX ('sex') and SMKC_202 ('type of smoker').

1. Identify the independent and dependent variables and state the null hypothesis (H_0) and the research hypothesis (H_i).

2. Set up a crosstabulation for the entire population and for cases 1 to 25 (do not weight your data). Look at the percentages. What do the crosstabs tell you about smoking patterns among males and females? Do a chi-square test using statistics both for the entire population and for cases 1 to 25. In each case, do you accept or reject the null hypothesis? Explain.

Analysis of Variance

Analysis of Variance (ANOVA)

Analysis of variance, or **ANOVA**, is similar to a *t*-test (discussed in chapter 10), but it allows us to compare more than two groups. In chapter 10 you looked at the relationship between students and alcohol consumption. Using ANOVA, discussed in chapter 15 of your text, you can compare the smoking habits of people with different religious affiliations or from different geographical regions—variables with more than two categories. ANOVA compares three things:

1. Differences between means

2. Differences in values within samples

3. Differences in values across samples

ANOVA compares the variation in a continuous dependent variable that is explained by the independent variable to the variation that occurs at random. For example, suppose you were examining the relationship between religion and voting patterns. Variation around the mean could be attributed either to differences between religious groups or to unexplained differences between individuals.

Let's review a few key terms. The **total sum of squares** is the total variation from the **grand mean** across all observations; it tells us whether there is more variation within groups than across groups.

This is the equation for the total sum of squares:

$$SS_{Total} = \sum (X - \overline{X})^2$$

The sum of squares within groups allows us to calculate the variation that exists within each group, rather than the total variance for all observations. This is the equation for the sum of squares within groups:

$$SS_{Within} = \sum (X - \overline{X}_{Group})^2$$

The sum of squares between groups treats each group as an observation and allows us to calculate the variation across groups. This is the equation for the sum of squares between groups:

$$SS_{Between} = \sum N_{Group}(\overline{X}_{Group} - \overline{X}_{Total})^2$$

The results for the sums of squares equations above will be dependent on sample size. Since we want a standardized value, we use the mean square instead of the sum of squares:

$$MS_{within} = \frac{SS_{within}}{df_{within}}$$

and

$$MS_{between} = \frac{SS_{between}}{df_{between}}$$

You'll recognize the numerators from our discussion above. The denominators represent degrees of freedom within groups and between groups. Use these formulas to calculate them:

$$df_{within} = N_{total} - k$$

and

$$df_{between} = k - 1$$

where k = the number of groups you are comparing.

For further elaboration on ANOVA, please see your textbook.

Calculating ANOVA with SPSS

Let's learn how to conduct an ANOVA with SPSS. We will use the CCHS2-1 data to examine whether individual body weight is related to total household income.

1. Open a blank syntax file. Click on **Analyze > Compare Means > One-Way ANOVA**. This brings up the **one-way ANOVA** window.

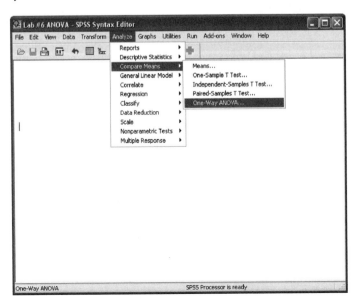

2. From the list of variables on the left side of the window, select the dependent variable, 'weight - kilograms', and move it into the box labelled **Dependent List**. Next, select your independent variable, 'total household income', and move it into the box labelled **Factor.** Click on **Options**.

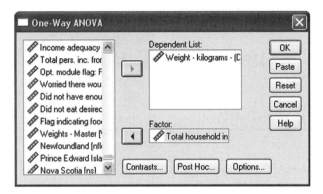

3. Within the options window, select **Descriptive** from the list of options and click **Continue.**

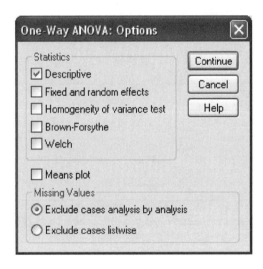

You will return to the **One-Way** ANOVA window. Click the **Paste** button to paste the commands into your syntax file, then run the analysis.

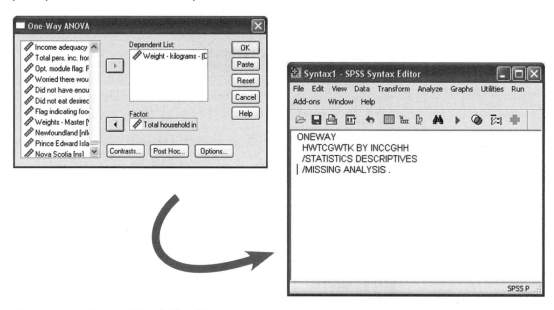

Your output file should look like this:

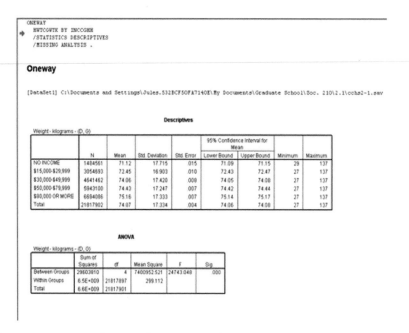

Look at the means. Respondents with no income have a mean body weight of 71.12 kilograms, and the relationship between income and mean body weight appears to be linear up through to the highest income level of $80,000 or more. But are these differences significant? Can we expect them to exist in the population?

To determine this, look at the ANOVA table. The between-group sum of squares has four degrees of freedom and a value of 29,603,810, and the within-group sum of squares has 21,817,897 degrees of freedom and a value of 6.5E+009 ($6.5 * 10^9$). As you can see from Appendix D, the critical F-distribution score, given four degrees of freedom for the between-groups score and more than 120 degrees of freedom for the within-group score, is less than 2.45. We can therefore conclude with 95 per cent confidence that there are significant differences between at least two groups.

Summary

In this section you were introduced to ANOVA, or analysis of variance, which allows you to compare differences between means across groups. You looked at whether individual body weight is associated with household income, and you were shown how to calculate ANOVA with SPSS and interpret your output.

Assignment 6

Determine which province smokes the most cigarettes. Use the variables GEOCGPRV (province of residence) and SMKC_204 (number of cigarettes smoked).

1. State null and research hypotheses about the relationship between province of residence and number of cigarettes smoked. Calculate the variance between provinces with respect to how many cigarettes respondents reported smoking, remembering to use only valid values for both variables. Which province is the most dispersed in its smoking habits? Which province smokes the most? The least?

2. State the value of the total sum of squares, the within-group sum of squares, and the between-group sum of squares. Calculate the F-ratio, using the mean square values. Based on these calculations, can you reject the null hypothesis? Is at least one province statistically different from the others?

LAB 7

Ordinary Least Squares Regression

In this section you will learn how to conduct an **ordinary least squares (OLS) regression** in SPSS.

Ordinary Least Squares (OLS) Regression and Dummy Variables

OLS regression allows us to create a regression line, an equation that represents the linear relationship between two or more variables. OLS requires that certain fundamental conditions be met:

1.   All variables must be interval, ratio, or dummy variables.

2.   All variables, and their errors, must be normally distributed.

3.   There must be linearity between variables. The relationship between an independent variable and a dependent variable must be the same across the range of scores for both variables.

4.   The data must be drawn from a random sample so that the sampling error is also random.

Condition 1 states that all variables must be continuous. If you want to test the differences between categories within a nominal or ordinal variable, you can create a series of variables with only two response categories, 0 and 1. These variables are often referred to as dummy variables. For example, instead of having a variable for 'sex', you might name your variable 'female'. You would code males as

0 and females as 1. Males, who are 0 per cent female, are therefore on one end of a spectrum, and females, who are 100 per cent female, are on the other end. This means you can rank individuals on their 'femaleness' and measure the distance between someone who is female and someone who is male. In other words, you have recoded a nominal variable so that it functions as an interval or ratio variable.

If the nominal or ordinal variable has more than one category, create a series of dummy variables for each category. For example, suppose your variable is religion. Since there are more than two religions, each religion, except for one, must become its own dummy variable (e.g., Catholic or not, Protestant or not, Muslim or not). Make one religion your reference group by leaving out its dummy variable. Usually this reference group is the most common or populous group, but selecting a reference group is up to the discretion of the researcher. Often the modal category is used as the reference, although that is not a statistical necessity.

Doing an OLS Regression Analysis with SPSS

To see how this is done in SPSS, for this example we will examine whether marital status affects the number of hours that women work outside the home. This question might be important to scholars who are interested in whether traditional family roles are still present among married women. Do married women work fewer hours outside the home than single women? To answer this question, we will need to prepare the data for an OLS regression analysis.

1. Open a blank syntax file. Run a frequency distribution on your independent variable, 'marital status'. To do this, click on **Analyze** > **Descriptive Statistics** > **Frequencies**.

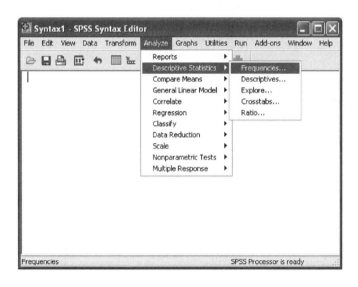

2. Move the 'marital status' variable into the variable list and click **Paste**. Then, within your syntax file, select **Run > All**.

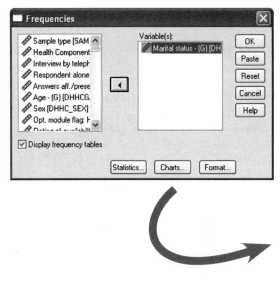

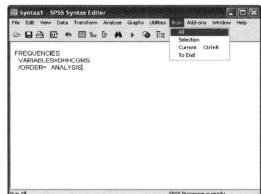

Let's take a look at the output file.

		Frequency	Percent	Valid percent	Cumulative percent
Marital status – (G)					
Valid	MARRIED	57826	43.1	43.2	43.2
	COMMON-LAW	9896	7.4	7.4	50.6
	WIDOW/SEP/DIV	25993	19.4	19.4	70.1
	SINGLE	40030	29.9	29.9	100.0
	Total	133745	99.8	100.0	
Missing	NOT STATED	327	.2		
	Total	134072	100.0		

Notice that the 'marital status' variable is categorical. In order to conduct a regression analysis, you must create a series of dichotomous dummy variables.

Creating Dummy Variables

To create these dummy variables, you can either use the point-and-click technique or simply write the syntax codes. Some syntax codes are more easily undertaken if written out. As you become more familiar with SPSS, you will learn which commands are more complicated to execute using the pull-down menus. First we will use the point-and-click technique to do a variable recode; then we will write out the syntax codes.

1. Select **Transform** > **Recode** > **Into Different Variables**. It is important to select this option because you are creating a series of new dummy variables derived from your original variable rather than altering the existing 'marital status' variable.

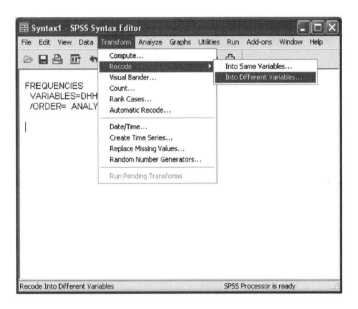

2. A window labelled **Recode into Different Variables** will come up. Specify the variable you want to work with, in this case, the 'marital status' variable (DHHCGMS). Bring that variable into the box labelled **Numeric Variable –> Output Variable**. Decide on a name and variable label for your new variable and type them into the **Output Variable** boxes. Then click on **Change**.

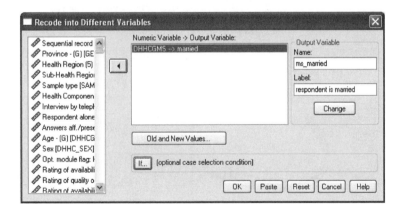

3. Next, click on **Old and New Values**. Since you want to create a dummy variable for respondents who are married, indicate that you want to keep those cases where respondents indicated '1 - married' at a value of 1; all other values should be coded as '0'. If you wanted to create a dummy variable for 'single', you would select '2 - single' equals '1' and all others equal '0', and so on for all the marital status categories. Once you have specified your conditions for each new dummy variable, select **Continue**.

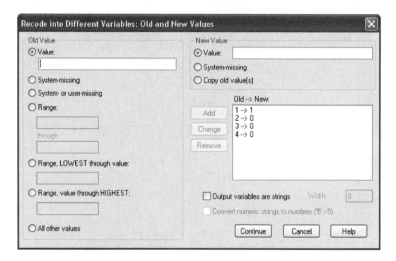

4. Once you return to the original window, select **Paste**.

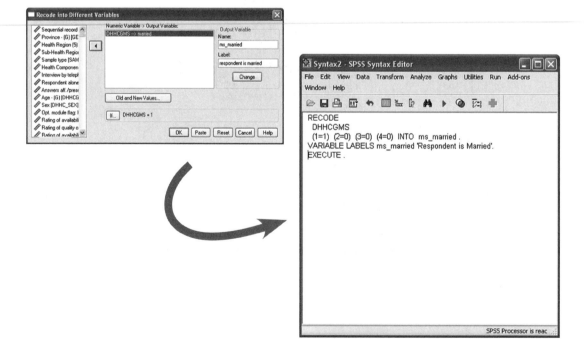

Repeat this procedure for each category of the 'marital status' variable until you have, in this case, four dummy variables: 'married', 'common law', 'widow/separated/divorced', and 'single'. Once you have completed these commands, highlight the recode variables and click **Run > Selection**. You can also manually type out the coding for a recode. These are the commands:

> COMPUTE married = DHHCGMS.
> RECODE married
>   (1=1)
>   (2,3,4=0)
>   (else=99).
> MISSING VALUES married (99).
> VARIABLE LABEL married "married".

The logic behind these codes is as follows: first, you are computing a new variable called 'married' based on the original 'marital status' variable, DHHCGMS. Then, you are recoding the new 'married' variable so that married respondents are coded as '1', all other marital status categories are coded as '0', and all other responses are coded as '99', which you will declare missing. Repeat this procedure for all of the other marital status categories to create a mutually exclusive and exhaustive list of dummy variables.

Now you can address your research question.

Selecting Cases

1. Since we are interested only in women, we need to select only respondents who indicated they were female. To do this, click on **Data > Select Cases**.

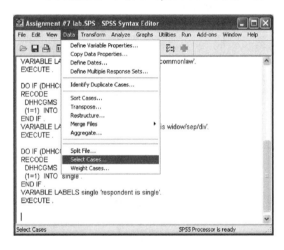

2. Within the window that opens up, select **If condition is satisfied**, and then hit the **If** button.

This brings up a window labelled **Select Cases: If**. Select the 'sex' variable (DHHC_sex). Since you are examining the effects of being female, you need to select cases where respondents indicated that they are female. Do this by specifying DHHC_sex=2: 'female', as in the box below.

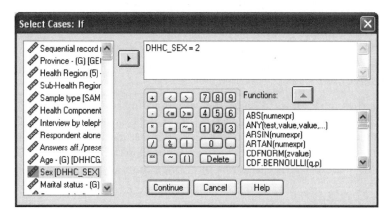

3. Then click **Continue**. This will bring you back to the original window. Hit the **Paste** button if you're using the syntax editor window. Highlight the commands and click **Run > Selection**.

Now you are ready to conduct a linear regression.

Conducting an OLS Regression

1. Click on **Analyze** > **Regression** > **Linear**.

2. Bring your dependent variable, 'total usual hours worked per week', into the **Dependent** box. Bring your independent variables, 'married', 'commonlaw', and 'widow/div/sep' into the **Independent(s)** box. Note that the variable 'single' was not included. Remember from your textbook that you need to exclude one reference category from your independent list. Hit **Paste**.

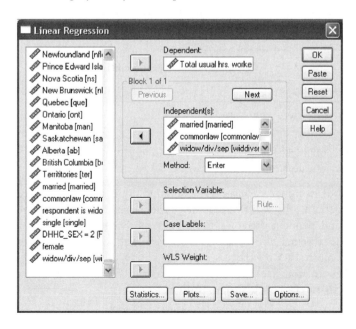

3. Your syntax should look like the following picture. Highlight the regression commands and hit **Run > Selection**.

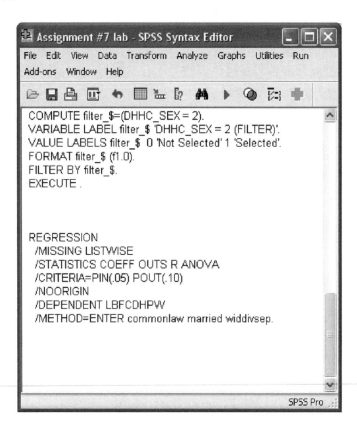

Let's look at the output file. First there is a summary of the variables included in the regression equation.

	Variables Entered/Removed(b)		
Model	Variables Entered	Variables Removed	Method
1	widow/div/sep, commonlaw, married(a)	.	Enter

a   All requested variables entered.

b   Dependent Variable: Total usual hrs. worked per week - (D)

Next, look at the model summary. Notice the R-squared figure value. R-squared measures how well the model fits the data; it tells you how much of the variation in the dependent variable can be explained by all the independent variables. In our example, we have only explained about 1 per cent of the variation in total usual hours worked weekly among women of different marital statuses. Therefore, although marital status matters, more variables should be included in this model to further explain this phenomenon. See chapter 14 to learn more about r-squared in bivariate analyses, or chapter 16 for a discussion in a multivariate context.

Model Summary				
Model	R	R Square	Adjusted R Square	Std. Error of the Estimate
1	.109(a)	.012	.012	15.352

a   Predictors: (Constant), widow/div/sep, commonlaw, married

The ANOVA table displays information on the variation, whether random or due to the independent variable, around the mean within groups and across groups. We find that the differences in variation between and across groups is statistically significant. For more information on ANOVA, see lab 6 and chapter 15 in your textbook.

ANOVA (b)						
Model		Sum of Squares	df	Mean Square	F	Sig.
1	Regression	109860.981	3	36620.327	155.372	.000(a)
	Residual	9137872.367	38770	235.694		
	Total	9247733.349	38773			

a   Predictors: (Constant), widow/div/sep, commonlaw, married
b   Dependent Variable: Total usual hrs. worked per week - (D)

Now look at the coefficients table. This table quantifies the **regression equation**, which looks like this:

$$Y = a + b_1 x_{1i} + b_2 x_{2i} + \dots + b_n x_{ni} + e_i$$

A regression equation expresses the relationship between two or more variables. The variable a is the constant term, the intercept value when all independent values are set to zero, and it equals 33.01. This means that single females work 33.01 hours in a usual week, a finding that is statistically significant at the 0.000 level. The bx term represents the independent variables. We can see from the output that women in common-law relationships work 4.68 more hours per week than single women, and this finding is statistically significant. Married women work 2.42 hours a week more than single women, and widowed, divorced, and separated women work 4.38 more hours than single women. The e_i at the end of the equation, the error term, indicates how much of the variation is due to random error, that is, how much is unexplained by the independent variables.

Coefficients (a)						
Model		Unstandardized Coefficients		Standardized Coefficients	t	Sig.
		B	Std. Error	Beta		
1	(Constant)	33.014	.143		231.547	.000
	Commonlaw	4.678	.278	.093	16.817	.000
	Married	2.423	.184	.078	13.147	.000
	Widow/div/sep	4.385	.247	.101	17.730	.000

a   Dependent Variable: Total usual hrs. worked per week - (D)

Summary

In this section you were introduced to OLS regression and dummy variables. You performed a regression analysis for which you recoded your variables into a series of dichotomous or dummy variables. After constructing your regression equation and computing the analysis with SPSS, you interpreted the output and analyzed the data.

Syntax Commands Learned in This Section

Recoding Variables:

COMPUTE \<new variable name\> = \<old variable name\>.

RECODE \<new variable name\>

      (old value = new value)

      repeat until all values are declared.

MISSING VALUES \<new variable name\> (XX).

VARIABLE LABEL \<new variable name\> "\<variable label\>".

Assignment 7

Do smoking patterns among Canadians differ by province?

1. Create at least one pair of research and null hypotheses that would help you answer the research question.

2. Recode variable GEOCGPRV as a series of dummy variables (i.e., one variable for each province).

3. Using SMKC_204, run an OLS regression. Use only valid values for each variable, and remember to leave a reference group for your independent variable.

4. Interpret your results. What are the dependent and independent variables? How do the groups compare? What does the *R*-squared value indicate? Which of your hypotheses (null or research) will you accept? Why? How do these results compare with the ANOVA results from the last lab?

5. Can you generalize to the Canadian population? Consider statistical significance.

An Introduction to Statistics for Canadian Social Scientists

A Companion Lab Manual for Stata

Julie Beth Hudson and Michael Haan

LAB 1

Introduction to Stata

What Is Stata?

Stata is a statistical program created in 1985 by the Stata Corporation. It allows you to analyze and describe data.

How Does It Work?

Stata applies a series of commands to a set of data. Within Stata, you select commands from a menu, and these commands are recorded in a review window. Stata then produces an output displaying the results of the commands. The commands will occur in the following order:

- Enter your data into Stata.
- Tell Stata to apply commands to the data.
- Wait for Stata to produce the output.

How to Begin a Stata Session

Once you have logged on to the computer, you will see the start icon at the bottom of your screen. Left click on the **Start Menu > All Programs > Stata > STATASE**.

What Will I See First?

You will see a window like this:

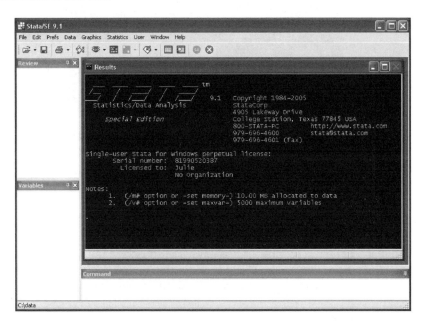

To open your data, select **File > Open > My Computer.** Find your data in **My Computer** and double click on the file. For the examples in this manual, you will be using CCHS2-1.dta. All the variables in the CCHS2-1.dta data set are listed along the left side of the screen in the box labelled **Variables**.

The Various Components of Stata

The Stata desktop contains several components:

- The standard menu bar
- The command window
- The Stata results window
- The variables window
- The review window

In addition, Stata has other windows that you will be using:

- The data editor
- The data browser
- The log

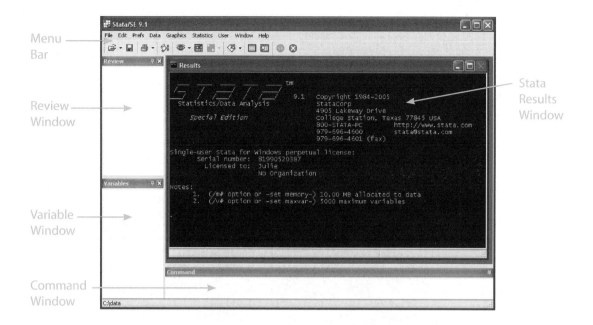

The Menu Bar

Along the top of the screen you will see the menu bar, which gives you access to all the available commands. The menu bar has a number of headings, dividing the commands into categories with similar functions (**File**, **Edit**, **Prefs**, **Data**, **Graphics**, **Statistics, User**, **Window**, and **Help**). Browse through these pull-down menus to become familiar with their contents.

The Command Window

To conduct an analysis within Stata, type the commands into the command window. For instance, to open the CCHS2-1 data set in the folder N:\courses folder\ SOC. 210, type

Use "N:\courses folder\SOC. 210\CCHS2-1.dta", clear

The path will vary according to where your data is stored. Remember that you can also execute this command by clicking **File > Open > My Computer**, finding your data file, and double clicking on it. 'Clear' closes any data files that are already open and, although it is not necessary here since there are no open files, it is a good habit to have when opening new data.

The Results Window

The results window displays the output from the statistical analysis you perform.

The Variables Window

The variables window lists the variables contained in your data set. Double click on any variable to bring it over to the commands window.

The Review Window

The review window lists all of the commands that have been executed in the current session. You can repeat these commands by double clicking on them, clicking anywhere in the command window, and hitting enter.

The Do-file (*.do)

The do-file is a text file containing a list of Stata commands. You can run it by entering the Stata prompt **do filename.do,** where 'filename' is the name of your do-file. This will save your syntax with a *.do extension, and you can give the file any name.

The Log File (*.smcl)

The log file is an output file—it records whatever appears in your Stata results window. You can ask Stata to keep a log of your session by typing **log using filename.smcl,** and Stata will name the log file filename.smcl. When you are done, type **log close**, and the log file will then be ready for you to view, edit, or print. You can ask Stata to open and close your log file within your do-file.

Saving Your Stata Files

To save your Stata files, click on **File** > **Save As**. Move to the directory in which you want to save the file and give your document a name. If you have previously saved your file and you have merely modified it, select **Save** from the **File** menu or click the icon in the menu bar that looks like a floppy disk.

Generating Frequency Tables in Stata

A frequency table shows you the number of cases associated with each value of a given variable. Generating frequency tables in Stata will help you to become familiar with the Stata windows introduced above.

First we will generate frequency tables using the dialogue boxes in your menu bar. When you are learning Stata these boxes will help you to become familiar with the language and component features of the program. This lab manual teaches you how to run Stata commands using the dialogue boxes. Eventually, however, you may want to skip the dialogue boxes and simply type the commands into the command window.

1. Open the data set. Then, in the menu bar, click on **Statistics > Summaries, tables, & tests > Tables > One-way tables**.

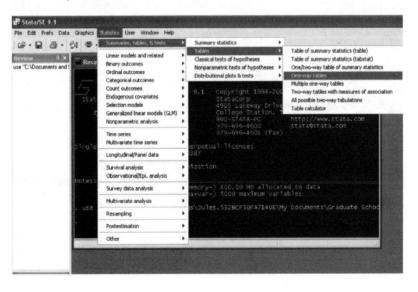

2. A dialogue box will open. From the pull-down menu under the heading **Categorical variable**, select **dhhc_sex.** Click **OK**.

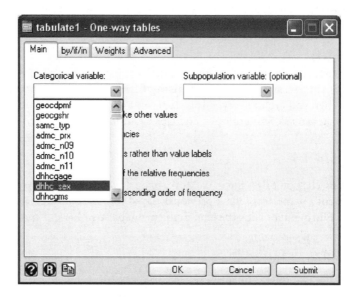

The output from this procedure will appear in your results window and will look like this:

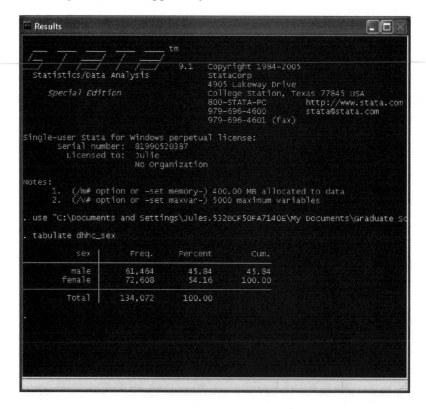

Note the following things about this output:

1. The commands are contained in the output. You can copy and paste these commands into a do-file to help track your progress and organize your analysis.

2. The column labelled 'Freq.' shows us how many cases are contained within the sex variable.

3. The table displays the distribution of males versus females by raw frequency and by percentage. It also displays the cumulative percentage.

This point-and-click technique is an easy way to see quick results, but there is one disadvantage. If you want to rerun this analysis later, you will have to go back through the menus to replicate the analysis. While this would not be very difficult for simple analyses like the one above, it will become increasingly difficult for longer series of analyses. You may find it preferable to use the do-file.

Within the do-file, you can create Stata codes in three ways:

1. Type them in yourself.
2. Open a do-file in which the commands are already written.
3. Paste the text commands from the pull-down menus into a do-file.

Writing Stata Codes

Let's see how you could generate frequency tables by writing the Stata codes yourself. In your command window, type the following code, then press enter:

Tab dhhc_sex

When you write Stata programming, you do not need to write out the entire command. Notice that 'tabulate' is not spelled out in full. Usually, you can just use the first few letters of key Stata codes. As the course develops, you will be exposed to a variety of codes that you may want to memorize.

If you do not have the commands memorized, you may want to copy and paste your commands from your review window into a do-file.

1. To open a do-file, select **Window > Do-File Editor > New Do-file**.

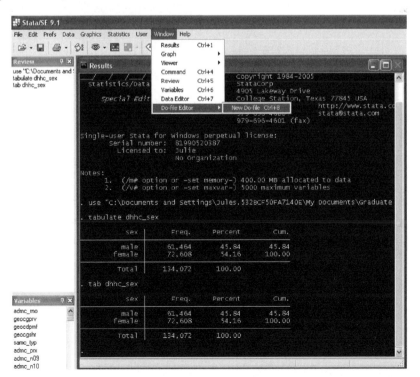

2. To copy and paste a command from your results window into your do-file, highlight the command and hit **CTRL + C,** or select **Copy** in the **Edit** pull-down menu. Then, within your do-file, hit **CTRL + V** or select **Paste** in the **Edit** pull-down menu.

3. Save your do-file. Click **File > Save As**, find the directory where you want to save your file, and give your file a name.

Summary

In this section you were introduced to the basics of Stata, including a variety of Stata windows and menus. You were taught three ways to enter Stata commands: writing the codes yourself, using existing codes from a do-file, and employing the point-and-click technique. Finally, you were introduced to a basic and frequently employed Stata procedure, tabulating frequencies.

Commands Learned in This Section

Frequency Distributions:

```
TABULATE <variable name>.
```

Assignment 1

1. What is the total number of variables in the CCHS2-1 database?

2. How many males and females are there?

3. Obtain a frequency distribution, both by using the point-and-click technique and by writing the Stata code, for the following variables: 'marital status' (dhhcgms), 'has food allergies' (cccc_011), and 'ever smoked whole cigarette' (smkc_01b).

4. Choose one of the above variables and interpret your results. How many observations are there for each response category? What is the most popular category for your chosen variable?

LAB 2

Presenting Data

Understanding how to present data is an important part of data analysis. This section will explore three methods of data presentation: pie charts, bar graphs, and frequency tables.

In the last section you learned how to obtain a frequency distribution both by using the point-and-click technique and by entering commands into your command window. This lab applies those skills to data-presentation techniques. In your textbook you were introduced to levels of measurement in chapter 2 and to univariate statistics in chapter 3. Understanding levels of measurement, frequencies, and measures of central tendency will help you decide when to use each of the formats for data presentation that will be introduced in this section.

Pie Charts

A pie chart is an effective way to summarize categorical data. (Remember: a set of data is categorical when the values or observations belonging to it can be sorted into groups.) Each value is chosen from a set of mutually exclusive categories. For example, 'sex' is a categorical variable with two categories, 'male' and 'female', and in the data set people cannot belong to both categories. We can then say that 'male' and 'female' are mutually exclusive. A pie chart is a circle divided into segments, where each segment represents a particular category. The area of each segment is proportional to the number of cases in the category it represents.

The following is an example of a pie chart for the 'marital status' variable (dhhcgms) found in the CCHS2-1 data set.

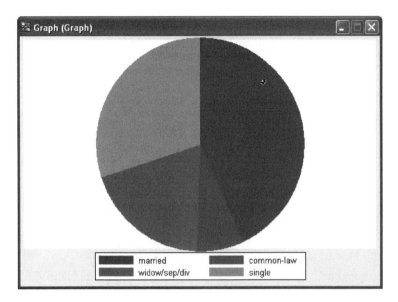

Here is how you can create a pie chart using the point-and-click technique within Stata.

1. Click on **Graphics** > **Pie chart**.

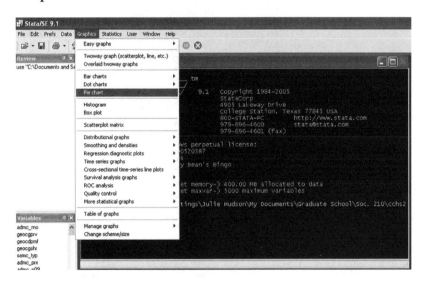

2. A dialogue box will open. From the pull-down menu under the heading **Categorical variable**, select **dhhcgms**, then click **OK**.

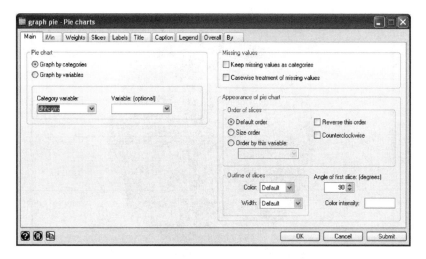

After running the commands, you should get an output file containing a pie chart that looks like this:

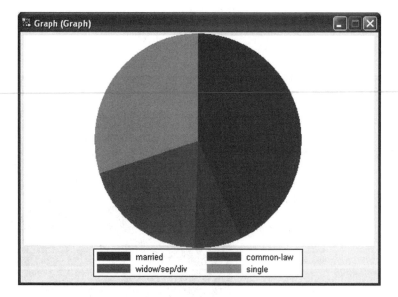

Bar Graphs

A bar graph is another way to summarize data. It displays the data using a number of bars, each of which represents a particular category. The length of each bar is proportional to the number of cases in the category it represents.

The following is an example of a bar graph for the 'province of residence' variable (geocgprv) found in the CCHS2-1 data set. Stata, unlike most statistics programs, assumes that the set of data you are graphing is continuous. If you try to plot categorical data, Stata will either give you an error message or, if your response categories are numeric, plot the mean of the value labels. To get around this limitation, we have to be creative.

In order to trick Stata into producing a bar graph from categorical data, generate a new variable that assigns a value of 1 to every individual, and then plot the counts for this new variable. You will learn more about creating new variables in lab 7, but for now, simply type this code in the command bar:

$$\text{gen freq} = 1$$

This will create a variable named 'freq' that assigns a value of 1 to every individual. Now that this is done, create a bar graph by selecting **Bar charts > Summary statistics**. Select 'freq' as the variable to be graphed, and then select **Count non-missing**. At the top of the box, click on the tab labelled **Over groups** and select **geocprv** under the heading **Over 1**. This procedure will yield the following graph:

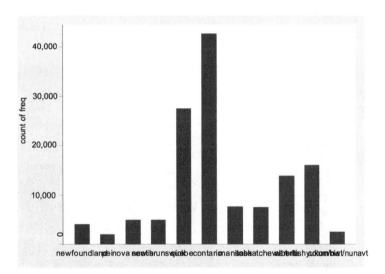

Notice that the province names overlap in the graph. Unfortunately, Stata doesn't have an easy solution for this problem. You can fix this within the graph options, but the procedure is complicated and beyond this manual. To get around this problem, plot the bars horizontally so that there will be more space for the province names. In the **Graphics** tab, change the orientation of the graph to **Horizontal**. This will give you the following graph:

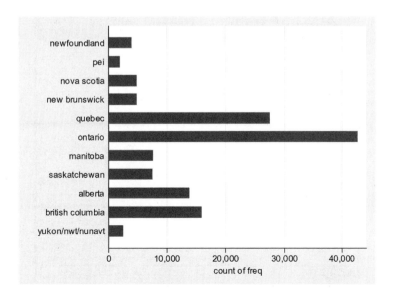

Frequency Tables

A frequency table is a way of summarizing a set of data. It tells you how often each value (or set of values) for a variable occurs and what percentage of values falls into each category. A frequency table can be used to summarize categorical, nominal, and ordinal data, and it may also be used to summarize continuous data, such as age, once the data set has been divided into sensible groups, such as age by ten-year increments. A frequency table created from a data set with more than one variable is sometimes called a contingency table because the figures found in the rows are contingent (dependent) upon those found in the columns.

Here is how to generate a frequency table for the variable 'last time visited the dentist' (denc_132), found in the CCHS2-1 data set.

1. In the menu bar, click on **Statistics > Summaries, tables, & tests > Tables > One-way tables**.

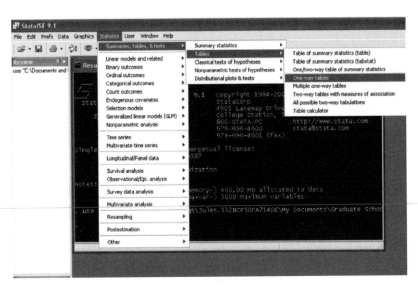

2. A dialogue box will open. From the pull-down menu under the heading **Categorical variable**, select **denc_132**, then click **OK**.

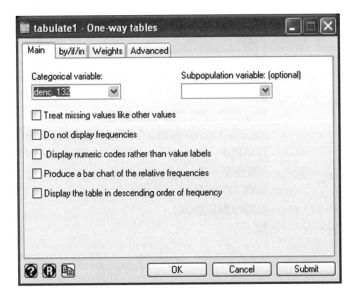

The output from this procedure will appear in your results window and will look like this:

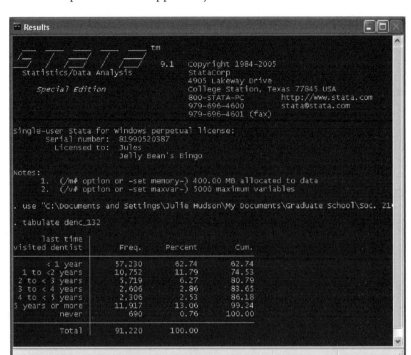

Note that 62.7 per cent of respondents visited the dentist within the last year, and approximately 13 per cent have not visited the dentist in five years or more.

Which Mode of Presentation Is Best?

Some presentation formats may be better suited to your data than others. When deciding which format to use, take into account the level of measurement of your selected variable and the number of response categories. For example, if you have a categorical variable with a large number of categories, a pie chart might crowd your presentation, whereas a bar graph would not.

Here are some general suggestions you may want to consider:

- Use tables to display data details that would be lost in graphs or charts.
- Opt for a bar graph when comparing data.
- Use a pie chart to show how percentages relate to each other within a whole.
- Identify the main point you want your chart to make and choose the format that emphasizes this point.
- Consider your audience. Try to think of what they would find most useful.

Summary

In this section you were introduced to the basics of data presentation. You explored three methods of data presentation: pie charts, bar graphs, and frequency tables. In addition to learning how to create these in Stata, you learned when and why you might prefer certain presentation types based on the level of measurement of your variables and the complexity of your data.

Assignment 2

1. In Stata, generate a frequency distribution, a bar graph, and a pie chart for a variable of your choice.

2. Imagine you have been hired to write a newspaper article on the topic of the variable you selected. Write a couple of sentences summarizing your findings. Which method of data presentation is most appropriate for this variable? Justify your answer, considering both your audience and the level of measurement of your variable.

The Normal Curve

In this section, you will learn about **measures of central tendency** (mean, median, and mode), as well as the relationship between the **standard deviation** and the **normal curve**.

Measures of central tendency allow you to understand or describe a single variable. In other words, they are **univariate** (one-variable) statistics. They are used to compare or generalize values across a population. For example, if you wanted a summary measure of the number of alcoholic drinks Canadians consume during any given month, you could use the mean, median, or mode, the three measures of central tendency. To recap what was covered in chapter 6 of the textbook, here's a reminder of what each term means:

The Mode

The mode is the most common or frequent score contained within a variable. It is not an arithmetic measure; rather, it is simply a frequency. The mode can be used with variables at all levels of measurement, but it is most often used with nominal variables.

The Mean

The mean is the arithmetic average, probably the most commonly reported measure of central tendency. It should only be used with interval- and ratio-level data.

The Median

The median is the middle score of any variable. If your sample is normally distributed, the median and mean will be the same. It cannot be used with nominal-level variables, and it can be used with ordinal-level variables only when there is an odd number of scores. To find the median in interval- and ratio-level variables for which you have an even number of observations, divide the difference between the two middle scores to create a mid-point between the two scores.

Calculating the Mode, Mean, and Median with Stata

You can calculate the mode using the tabulate function demonstrated in labs 1 and 2.

1. In the menu bar, click on **Statistics > Summaries, tables, & tests > Tables > One-way tables**.

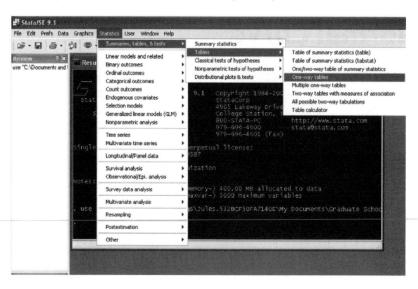

2. A dialogue box will open. From the pull-down menu under the heading **Categorical variable,** select **dhhcgms,** the 'marital status' variable, and click **OK.**

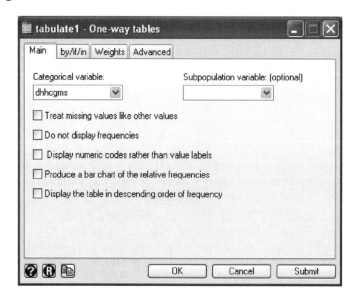

Take a look at your output. While we have not obtained the mode as an explicit statistic, we can determine the mode by looking at the frequency distribution of the 'marital status' variable. Recall that the mode is the most frequently occurring value. From the frequency distribution we can see that 'married' is the most frequently occurring value for the 'marital status' variable. Notice also the value 'p50' in the table above your frequency distribution. This is the fiftieth percentile, or the median.

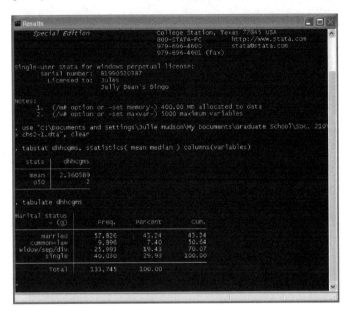

Calculating the mean and median in Stata is slightly different from calculating the mode. For these calculations we will use the variable hwtcgwtk, 'weight in kilograms', since the mean is only meaningful for an interval- or ratio-level variable.

1. In the menu bar, click on **Statistics > Summaries, tables, & tests > Tables > Table of summary statistics (tabstat)**.

2. A dialogue box will open. From the pull-down menu under the heading **Variables**, select **hwtcgwtk**. Under **Statistics to display**, select both **mean** and **median.** Click on **OK**.

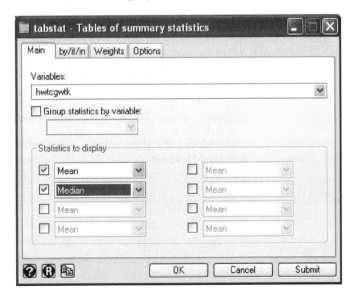

Your output should look like this:

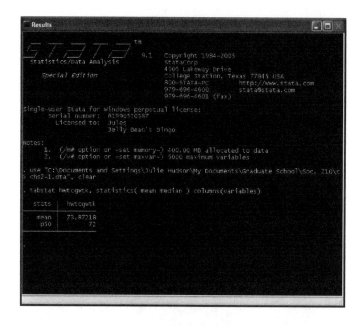

The mean value is 73.87 kilograms and the median is 72 kilograms.

Standard Deviation and Variance

Now that you know how to calculate the mean, median, and mode in Stata, it is time to learn how to obtain the **standard deviation** and **variance**. Variance, as defined in your textbook, is the average of the squared deviations from the mean value. The equation is as follows:

$$s^2 = \frac{\sum (X - \overline{X})^2}{n - 1}$$

Where s^2 equals the variance (the standard deviation is the square root of the variance.), X is any variable, $\overline{X}$ is the mean of that variable, and N is the number of observations. Understanding standard deviation allows you to visualize the proportion of your sample, or population, that falls within certain key values of the normal curve. For more information on this topic, see chapter 6 of your textbook. This is the equation for standard deviation:

$$s = \sqrt{\frac{\sum (X - \overline{X})^2}{n - 1}}$$

To calculate the variance and the standard deviation within Stata, follow the same steps you did to calculate the mean and median. When you are looking at the window labelled **tabstat – Tables of summary statistics**, select **Variance** and **Standard Deviation** under the heading **Statistics to display**.

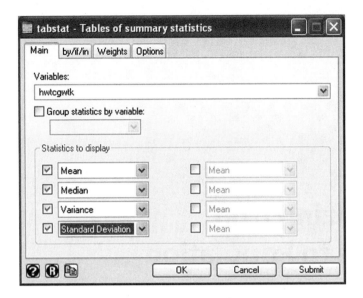

Summary

In this section you were introduced to the properties of the normal curve through an examination of measures of central tendency. Specifically, you learned how to obtain the mean, median, and mode, along with the variance and standard deviation, using the point-and-click technique within Stata.

Assignment 3

How often do Canadians consume alcoholic beverages?

1. Using the CCHS2-1 database within Stata, calculate the following for observations 15–21:
   a. The mean, median, and mode on variable alcc_5a6, 'number of drinks on Fridays'.
   b. The standard deviation and the variance of the mean.
   c. Calculate the mean, median, mode, standard deviation, and variance by hand. Compare your calculations with those done by Stata.

2. When considering which measure of central tendency you should report, think about:
   - The level of measurement.
   - The nature of the information you seek.
   - The number of observations.
   - The distribution of values.

Given these considerations, which measure of central tendency is most appropriate if you are reporting on Canadian drinking habits? Why?

Generalizing from Samples to Population

This section will introduce you to sampling and sampling distribution. As you work through the section, keep these two things in mind:

- The larger the sample, the more accurate the estimates will be in relation to the population from which it is drawn.
- The means of repeated samples from a population will form a normal distribution.

Populations and Sampling

A **population** is a group of persons, institutions, events, or other subjects of study that a researcher wants to describe or generalize about. Researchers will often generalize about a population based on representative samples drawn from the original population of interest.

Since the data we study is usually not from a complete population, we must try to create a more accurate representation of the population. To do this, we apply weights to the data. Weights are multiplication factors that make the data more reflective of the population it is intended to represent. They adjust for differences in the number of population units and the number of cases within a variable. For example, suppose we want to generalize about elderly people's attitudes towards health care and we have a sample of one hundred 85-year-old women and one hundred 85-year-old men. We might want to give more weight to the elderly women's attitudes on health care since we know that, due to differences in women's and men's life expectancies, the population of 85-year-olds includes more women than men. The weights would normalize the sample so that it is more reflective of the entire population, correcting for any over-sampling or under-sampling.

Sometimes weighting data can create other problems in statistical analysis—for example, it can inflate any standard errors. Consequently, we usually use normalized weights, or weights with an average value of one. Stata's analytic weights option automatically normalizes weights.

In many data sets, there is a predefined variable that will adjust for over- or under-sampling to make the data set more representative of the general population. For example, in the CCHS2-1 data, the predefined weight variable is wtsc_m. Read on to see how the weight variable works.

How to Weight Data in Stata

Look at the frequency of males and females in the sample before applying the weight variable. To do this, we will run a frequency distribution on the 'sex' variable (dhhc_sex).

1. In the menu bar, click on **Statistics > Summaries, tables, & tests > Tables > One-way tables**.

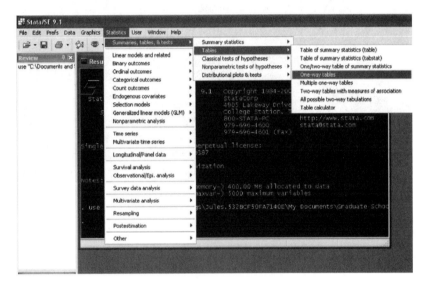

2. A dialogue box will open. We want to know the frequency distribution for the 'sex' variable. From the pull-down menu under **Categorical variable**, select **dhhc_sex**, then click **OK**.

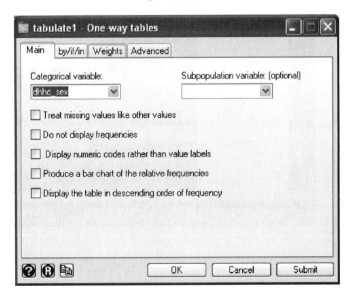

The analysis should appear in the results window. Note that there are 134,072 cases, of which 61,464 (45.84 per cent) are male and 72,608 (54.16 per cent) are female.

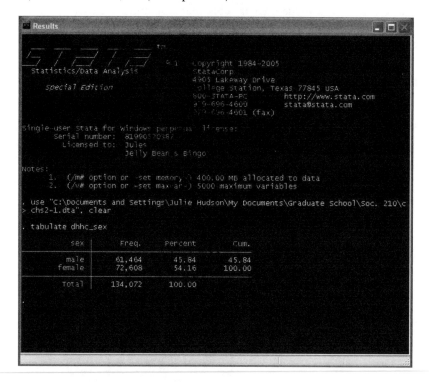

Let's apply the weights and rerun the analysis.

1. In the menu bar, click on **Statistics > Summaries, tables, & tests > Tables > One-way tables**.

2. A dialogue box will open. From the pull-down menu under **Categorical variable**, select **dhhc_sex**. Click on the tab labelled **Weights**. Select **Analytic weights**, choose the variable **wtsc_m**, then click **OK**.

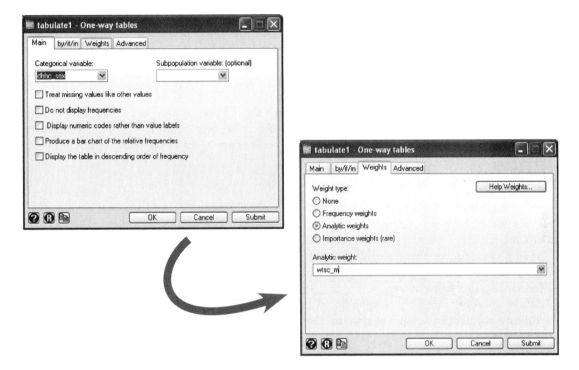

You will get the following output:

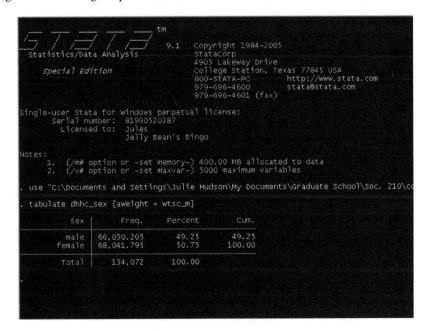

Consider some of the differences between the initial output, obtained before weighting, and the current output, obtained after weighting. The percentage of cases in each group changes, but the total number of cases remains the same. Even though we are using analytic weights, Stata retains the same number of observations instead of inflating the number of observations. Sample size determines standard error to some extent, and inflating the number of observations might cause users to underestimate standard error. For this reason, Stata normalizes the weights and reports these normalized numbers.

Now, with the weights applied, 50.75 per cent of the cases are female and 49.25 per cent male, compared to 54.16 per cent female and 45.84 per cent male before weighting. Usually weight variables are determined by the survey taker (in this case, Statistics Canada) and are designed to make the sample resemble the population more closely. Here, since women were over-sampled, the weights decreased the proportion of women so that the sample would better represent the Canadian population.

Taking a Random Sample from a Population

When researchers cannot obtain information from every member of a population, they gather data from a **sample** of the population, or a selection of cases that represent the population. Researchers can then generalize the data from their sample to the larger population.

Let us pretend for a moment that our weighted sample is a population and take a random sample from it. Random sampling means selecting a group of subjects entirely by chance. In this lab, you will learn how to take a random sample.

To take a random sample, you will employ the resampling command. This command allows you to indicate how large a sample you would like to obtain. In this example, we will ask for a 2 per cent random sample.

1. To execute the resampling command, select **Statistics > Resampling > Draw random sample**.

2. In the box labelled **Percentage of current data to sample**, type '2', then click **OK**.

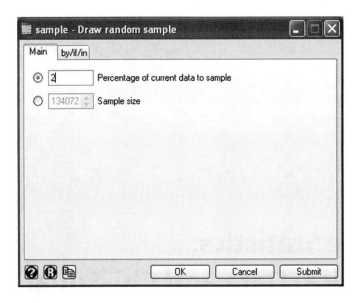

Now that you have selected a 2 per cent sampling frame, rerun your frequency distribution on gender. Compare your totals to the weighted totals. Notice that now you have far fewer observations than you had in the full sample. These new numbers should be roughly 2 per cent of the larger numbers.

Summary

In this lab you were introduced to the concept of sampling. You used the weight command to create a normalized sample of the Canadian population, and from this normalized sample you drew a random sample.

Assignment 4

1. In Stata, calculate the mean, median, mode, and standard deviation of variable dhhcgage using the weighted data.

2. Obtain 10 repeated samples using a 5 per cent sampling frame. (Hint: run the same command ten times.) Record the mean, the standard error of the mean, and the standard deviation for each of the 10 samples.

3. Calculate the mean of the 10 means, the mean of the 10 standard errors of the means, and the mean of the 10 standard deviations. On average, how close are your sample estimates to the population mean?

4. Now that you have the average mean and the average standard deviation, use the formula below to compute the coefficient of variation, a measure of relative dispersion.

$$\text{coefficient of variation} = (\text{standard deviation}/\text{mean}) \times 100$$

A higher coefficient of variation suggests wider dispersion. Given this, what can you conclude about your samples? Do they have the same relative dispersion? How do they compare to the weighted mean for the entire sample?

To get a sense of what these values mean, use the following conventions:

0% to 16.5%	Estimates can be considered accurate
16.6% to 33.3%	Estimates can be used with caution
Over 33.3%	Estimates should be used only with extreme caution

Bivariate Statistics:
Categorical Data and Chi-Square

Learning Objectives

In this section, you will learn how to answer simple research questions in Stata by examining basic bivariate statistics through crosstabulations (often abbreviated as crosstabs).

Bivariate Statistics and Contingency Tables

Bivariate statistics, as introduced in Part II of your textbook, quantify the relationship between two variables, such as gender and university attendance, family size and religion, or political party affiliation and sexual orientation. Crosstabulations are usually presented within a **contingency table**, which looks similar to the frequency table you learned about in lab 2. However, while a frequency table presents the distribution of one variable, a contingency table presents the distribution of two or more variables simultaneously. Each cell within a contingency table shows the number of respondents that gave a specific combination of responses (e.g., how many respondents are female and attend university). In other words, each cell contains a single crosstabulation, and an entire contingency table is comprised of many crosstabulations. (See chapter 12 of your textbook for a fuller discussion on bivariate statistics at the nominal level.)

Creating Contingency Tables with Stata

To learn how to create contingency tables in Stata, for this example we will examine whether men and women differ significantly in their opinions about their own weight.

1. Once you have opened the CCHS2-1 data set, click on **Statistics > Summaries, tables, & tests > Tables > Two-way tables with measures of association**. We will not be using weighted data in this lab in order to provide a more accurate representation of chi-square.

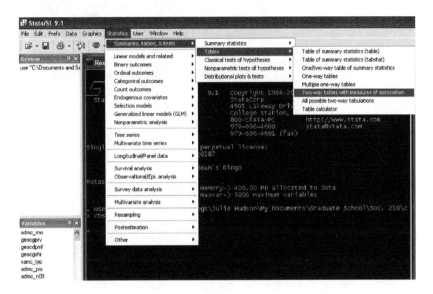

2. This will bring up a window labelled **tabulate2 - Two-way tables**. In this window, select your dependent variable, 'respondent's opinion of their weight' (hwtc_4), from the pull-down menu under **Row variable**, and select your independent variable, 'sex' (dhhc_sex), from the pull-down menu under **Column variable**. Select **Pearson's chi-squared** under **Test statistics**, and then select **Within-column relative frequencies** under **Cell contents**. Click **OK**.

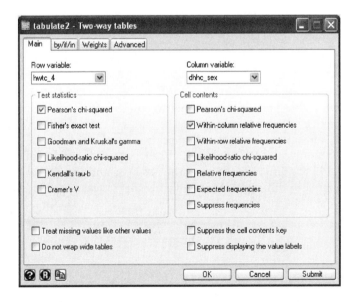

Take a look at the output in your results window. You have created a contingency table displaying the number of observations (128,149 cases) and both the raw frequencies and the percentages of males and females who feel that they are either overweight, underweight, or just about right.

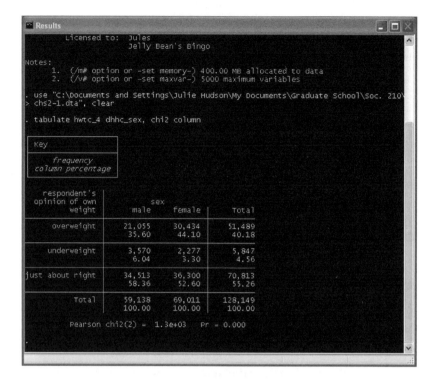

Now interpret these results. There do appear to be differences between men and women in their opinions about their weight. Women are more likely to report being overweight than men—44.1 per cent of women report this, compared to 35.6 per cent of men. But are these differences statistically significant? How do we know the observed differences did not occur by chance? That is, how do we know if the differences seen in the sample also exist within the population? One way is to use a chi-square test.

Chi-Square Tests

A chi-square test can help you determine whether differences seen in a sample are also likely to exist in a population. Since chi-square is nonparametric, you can use it for all levels of measurement without having to make any assumptions about the data's distribution (such as that the data is normally distributed). Chi-square tests the **null hypothesis** and measures the discrepancy between observed and expected occurrences (see chapter 11 for a lengthier discussion of null hypotheses). To calculate chi-square, find the difference between the observed and theoretical frequencies for each possible outcome, square this difference, divide it by the theoretical frequency, and take the sum of the results:

$$\chi^2 = \sum \frac{(f_o - f_e)^2}{f_e}$$

Where:

f_o = the observed frequency
f_e = the expected (theoretical) frequency if no relationship exists, as asserted by the null hypothesis

To evaluate whether differences observed in the sample are also likely to exist in the population, we need to determine the degrees of freedom, which can be found in the Stata output, and we need to decide on our level of significance (often we use a 95 per cent confidence interval). For our results, the degrees of freedom equal 2. Since chi-square has a known distribution, we know that the critical chi-square value at a 95 per cent confidence interval for 2 degrees of freedom is 5.991 at the 0.05 level of statistical significance. Our chi-square value is 1.3e+03. Since our chi-square value exceeds the critical chi-square value, we can conclude from our sample that there are statistically significant differences between males and females in the population with respect to their opinions about body weight.

Summary

In this section you were introduced to the basics of crosstabulations and chi-square tests. You explored the relationship between two variables and answered simple research questions. Part of examining the relationship between two variables is establishing whether the relationship seen in the sample also likely exists in the population, that is, whether the relationship is statistically significant. In this lab you used chi-square to determine whether a statistically significant relationship exists between men's and women's opinions of their weight.

Assignment 5

Who smokes more cigarettes, men or women? Use the variables dhhc_sex ('sex') and smkc_202 ('type of smoker').

1. Identify the independent and dependent variables and state the null hypothesis (H_o) and the research hypothesis (H_i).

2. Set up a crosstabulation for the entire population and for cases 1 to 25 (do not weight your data). Look at the percentages. What do the crosstabs tell you about smoking patterns among males and females? Do a chi-square test using statistics both for the entire population and for cases 1 to 25. In each case, do you accept or reject the null hypothesis? Explain.

LAB 6

Analysis of Variance

Analysis of Variance (ANOVA)

Analysis of variance, or **ANOVA**, is similar to a *t*-test (discussed in chapter 10), but it allows us to compare more than two groups. In chapter 10 you looked at the relationship between students and alcohol consumption. ANOVA, discussed in chapter 15 of your text, lets you compare the smoking habits of people with different religious affiliations or from different geographical regions—variables with more than two categories. ANOVA compares three things:

1. Differences between means

2. Differences in values within samples

3. Differences in values across samples

ANOVA compares the variation in a continuous dependent variable that is explained by the independent variable to the variation that occurs at random. For example, suppose you were examining the relationship between religion and voting patterns. Variation around the mean could be attributed either to differences between religious groups or to unexplained differences between individuals.

Before we begin, it is useful to review a few key terms. The **total sum of squares** is the total variation from the grand mean across all observations, and it tells us whether there is more variation within groups than across groups.

This is the equation for the total sum of squares:

$$SS_{Total} = \sum (X - \overline{X})^2$$

The sum of squares within groups allows us to calculate the variation that exists within each group rather than the total variance for all observations. This is the equation for the sum of squares within groups:

$$SS_{Within} = \sum (X - \overline{X}_{Group})^2$$

The sum of squares between groups treats each group as an observation and allows us to calculate the variation across groups. This is the equation for the sum of squares between groups:

$$SS_{Between} = \sum N_{Group} (\overline{X}_{Group} - \overline{X}_{Total})^2$$

The results for the sums of squares equations above will be dependent on sample size. Since we want a standardized value, we use the mean square instead of the sum of squares:

$$MS_{within} = \frac{SS_{within}}{df_{within}}$$

and

$$MS_{between} = \frac{SS_{between}}{df_{between}}$$

You'll recognize the numerators from our discussion above, and the denominators represent degrees of freedom within groups and between groups. Use these formulas to calculate them:

$$df_{within} = N_{total} - k$$

and

$$df_{between} = k - 1$$

where k = the number of groups you are comparing.

For further elaboration on ANOVA, please see your textbook.

Calculating ANOVA with Stata

Let's learn how to conduct an ANOVA with Stata. We will use the CCHS2-1 data set to examine whether individual body weight is related to total household income.

1. Open the data set. Click on **Statistics > Linear models and related > ANOVA > One-way ANOVA**. This will bring up the ANOVA window.

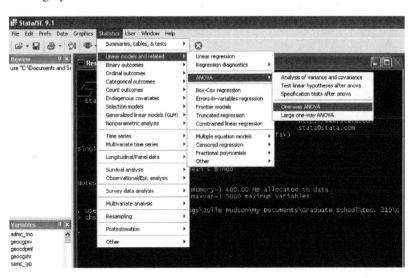

2. Select your dependent variable, 'weight in kilograms' (hwtcgwtk), from the pull-down menu under **Response variable**. Select your independent variable, 'total household income' (inccghh), from the pull-down menu under **Factor variable**. Then, under **Output**, select **Produce summary table**. Click **OK**.

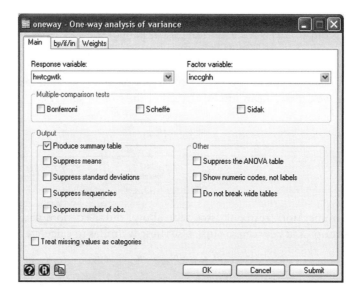

You will get the following output in your results window:

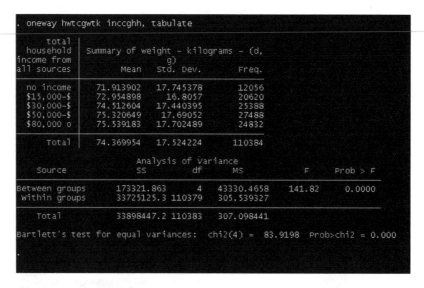

First, look at the means. Respondents with no income have a mean body weight of 71.91 kilograms, and the relationship between income and mean body weight appears to be linear up through to the highest income level of $80,000 or more. To determine if these differences might also exist in the population, we need use ANOVA.

The between-group sum of squares has 4 degrees of freedom and a value of 173,321.863, and the within-group sum of squares has 110,379 degrees of freedom and a value of 33,725,125.3. As you can see from Appendix D at the back of the textbook, the critical F-distribution score, given 4 degrees of freedom for the between-groups score and more than 120 degrees of freedom for the within-group score, is less than 2.45. Since the critical F-distribution score is much smaller than our value of 141.82, we can conclude with 95 per cent confidence that there are significant difference between at least two groups.

Summary

In this section you were introduced to ANOVA, or analysis of variance, which allows you to compare differences between means across groups. You looked at whether individual body weight is associated with household income, and you were shown how to calculate ANOVA with Stata and interpret your output.

Assignment 6

Determine which province smokes the most cigarettes. Use the variables geocgprv (province of residence) and smkc_204 (number of cigarettes smoked).

1. State null and research hypotheses about the relationship between province of residence and number of cigarettes smoked. Calculate the variance between provinces with respect to how many cigarettes respondents reported smoking. Which province is the most dispersed in its smoking habits? Which province smokes the most? The least?

2. State the value of the total sum of squares, the within-groups sum of squares, and the between-groups sum of squares. Calculate the F-ratio, using the mean square values. Based on these calculations, can you reject the null hypothesis? Is at least one province statistically different from the others?

Ordinary Least Squares Regression

In this section will you will learn how to conduct an **ordinary least squares (OLS) regression** with Stata.

Ordinary Least Squares (OLS) Regression and Dummy Variables

OLS regression allows us to create a regression line, that is, an equation that represents the relationship between two or more variables. OLS requires that certain fundamental conditions be met:

1. All variables must be interval, ratio, or dummy variables.

2. All variables, and their errors, must be normally distributed.

3. There must be linearity between variables. That is to say, the relationship between an independent variable and a dependent variable must be the same across the range of scores for both variables.

4. The data must be drawn from a random sample so that the sampling error is also random.

Condition 1 states that all variables must be continuous. If you want to test the differences between categories for a nominal or ordinal variable, you can create a series of variables with only two response categories, 0 and 1. These variables are often referred to as dummy variables. For example, instead of having a variable for 'gender', you might name your variable 'female'. You would code males as 0 and females as 1. Males, who are 0 per cent female, are therefore on one end of a spectrum, and females, who are 100 per cent female, are on the other end. This means you can rank individuals on their 'femaleness' and measure the distance between someone who is female and someone who is male. In other words, you've recoded a nominal variable so that it functions as an interval or ratio variable.

If the nominal or ordinal variable has more than one category, create a series of dummy variables for each category. For example, suppose your variable is religion. Since there are more than two religions, each religion, except for one, must become its own dummy variable (e.g., Catholic or not, Protestant or not, Muslim or not). Make one religion your reference group by leaving out its dummy variable. Most often this reference group is the most common or populous group, but selecting a reference group is up to the discretion of the researcher. Often the modal category is used as the reference, although this is not a rule.

Doing an OLS Regression Analysis with Stata

Let's see how this is done in Stata. For this example, we will examine whether marital status affects the number of hours that women work outside the home. This question might be important to scholars who are interested in whether traditional family roles are still present among married women. Do married women work fewer hours outside the home than single women? To answer this question, we will need to prepare the data for an OLS regression analysis.

1. Run a frequency distribution on your independent variable, 'marital status'. To do this, click on **Statistics > Summaries, tables, & tests > Tables > One-way table**.

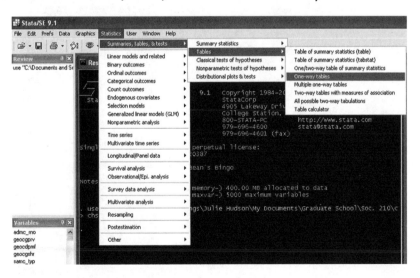

2. Select the 'marital status' variable (dhhcgms) from the pull-down menu under **Categorical variable**. Click **OK**.

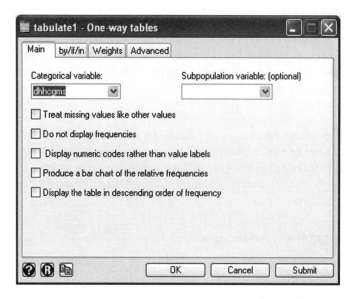

Let's take a look at the output in the results window. Notice that 'marital status' is currently coded as a nominal variable. In order to conduct a regression analysis, you must create a series of dichotomous dummy variables.

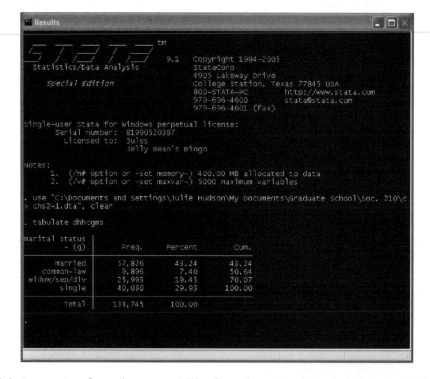

We will derive a series of new dummy variables from the original 'marital status' variable.

Creating Dummy Variables

1. Select **Data > Create or change variables > Other variable transformation commands > Recode categorical variable**. You must select this option because you are creating a series of new dummy variables from your original variable rather than altering the existing 'marital status' variable.

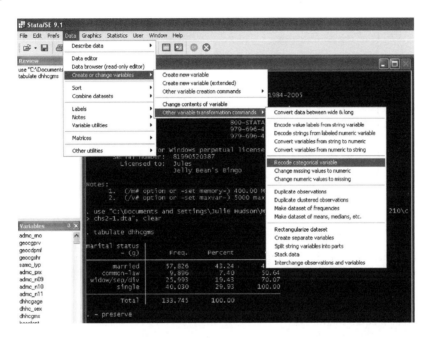

2. A window labelled **recode – Recode categorical variables** will come up. Specify that you wish to work with the 'marital status' variable (dhhcgms) by selecting it from the **Variables** list. Under **Required**, select the **(#=#)** option. Replace both # signs with the numeral 1 so that the option reads **(1=1)**. This indicates that you want the value 1, 'married', to equal 1 in your new variable. Under **Optional**, select **(else=#)** and replace # with 0, indicating that you want all other values to equal 0. You have now recoded the new variable so that married participants are coded as '1' and all other marital status categories are coded as '0'.

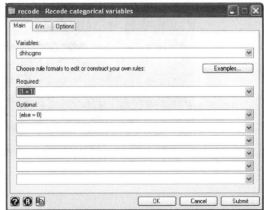

3. Click on the **Options** tab. Select **Generate new variables** and create a new variable called 'married'. Click **OK**.

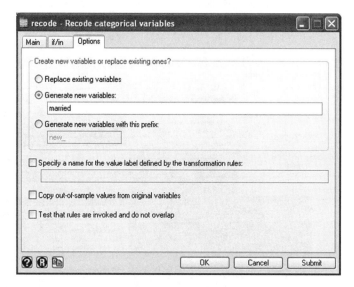

4. These commands should now appear in your results window. If you would like to confirm that you have recoded the variable correctly, type 'tab married' and hit **Enter**. Look at the frequency distribution of your new 'married' variable. In your original 'marital status' variable (dhhcgms), the 'married' value was 57,826, so now in your dummy variable, 'married', or value 1, should still equal 57,826.

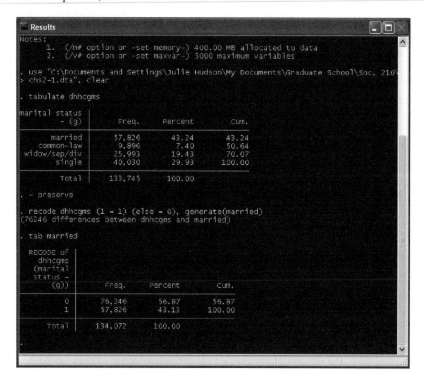

Repeat this procedure for each category of the 'marital status' variable until you have, in this case, four dummy variables: 'married', 'common law', 'widow/separated/divorced', and 'single'.

Now you can address your research question. Let's do a regression analysis.

OLS Regression

1. Click on **Statistics > Linear models and related** > **Linear regression**.

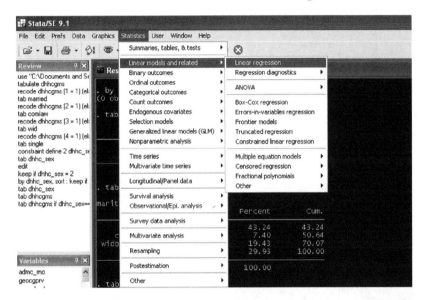

2. Select the variable lbfcdhpw, 'total usual hours worked per week', from the **Dependent variable** menu. Select the variables 'married', 'common law', and 'widow/div/sep' from the **Independent variables** menu. Note that the variable 'single' is not included. Remember from your textbook that you must leave one reference category out of your independent variable list.

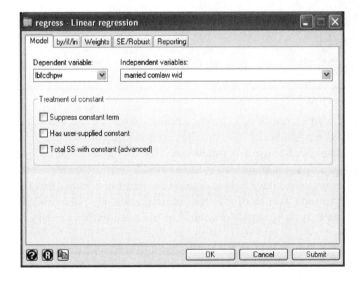

3. Click on the **by/if/in** tab. To specify that you are only interested in female respondents, type dhhc_sex==2 under **Restrict to observations**. This tells Stata you want to select only cases in category 2, 'female'. Then click **OK**.

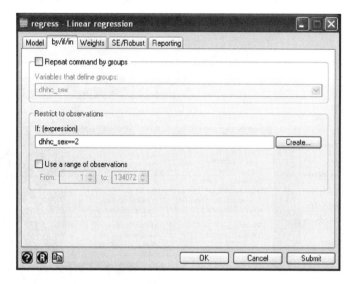

Now let's look at your results window. First you will see a summary of the variables included in the regression equation:

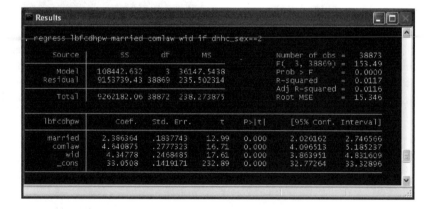

On the right side of your screen is your model summary. Notice the *R*-squared figure. *R*-squared measures how well the model fits the data; it tells you how much of the variation in the dependent variable can be explained by all the independent variables. Acceptable levels of *R*-squared vary by discipline. In the social sciences, an *R*-squared value of 10 per cent is considered a reasonable amount of variation. In our example, we have only explained about 1 per cent of the variation in total usual hours worked weekly among women of different marital statuses. Therefore, although marital status matters, we can see that more variables should be included in this model to further explain this phenomenon.

   The table in the top left corner of your results screen displays information about both the variation in the dependent variable that can be explained by the independent variables and the variation that is unexplained or random. The column heading 'SS' refers to the sums of squares, like in ANOVA. *R*-squared is equal to the model sum of squares divided by the residual sum of squares. For more information on ANOVA, see lab 6 and chapter 15 in your textbook.

Underneath is the coefficients table. This table quantifies the **regression equation**, which looks like this:

$$Y = a + b_1 x_{1i} + b_2 x_{2i} + \ldots + b_n x_{ni} + e_i$$

A regression equation expresses the relationship between two or more variables. The variable a is the constant term, the intercept value when all independent values are set to zero, and it equals 33.01. This means that single females work 33.01 hours in a usual week, a finding that is statistically significant at the 0.000 level. The bx term represents the independent variables. We can see from the output that women in common-law relationships work 4.68 more hours per week than single women, and this finding is statistically significant. Married women work 2.42 hours a week more than single women, and widowed, divorced, and separated women work 4.38 more hours than single women. The e_i at the end of the equation, the error term, indicates how much of the variation is due to random error, that is, how much is unexplained by the independent variables.

Summary

In this section you were introduced to OLS regression and dummy variables. You performed a regression analysis for which you recoded your variables into a series of dichotomous or dummy variables. After constructing your regression equation and computing the analysis with Stata, you interpreted the output and analyzed the data.

Assignment 7

Do smoking patterns among Canadians differ by province?

1. Create at least one pair of research and null hypotheses that would help you answer the research question.

2. Recode variable geocgprv as a series of dummy variables (i.e., one variable for each province).

3. Using smkc_204, run an OLS regression. Remember to leave a reference group.

4. Interpret your results. What are the dependent and independent variables? How do the groups compare? What does the R-squared value indicate? What does the t-test indicate? Which of your hypotheses (null or research) will you accept? Why?

5. Can you generalize to the Canadian population? Consider statistical significance.

Index